DISSOCIATION OF TRAUMA: THEORY, PHENOMENOLOGY, AND TECHNIQUE

DISSOCIATION OF TRAUMA: THEORY, PHENOMENOLOGY, AND TECHNIQUE

Ira Brenner, M.D.

International Universities Press, Inc.

Madison   Connecticut

Library of Congress Cataloging-in-Publication Data

Brenner, Ira, 1950–
    Dissociation of trauma : theory, phenomenology, and technique / Ira Brenner.
        p. cm.
    Includes bibliographical references and index.
    ISBN 0–8236–1289–9
     1. Multiple personality. 2. Psychic trauma. I. Title.

RC569.5.M8 B74 2000
616.85′236—dc21

                                                                00–046124

Manufactured in the United States of America

This book is dedicated to my patients who have taught me so much about humanity in the face of cruelty and degradation, for they have devoted their lives to breaking the cycle and building new traditions.

CONTENTS

INTRODUCTION AND ACKNOWLEDGMENTS

This book deals with the psychoanalytically informed treatment of adults who were severely traumatized in childhood and who employ defensive altered states of consciousness. It is an area fraught with confusion, controversy, and anxiety, which I hope at least in some small measure, will be alleviated by this contribution. A highly specialized topic which might seem to be of interest only to those who work with these patients, the issues which are addressed and the questions left unanswered have far-reaching implications. The question of trauma and how it impacts on symptom, defense, and character formation has been simmering in the psychoanalytic crucible for the last 100 years, as no model of the mind seems to adequately explain all the data. As a result, I have drawn on elements of drive theory, ego psychology, object relations theory, self psychology, and intersubjectivity to help me understand what I have observed and experienced with this remarkable patient population. Utilizing existing theory and, when empirically helpful, extending it, I offer a scaffold on which to climb, or, at times, to cling to, in order to meet the patient where he or she is, rather than to prove a given point of view.

To illustrate my hypotheses, I have presented clinical material in each chapter, from vignettes and composites to extensive case histories. All patient material is disguised in order to protect confidentiality (Clifft, 1986), and I found myself walking that well-known tightrope of trying to find an appropriate balance between maintaining the necessary safeguards for privacy and the need to accurately portray the clinical process (Goldberg, 1997). Given the problems of psychic reality, memory, and reconstruction (Kris, 1956; Arlow, 1969, 1996; Calef and Weinshel, 1981), especially in situations of physical and sexual abuse, I have included only those cases when there was corroboration of the past. This collateral support was obtained either before, during, or after treatment, and came in various forms, such as eyewitness reports, legal documentation, or admissions by the perpetrators themselves.

The book is divided into three parts. Part I is an overview of the problem. It begins with a clinical chapter addressing the issues of resistance and interruption of analysis due to unrecognized dissociative psychopathology. Chapters 2 and 3, revised and expanded versions of previously published papers, present my hypothesis of the characterological basis of "multiple personality," and the continuum of "dissociative character" pathology. I also offer a psychoanalytic definition of dissociation which enables the clinician to appreciate its dual nature as both as altered state associated with previous trauma, and one which may be reactivated and employed to ward off anxiety due to intrapsychic conflict in the here-and-now.

What was known in Freud's day as "multiple personality" was included in the psychiatric nosology as multiple personality disorder (MPD), and subsequently renamed "dissociative identity disorder" (DID) (A.P.A., 1994). This name change was intended to eliminate the controversy and disbelief over the validity of the condition. It was also intended to reflect contemporary thinking that the problem was not due to too many personalities, but to not enough of one personality, i.e., a disturbance of identity formation. Nevertheless, the patient's subjective experience is of being inhabited by others or having to share his or her body with the "inside people." Therefore, I will use these labels interchangeably throughout the book.

The hallmark of this aberrant mental development is the presence of seemingly different identities which are kept separate through an amnestic, autohypnotic mechanism. The uncertainty over the genesis of these personifications is part of the controversy surrounding the condition, and Part II addresses those most prevalent influences which have thus far come to light through psychoanalytic exploration. Chapter 4 examines the role of perverse sexuality as an organizing influence in which the individual may follow more than one sexual developmental pathway, encapsulating aggression, anxiety, and traumatic memory. An extensive case history of a patient with the triad of sadomasochistic heterosexuality, homosexuality, and transsexualism illustrates this thesis. Chapter 5 considers the role of the ego in the dream state, especially focusing on the capacity to symbolize one's own alterations of consciousness, i.e., the functional phenomenon. Clinical examples of the anthropomorphization of hypnagogic, hypnopompic, and traumatic states demonstrate how this aspect of ego functioning also contributes to the sense of separateness. Chapter 6 is an application and extension of findings from Holocaust research pertaining to the intergenerational transmission of trauma. The patient's internalization of the traumatizing adult's own early trauma may be demonstrated to contribute to the creation of a separate biography in certain alter personalities.

The concluding chapter of Part II, Chapter 7, is a revisiting of the death instinct. This theory, regarded by many to have only historical significance, seems to have usefulness in understanding trauma. At the very least, I feel that this concept has metaphorical value in conceptualizing the personified inner battle between life and death forces in these patients. A case history of a patient with HIV disease and multiple personality illustrates the effect of dissociated internalized aggression on the clinical course of both psychiatric and medical symptoms.

In a clinical volume such as this, theoretical and technical issues are intermingled throughout, so while Part III focuses on therapeutic issues, additional theory is advanced.

Chapter 8 discusses a unique facet of the treatment of these patients, the integration of personifications. Unlike most descriptions in the literature, this phenomenon is examined here from an analytic perspective. Instead of active hypnotic intervention to join the different parts, I favor efforts at dissolving those forces actively keeping the mind divided, a crucial therapeutic step which then permits the psyche to reorganize on its own. Therefore, my emphasis is on the dissolution of the "dissociative self," a structure which I postulate is designed to keep mental contents separate, and inaccessible. This defensive construct, the dissociative self, maintains the position that whatever the problem may be, it belongs to someone else. It essentially says, "It's not me!" Its function, therefore, is to disown (Sullivan, 1953) unacceptable mental contents, so that drives, affects, dreams, memories, fantasies, perceptions, and somatic representations are all potentially subject to extrusion by this superordinate structure. To assist in this process, the previously described organizing influences, i.e., perverse sexuality, the dream ego, and intergenerational issues are recruited by this "It's not me!" self.

Through this complex defensive process, which consists of a type of negation (Freud, 1925a) and a pseudoexternalized displacement, the patient's subjective experience, that, "It's not me!" leads her to conclude that since it is not her, then it surely must be somebody else. That "somebody" is what has been termed an "alter personality," or personification. These "inside people" are often experienced as completely separate entities who have various functions and who share or fight for exclusive possession of the body. One patient quipped that the battle over her body felt analogous to time-sharing of a condominium. In contrast to frank psychosis, reality testing, although impaired, usually is intact enough to allow the patient to distinguish the external object world from his or her "inside people," but some confusion may exist. The conviction of separateness, however, may approach delusional proportions, resulting in a most formidable resistance.

It is of great historical significance that at the end of his career, Ferenczi's work with sexually abused patients brought him to the point of recognizing this phenomenon also. He summarized the problem as follows: "If the shocks increase in number during the development of the child, the number and the various kinds of splits in the personality increase too, and soon it becomes extremely difficult to maintain contact without confusion with all the fragments, each of which behaves as a separate personality yet may not know of even the existence of the others" (Ferenczi, 1933, p. 165). I am simply elaborating upon Ferenczi's formulation, examining how it happens, not if it happens, and exploring how to treat it, not whether to treat it.

Involving such patients in the treatment process is in itself a great challenge, because the awareness of these seemingly separate lives may be completely unknown at first, such as it was portrayed by Joanne Woodward in the film adaptation of *The Three Faces of Eve* (Thigpen and Cleckley, 1957). For the patient to even consider the possibility of the diagnosis of "multiple personality" may take years in and of itself. The clinical work may be so complex and overwhelming, that the opportunity to fully appreciate the ever present but elusive dissociative, or "it's not me!" self, is frequently lost. Therapeutic engagement of this chameleonlike moving target of a self is absolutely necessary, but the patient will usually try to avoid this aspect of the alliance with every diversionary tactic, ruse, and resistance in his or her defensive arsenal. Substance abuse, eating disorders, hysterical symptoms, psychosomatic illness, suicidal regressions, violence, and the proliferation of an expanding universe of alter personalities are often enough to induce such disbelief, exasperation, frustration, and countertransference enactments, that discontinuing treatment or rapid referral to an unsuspecting colleague may result. For those patients and those analysts who persist, however, the work can be extremely gratifying and even exhilarating at times. Chapter 8 describes such an odyssey, and Ferenczi's caveat about the analyst becoming confused is well taken. It may help the reader to jot down the cast of characters and their functions, if he or she becomes temporarily confused by the pathology.

Chapter 9 describes the adjunctive use of psychotropic medication and reviews some of the empirical evidence of its limited efficacy. Because it may have some value, and is often prescribed to such patients, clinical material is presented to illustrate how it can get woven into the therapeutic process. Chapter 10 explores the realm of intersubjectivity, unconscious communication, and transference–countertransference issues. This patient population reports an unusually high rate of paranormal experiences, and this aspect of intercommunication presents special challenges which are illustrated in a case history. An unusual organizing influence, a near-death experience in childhood, is also considered here. And, finally, the last chapter addresses the issue of termination and terminability of these long-term cases. Through the use of the patient's dreams and a countertransference dream, the process of termination is illustrated with extensive case material.

My interest in the subject of defensive altered states goes back more than twenty years, when during my residency I coauthored a paper on fugue states with Salman Akhtar (Akhtar and Brenner, 1979). Interestingly, I all but forgot the paper until years later, as I pursued other areas of interest along the way. But from that point on, Akhtar encouraged me to write about the clinical process, and his own work has continued to be a great inspiration to me. After a long incubation period, I began to formulate my ideas about the dissociative character, but I first suggested that he develop the concept further and write such a chapter in his book on severe character pathology (Akhtar, 1992). We had a very stimulating exchange of ideas, but then he suddenly got quiet, smiled enigmatically, and then simply said that I would have to write about *that* subject myself! Until that moment, it did not occur to me that it was I who might have had enough understanding to actually write about it, let alone take any credit for a new contribution that could be offered on the subject.

Three other people I met during my training at the University of Virginia also bear mentioning. D. Wilfred Abse first taught me that multiple personality was a bona fide condition and his now classic writings (Abse, 1987) on the subject of hysteria have been most helpful. Bruce Greyson, who has done important research on near-death experiences and paranormal phenomena, exemplifies the solid clinician who has the courage and self-confidence to study areas on the fringe of "respectability" in our very conservative field. And, of course, there is Vamik Volkan, my mentor extraordinaire. He epitomizes the classically trained psychoanalyst who has incorporated his brilliant creativity and use of the self to further theory and to apply analytic thinking to many realms. His work on the traumatic effects of sudden object loss and pathological grief demonstrated to me early on, how psychic trauma could result in very strange symptoms which could be psychoanalytically understood and worked through (Volkan, 1981).

As I moved to Philadelphia and continued my training as a candidate in psychoanalysis, I was subsequently accepted into the New York based Holocaust study group, chaired by Judith Kestenberg, Martin Bergmann, and Milton Jucovy. I commuted to New York for this rare opportunity, which enabled me to learn about massive psychic trauma and its transmission to succeeding generations. My apprenticeship with Judith Kestenberg continued for many years until the decline in her health, which unfortunately occurred while we were finishing our book on child survivors (Kestenberg and Brenner, 1996). Her attention to detail and ever inquisitive mind kept me on my toes, pursuing lines of inquiry until she was satisfied with an analytic understanding of the issues at hand. This immersion in Holocaust related work prepared me as well as could be expected to listen to the veiled stories of suffering, degradation, and exploitation from another group of victims, the adult survivors of sexual abuse. Though frequently accompanied by bizarre symptoms and seemingly incredible accounts which did not become comprehensible until well into treatment, their affects, psychic pain, and internalized aggression were powerful indicators of something very seriously wrong. My extensive contact with this patient population was made possible by fortuitously meeting Richard Kluft, who along with his associates Catherine Fine and David Fink, was thoroughly involved in the treatment of such individuals at The Institute of Pennsylvania Hospital. Their dissociative disorders unit had acquired an international reputation and I gained considerable experience working with them. Our clinical and theoretical discussions were enriching and invaluable, as I struggled to understand psychoanalytically, what I saw and felt on the unit.

During this time, my senior colleagues at the Philadelphia Psychoanalytic Institute were extremely supportive of my efforts to bridge the gap between analysis and dissociative phenomenology. I especially wish to thank J. Alexis Burland, LeRoy Byerly, Philip Escoll, Newell Fischer, Ruth Fischer, Selma Kramer, Eric Lager, Leo Madow, William O'Brien, Henri Parens, and Sydney Pulver. In addition, my study group, consisting of Marc Lipschutz, Michael McCarthy, Katherine Reed, Neal Shore, and Barbara Young, has been a very important place to discuss emerging ideas and get candid feedback. I also wish to acknowledge the following colleagues who have helped me by either reading my manuscripts, discussing my papers, exchanging views, or inviting me to present: Jacob Arlow, Alice Brand-Bartlett, Bonnie Buchele, Charles Brenner, Eleanor Galenson, Jane Jedwabney, Ilany Kogan, Henry Krystal, Dori Laub, Howard Levine, Steven Marmer, Leonard Shengold, Melvin Singer, Charles Socarides, Richard Waugaman, and Stan Zuckerman. Ellen Young and Betty Ankerson have worked tirelessly trying to read my handwriting and translate it into a typed manuscript, so the editorial staff at International Universities Press could transform it into a book. And throughout this process, my wife Roberta, knowing how important this project had become, has always been there for me.

Ira Brenner, M.D.

Part I

An Overview

Chapter 1

AN INTERRUPTED ANALYSIS

> One cannot say that the time between the individual work-
> ing periods passes without leaving a trace on these patients;
> a certain subsequent assimilation, a working out of what has
> been learnt during the treatment is sometimes undeniable
> [Sandor Ferenczi, 1914b, pp. 234–235].

The premature disruption of analysis, the bane of the analytic candidate's existence, may occur in the seasoned clinician's practice also. Interestingly, there is not much written about it in the classic texts on technique (Fenichel, 1941, 1945; Nunberg, 1955; Glover, 1958; Greenson, 1967), and even Freud referred much more often to "coitus interruptus" than to what might be considered "analysis interruptus." Early in his work, however, he very succinctly states that "whatever interrupts the progress of analytic work is resistance" (Freud, 1900, p. 517), and he certainly understood how resistance may come from the analyst, too. Indeed, it may be overstating the case only just a bit to ascribe every interruption to countertransference problems rather than to technical limitations (Reich, 1949, p. 139), and contemporary psychoanalysts are more aware than ever of the mutual influences that each member of the analytic dyad has on the other (Jacobs, 1991).

In my view, however, psychoanalytic technique has not yet fully evolved, and this shortcoming does account for some of the problems in the treatment of adults who have sustained severe early trauma. But, the extent to which psychological trauma may be a factor in the fate of analysis is hardly a new concept, having been a central idea in Freud's thinking, continuing through his last major work. In "Analysis Terminable and Interminable" (1937), he

3

indicated that the nature of trauma had prognostic implications, in that relatively uncomplicated cases could do quite well, if "the patient's ego had not been noticeably altered and the aetiology of his disturbance had been essentially traumatic" (p. 220).

However, the sequelae of severe early childhood trauma, such as ongoing incest and physical abuse, may result in not readily recognized "ego alterations" and an inability to obtain a cogent history at the outset. Although both analyst and analysand may suspect as much, the active quest to confirm such a past is not only undesirable but also contraindicated, at first. Consequently, treatment may begin with a nebulous cloud of uncertainty regarding this issue, a state of affairs that the nonanalytic world might find incomprehensible. And, as a result of this clinical stance, there may be surprises found along the tortuous analytic path, as resistances, defenses, and the propensity for regression can prove too much for the traditional psychoanalytic framework. Unusual symptoms and characterological formations may manifest themselves, which can bring the analytic process to a halt.

I found myself in this position early in my career, before my ideas had fully taken form about "dissociative disorder patients." The analysis of a very troubled woman reached an impasse, and, for reasons which I will describe below, the process was interrupted for almost two years. Throughout this period of time, however, my experience with and understanding of defensive altered states had grown, which had given me a new perspective on what had been happening in the analysis. I could not apply it during her "first" analysis, but when treatment resumed, I was able to view her situation from a fresh vantage point, feeling freer and more willing to be flexible in certain technical areas. What would have been unthinkable years before seemed to be a natural conclusion after working simultaneously with much more severely ill patients in both the inpatient and outpatient setting. I suspect that having become a more experienced analyst overall contributed to the successful resumption of the process, also, and these intangibles enabled me to listen to her more comfortably. By incorporating some modifications in my approach, especially during the beginning of the second "installment" (Kohut, 1979) of analysis, the treatment was then able to proceed. I will present a synopsis of the crucial elements, keeping in mind that the reader will not yet have had the advantage of being familiar with subsequent chapters which informed much of this work with her.

CASE REPORT

Ms. Julie G was referred for analysis while in her early thirties, after a three-year course of dynamic psychotherapy yielded little relief from her suffering.

Essentially, she felt doomed to be a failure in life, having taken many years to complete her freshman year of college and complaining of never having been asked out on a date. In a desperate effort to prevent her daughter from becoming an old maid, her mother pushed her into a humiliating arranged marriage which was annulled in days, before it was consummated. With a compulsion to maximize unattractiveness and hide her natural beauty through a variety of conscious and unconscious means, a life-style she described years later as "protection through mutilation," Ms. G kept a distance from everyone except her mother. It became clear to her psychotherapist that her problems with intimacy were so profound that any attempt to help her address the issue only drove her further into an unreachable despair. As material was emerging that raised suspicions of early sexual trauma, she became more inaccessible. The decision to refer was out of frustration and a recognition that she needed more intensive work, and analysis was seen as her best and only chance. The deciding factor was her revelation that she had befriended a parking lot attendant near the therapist's office, a much older man from a very troubled and a very low socioeconomic background. Seen as destructive acting out and not amenable to exploration, the therapist got worried. Ms. G, on the other hand, was pleasantly surprised and privately relieved to find herself in what quickly became a sexual relationship. This being the first of its kind, she was eager for the experience, but stopped short of intercourse for religious and moral reasons, a position which had thinly veiled her underlying repugnance and terror. She subsequently broke off this secret affair when she terminated with her psychotherapist and bemoaned the loss of both relationships for the first several years of analysis.

When I first met Ms. G, I was struck by a pervasive sense of grim resignation, an attitude, along with her intelligence, which made her seem older than she actually was. Being her mother's confidante who interposed herself between estranged parents and who listened in on all of the neighborhood gossip, she lived vicariously "over coffee," as though she were hoping to bypass young adulthood and slip into middle age unnoticed. After several initial sessions sitting up, which were cordial, formal, and otherwise unremarkable, we negotiated a fee and she dutifully lay on the couch. As a senior analytic candidate at the time, whose graduation was imminent, I felt delighted to start another analysis. My enthusiasm for analysis was boundless, so I thought my colleague's caveat that Ms. G's analysis would be very long and difficult might have been a bit pessimistic. Perhaps she was underestimating the therapeutic power of the process, and I did not think I was being unduly idealistic. Ms. G seemed motivated enough. While I realized that I had only a limited amount of history, I felt optimistic that her prior psychotherapy experience, her seemingly insightful powers of observation, and her desperate discomfort with herself were all important ingredients to a workable analysis.

On the appointed day she was to begin using the couch, she wore a sweater with large, bright butterflies embroidered on the front, covering her abdomen. I was immediately aware of the colorful departure from her previously drab, dark clothing but was unsure if she was conscious of it. Given her previous demonstration of psychological mindedness, I listened for any references to anxiety or "butterflies in her stomach" about commencing analysis but heard nothing. Instead, she became more tentative and intellectualized, getting extremely preoccupied about minute details of conversations with casual acquaintances that had taken place months before. We were approaching the end of the hour and my opportunity to share this observation was slipping by quickly, as I was apparently determined to see how she would accept my trial interpretation (Friedman, 1985; Levy, 1992). As though it were a harbinger of things to come, my comment about whether she had any "butterflies in her stomach," landed with a thud. Not only did she have no idea how she was feeling at the time, but she could not even see the connection, as to why I might have hypothesized such a thing. Consequently, I was the one left with a feeling in *my* stomach, a sinking feeling (Hitchcock, 1984), being unpleasantly surprised and puzzled by her obtuseness. This ill-fated intervention revealed what I was unwilling or unable to see in the evaluation, that she was totally removed from her affect in the present, like alexithymia (Krystal, 1978), and did not seem to comprehend the concept of unconscious symbolism. Although I considered that my comment may just have been poorly timed and forced for my own reasons, I began to suspect that my colleague might have had a point after all.

The history that was elicited from Ms. G during the evaluation and early weeks of analysis was as follows: she was the youngest of four children, adopted at birth, growing up with the knowledge that she as well as her siblings were adopted. Her developmental milestones were reportedly unremarkable, and she described herself as a quiet and obedient child whose zest for living peaked at the age of 3. While she could not elaborate further upon what was either a screen memory or the memory of her mother's repeatedly telling her the story, Ms. G reported that at age 3 she made drawings depicting a girl being sodomized by a big man. She did not know what to make of this information which seemed even more disconnected from her than her vague but never forgotten memory of licking her adopted father's penis when she was 5. These isolated fragments were in stark contrast to an idealized childhood of family harmony, maternal attunement, friends, intellectual stimulation, travel, and the finer things of life. Upon closer reflection, however, she reported so many gaps in the memory of her childhood that she was not even sure when her parents separated or who some of her teachers were. Ms. G was unclear about her parents' marital problems, but the official story was that, due to military obligations, her father needed to relocate, and her mother was unwilling to uproot the growing family. Father, consequently, lived elsewhere, flying home on weekends, perpetuating the illusion that everything was normal, fine, and as it always was. In fact, Ms. G lived for the weekends and holidays, waiting, oftentimes in vain, for father to come home, a practice which extended well into the analysis.

Ms. G described herself as shy, introverted, and socially awkward, preferring to be with one girl friend rather than a group of friends. Though her teachers recognized her considerable intellectual endowment, her academic record was wildly erratic. Her psychotherapist had helped her recognize a pattern, however, in that after she would get an A and attract her teacher's attention, she inevitably would panic and withdraw, disappointing them subsequently with a series of F's. Their efforts to help her were met with ambivalence and she would experience a claustrophobic sensation impelling her to run or drop out. She would find solace in her private little world of books, dolls, figurines, and stuffed animals, creating a perfect sanctuary for herself. Her two sisters and brother were older by a span of eight to twelve years, leaving her somewhat isolated from them and never able to catch up.

Despite her not questioning her mother's love for her, she cautiously complained about a certain unevenness about her too, fluctuating from overprotective zeal to naive obliviousness, leaving Ms. G to wonder, as she got older, who was taking care of whom. Father, on the other hand, was consistently arrogant, self-righteous, perfectionistic, demanding, in control, and constantly dismayed at his daughter's seeming inability to succeed the way he had. Coming from an underprivileged background of poverty and deprivation, which he presumably overcame, he was intolerant of ignorance, weakness, or excuses, so he would constantly instruct and test her. As hungry as she was for his approval and love, she could only begin to describe a certain iciness in his demeanor which paralyzed her with fear. Ms. G and her family were apparently very good at putting up a social veneer of normalcy and harmony, a facade that she too believed until her psychotherapist began to question her.

In her midtwenties, a beloved aunt, who took a special interest in her, bequeathed a modest sum of money for her education and personal growth. At that time, she was thought to be quite depressed and was referred by her physician for treatment. A course of tricyclic antidepressants and counseling had minimal effect except to let her know that others might take an interest in her well-being. She returned to school part-time and allocated some of her funds to psychotherapy, knowing intuitively that it was her only chance for survival. Her father jeered at her, devaluing psychiatrists as greedy manipulators of the mind who were all secretly crazy, while her mother wrung her hands in despair worrying what the neighbors would say if they found out. Feeling utterly unsupported, her decision to get help felt like a rebellious act, which both pleased and invigorated her, but also increased her sense of alienation. Yet, nothing seemed to help her, and now she was exiled to analysis.

Analysis was tedious, laborious, and very dry. A certain predictability set in almost from the onset, characterized by lateness, intellectual rambling, and a penchant for talking about what she thought she might have felt the week before. On the days she did show up on time, she would appear lost in thought and surprised when I would greet her in the waiting room. When she entered the office, she customarily placed her belongings on the desk, waiting for me to cross the room to sit down first before she lay on the couch. Years later, she was able to acknowledge how essential it was to know I was safely seated before she got horizontal. Each hour seemed to be an ordeal for her to get through, and she seemed visibly relieved to exit each day, avoiding eye contact and with her head held low. She was typically late with payments, questioned her ability to sustain the financial commitment to treatment, and made overtures to drop out every several months.

Ms. G appeared to be blasé about absences, breaks, and vacations, determined to be immune to any emotional reaction pertaining to analysis. She vowed not to succumb to that dreaded "T-word," the transference, a concept that she had read about and wanted nothing to do with. She soon began to complain that she believed she was being harshly judged, ridiculed, or tested during my silences. Her father was very secretive and silent, so the basic analytic stance evoked a strong negative reaction which she perceived as depriving, unapproachable, and mean. As time passed, she revealed that she was being regularly tortured by nightmares of being chased or terrorized by her father. She also revealed a tendency to binge and to tear open the skin all over her body until she bled, two habits which filled her with deep self-loathing and shame. Feeling that she was totally despicable and beyond redemption, she alternatively sought reassurance of my continued interest in working with her while she progressively but passively sabotaged treatment. Not surprisingly, she showed remarkably little curiosity about me, having grown up knowing virtually nothing about her father's "other life" in the military. Underneath this mystery was perhaps the question of her biological parents' identity, which she never pursued. Once again, her deferential respect and pseudounderstanding about my privacy belied deep feelings, those of profound insecurity and feeling left out.

Ms. G complained of her life with her mother, whose advancing age and, "Oh, don't worry about me, just go and live your life," speeches made her feel that she would never have the strength to break free. Her sense of the futility of life and of analysis colored every session in which she began to talk about how successful and happy so many of her childhood peers had become. Perhaps there really must be something dreadfully wrong with her, she wondered, but dare not let herself probe the question too deeply nor contemplate her aspirations in life. It became clear to me that she was working very hard, unconsciously, to make things go "nowhere," but any effort to help her try to recognize or understand her contribution to her misery seemed futile.

Analysis continued in this vein for more than six years, with minimal change in her overall functioning and intrapsychic life. When Ms. G allowed herself to believe that I might have been well-intentioned, she could not explain to herself how someone in my position would genuinely care about her welfare. It seemed much more natural for her to believe that I was just biding my time until she let her guard down, at which point I would reveal my true malevolent intentions and exploit her in an as yet unspecified, sexual way. For her to consider that indeed her analyst was a "good guy" was not only too good to be true, it also would have posed the obvious problem of never wanting to leave me and craving more of a relationship with me. She had absolutely no confidence in her judgment of men's character as she revealed that she had a tendency to feel attracted to older men in a position of authority. More recently, one man had wanted to engage in bondage, while another had forcefully insisted on fellatio, which she dutifully performed, much to her surprise. She felt baffled and mortified to acknowledge how familiar it had seemed to her, despite her insistence that she was so inexperienced. As she described an almost dejâ vu quality to this sexual episode, Ms. G became nauseated to consider that she might have done such things as a young girl. This topic was absolutely off limits, and she was relieved that I did not push her to "find out" more. Affectively, the patient would continue to speak about herself in a distant, almost third person way, using phrases such as, "there is a feeling of excitement," or "on some deep level there could be fear." Similarly, there would be pauses and delays in her responses, as though I were speaking to her overseas on a cut-rate long distance service. Ms. G could not decide whether it was more painful to pursue transferential issues or the question of sexual boundary violations in childhood, hoping to avoid both, but finding that one led to the other. The analysis began to feel very "real." An exacerbation of insomnia, binging, and self-mutilation would accompany these issues as Ms. G's private "craziness" seemed impervious to analysis. Her fear of becoming hospitalized, needing medication, and becoming a homeless, chronically ill vagrant consumed her endlessly, as she felt able to handle only entry level, minimum wage jobs. I was, at times, surprised at the dismal terms in which she saw her future, seeing much more potential and ego strength in her than she obviously felt. I wondered if I were missing something but at the time did not know what.

Ms. G then reached an even lower point after mustering up the courage to confront her father about her childhood. It was an idealistic plan where she had naively hoped that if he would just admit the truth and ask forgiveness, he could give her her mind back so she could magically be freed up to get on with her life. In this ill-fated meeting, Ms. G did not realize until later in analysis just how tense and stiff her body felt in his presence. These musculoskeletal signs came to be recognized as part of her feeling absolute terror, i.e., frozen stiff. But, at the time, Ms. G stoically told him just how strange she felt in the presence of men, how unable she was to have a long-term relationship, and how, in her most recent encounter, was told rather rudely that she was really weird, and she might have been sexually abused. She beseeched her father to help her out if he could, secretly praying inside that he would redeem himself by coming clean. Instead, he was steadfast in his denial, conveying, as Ms. G described it, a somewhat distracted but superficially pleasant demeanor throughout. Dismayed and almost convinced she must have been wrong about her suspicions, she ended her meeting and got up to walk away. At the last possible moment, he called her back and Ms. G's heart skipped a beat. Hoping for words of encouragement, support, or even love, she eagerly returned, and through a faint smile he said to her, "You know, your boyfriend *is* right, you really are weird! You must be having those dreams again!" Ms. G was devastated and became speechless, unable to process this last interchange for several weeks. During this interval, she became "dumb," unable to think for herself. The words, "I don't know" became her standard response to every query, as she repeated this phrase at least twenty to thirty times a session. Ms. G doubted every perception, thought, and feeling, unable to link this "brainwashing" (Shengold, 1989) with her meeting with her father.

Ms. G's confidence in her ability to think took many weeks to return, and I noticed more forgetfulness, more day dreaminglike tendencies, and more intellectualized removal from any affective experience. As had been her tendency in the past, she would set arbitrary termination dates for herself about every nine to twelve months, feeling safer in the knowledge that she had an escape plan. As she had accrued considerable debt from time to time, these potential points of departure were further rationalized as time needed to catch up on her sizable bill. Interruptions were narrowly averted at the last minute on several occasions, as Ms. G would rededicate herself to analysis, manage to become current in her payments, and most importantly, acknowledge that she wanted to continue. Her sense of propriety did not allow her to ask for a lower fee in light of her debt, but she had not paid anything in six months. I got the sense that Ms. G was really pushing for a break this time, as things were going very "far" into the taboo realm that she swore she would never deal with. She had passively let her bill mount up over the months, masochistically daring me to catch her, confront her, and punish her by setting a limit. Knowing that she could not continue without paying, she allowed herself to lose her job, reportedly depleted her savings, and refused to ask for any financial help. She forced the issue once and for all, insisting that she needed at least several months off to catch up. I felt in a quandary, knowing that I could not prevail upon her at this point to do what she was unwilling or unable to do. Yet, it was quite clear that she was in flight from the erotic transferential (Jackel, 1966) and childhood sexual issues, and I had hoped we could work through her resistances. However, it seemed that her need not to know outweighed all else, and I needed to respect that or I would be subjecting myself to a masochistic experience which would be rife with countertransference pitfalls. In retrospect, it almost seemed as though Ms. G were unconsciously directing me to implement Alexander's "principle of flexibility" (Alexander and French, 1946) by insisting on an interruption in the hopes of catalyzing later progress. It gave us both time to regroup, as it were, and try it again. So, Ms. G set an interruption date for several weeks hence, and we continued to analyze up to the last moment (Lipton, 1961). She offered a repayment schedule which she hoped would be completed within six months and promised to contact me at that time to resume analysis.

In the last week of this phase of treatment, Ms. G produced two new, disturbing dreams, a goodbye gift of sorts (Peck, 1961), which foreshadowed things to come. In the first dream, Ms. G was being taken to the bathroom of her childhood house by her father. Just as something horrible was about to be done to her by him, she found herself atop a mountain in winter. There she discovered a young girl trapped in a glacier. Peering through the ice, she saw that the young girl was cowering in a fetal position. The child was very pale, slightly blue, and immobile, as though she were suddenly frozen in that position. She thought the girl looked a lot like her and was confused. The patient awoke in a cold sweat and was terrified, as she became haunted by the image of this strangely familiar young girl. The second dream, the next night, consisted of a bizarre interrogation by the police in which two detectives were confronting her about a crime. One agent was friendly, while the other was mean, as they took turns trying to get a confession out of her. Then, suddenly, she became naked, while they stood behind her manipulating her back. She felt an icy hand hold her tightly around the neck and then a warm sticky liquid drip down her buttocks. They told her it was for a special back massage, but she became frozen in a bent over position and could not move. When she awoke after this dream, she felt a chill so deep throughout her body that she could not get warm. The tactile sensations in her neck and buttocks from the dream persisted for hours, making her feel that she could not quite shake off the dream and fully wake up. In an unusually direct way for her, she experienced disgust, revulsion, and terror. The timing of these very "real" dreams was not lost on her, in that they emerged in the closing moments of this phase of her analysis, precluding exploration, but making an indelible impression on her conscious mind. She had the intuitive sense in her bones, as it were, that these dreams had traumatic sexual significance and felt a peculiar longing to find out more about the cyanotic, frozen little girl in the glacier, a pathetic young figure who seemed to beckon her in a haunting way.

Ms. G was essentially "saved by the bell" and was not about to change her plans, essentially determined to take her hiatus from treatment, vowing to return at some vague point in the not too distant future. At the time, I believed that she believed herself, but, given her tendency toward procrastination and her great difficulty in completing anything, I had a doubt about what would ultimately happen. It was not clear if it would be a permanently interrupted analysis or whether it would be more like a "discontinuous analysis" where, with any luck, treatment would pick up where we left off, after a period of modest personal growth (Ferenczi, 1914b). Ms. G was overwhelmed by the dream material which dominated the remaining time, as she recalled a recent conversation with an older sister who had run away from home as a teenager and avoided contact with the family. The sister, who told her that she had fled the house to escape her own abuse, had once walked into Ms. G's bedroom to find her father "examining" her backside in the middle of the night. Ms. G was shocked and horrified to hear this story, reporting it at the time in passing, in her usual detached way. The dream had unnerved her, however, and she could not elaborate on it, other than associate to her sister's account. And, then the girl in the glacier from the other dream loomed larger than ever, as she realized that she was about the same age that Ms. G was when her sister had walked in on her and her father. These connections induced a vagal reaction, characterized by nausea, dizziness, and clammy perspiration. Such psychosomatic reactions (see chapter 7 on the Death Instinct) were rare for Ms. G, and she felt that their coinciding with intense material was very meaningful. I offered to continue this exploration when we reconvened, a gratuitous invitation that the patient regarded with dreaded anticipation as she knew quite well that she had found herself in important territory. Our last meeting was then fairly unremarkable, intellectualized, and somewhat hollow, as she expressed great ambivalence over the interruption but "knew" she had no choice.

Julie paid allotments of the balance on a monthly basis, and four months after our last session, she included a brief note with her check, informing me that it would take several months longer than expected to get caught up (a total of about nine months). She said that she would call me for an appointment at that time to resume treatment. I felt pleased to hear from her, and when I received her last payment, I patiently waited to hear from her, but she never called. I wondered what was going on and decided to give it several weeks, knowing her tendency to procrastinate. After three months, however, I sensed that something was amiss, because this delay seemed beyond even her pattern, so I debated whether to contact her myself. Initially concerned that she might feel intruded upon, I eventually did decide to call her and inquire as tactfully as I could where she stood with things. Ms. G was totally taken aback by my call. While she was not unhappy to hear from me, she was completely surprised to hear that I had been waiting for her call, having no recollection of what she had written in the note! I thought that this amount of forgetting about a decision as important as analysis seemed a bit excessive, and my index of suspicion further increased that she was employing more than ordinary repression at such times. I was reminded of the countless times when I would find her so completely self-absorbed in the waiting area that she was startled to see me (Morgan, Grillon, Lubin, and Southwick, 1997). Ms. G seemed to have become so caught up in her private little world that she had no idea that I would have given her another thought. She sounded reluctant to make any decision and suggested we meet in a month to discuss what she wanted to do. I was intrigued by her amnesia and by this time had enough distance from the analysis to consider that our meeting might shed new diagnostic light. During that meeting and the several monthly meetings that followed at Ms. G's request, she indicated that she might have never contacted me if I had not called but could not say why. But, rather than having an "as if" (Deutsch, 1942) and unauthentic quality, she came across more as being in a dreamlike state. Yet, in spite of this "spacey" demeanor, we had a series of fascinating conversations where we shared observations of each other during the analysis, almost reminiscing about "what went wrong." Ms. G found it both comforting and titillating to sit face-to-face now, telling me how different and how much less terrifying my voice sounded. She then revealed how she would drift off regularly, struggling to stay oriented to the here-and-now (Lewin, 1955). She was too scared and too busy trying to stay in control to inform me, convinced that I would have locked her away in the hospital if I knew how on the edge of losing her sanity she regularly felt. Now, she could keep her composure, and the infrequent visits gave her time to collect herself before she saw me again. Ms. G described what sounded like psychotic transference manifestations (Lowenstein, 1993), in that she, at times, was totally convinced that I was just like her father, feeling that no amount of reassurance could convince her otherwise.

As I listened to her during this interlude, I told her that it felt as though we were having an extended coffee break, alluding to her pseudomature conversations with her mother which characterized much of their relationship. She was mildly amused at the observation, and we both enjoyed a moment of levity, as I realized more than ever that if she were ever to take another chance at analysis I must utilize much more of my self, i.e., my sense of humor, some disclosure about how my mind works, and, to some extent, my affective state, as well as perhaps countertransference (see chapter 10 on Intersubjectivity). Furthermore, it was imperative that we find a way to explore her amnesia and altered states which were well disguised by her obsessional character traits. Most significantly, however, were the terrifying transference regressions which we discussed in such a casual way that it felt like we were having a chat about someone else's problems. Indeed, that was exactly the point. She appeared to talk about herself in the third person although she really knew it was her, i.e., "It's me and it's not me" (see chapter 8 on Integration, and the discussion of the "It's not me!" self). But, Ms. G was surprised to find how much she began to look forward to our meetings, and she requested more frequent sessions, which then became weekly at this point. Her comfort and increased contact triggered off new anxiety, as she found her capacity to keep her intellectualized distance beginning to slip. She did not want to let it get "real" again, as she revealed, very cautiously, that she even heard voices at times. At this point, I was not at all surprised, nor particularly concerned, as these symptoms seemed more in the realm of hysteria, dreamlike phenomena, and posttraumatic symptoms with varying degrees of observing ego, rather than being frankly psychotic or schizophreniform in nature. For example, there was no deterioration in hygiene or functioning, and, in fact, she had advanced in her work. Furthermore, by this point, I had seen a great number of patients who very likely had sustained severe early trauma, who had more profound symptoms, and who were able to somehow create a psychological firewall, in order to function over long periods of time. I essentially told Ms. G all of the above during this "coffee break," and also told her that her concerns about needing hospitalization might not have been completely unfounded. We even discussed practical details such as how many days of inpatient coverage she had and whether medication at some point might be indicated. I also told her that I could not predict what would happen to her if she continued or if she did nothing and decided to stop before she got any deeper. I believe that Ms. G appreciated my forthrightness about the uncertainty of her prognosis as well as my willingness to take her back into intensive treatment, wherever it might take us. By now, I was less concerned about the "purity" of an analysis without parameters, and since I finally knew I was working with a patient with dissociative pathology, I needed to be prepared for any eventuality. She seemed to correspond to the upper level dissociative character in my continuum (see chapters 2 and 3) and I now had a road map. I must have conveyed my confidence in being able to handle the situation, and Ms. G seemed greatly relieved. In fact, she never required psychiatric medication, hospitalization, or even phone calls between sessions, but the assurance that I would be able to see her through and do whatever was necessary, not only in my role as psychoanalyst but also as a psychiatrist, if necessary, was an aspect of reality that seemed to anchor her.

Ms. G began to seriously contemplate resuming her analysis, and I anticipated with her the likelihood that she would have urges to flee again. She wholeheartedly agreed, and I asked her if she would be able to verbalize these impulses as they arose so we could learn about the pattern. At this point, she suddenly had a sensation in her head and began talking about the girl in the glacier from her dream. She had a peculiar expression on her face and seemed to be listening to something, which, if I did not directly ask about it she would not have reported. Indeed, she confirmed that she thought she "heard" sounds and could not tell if it were like rustling wind or murmuring. Because I waited for clinical cues and self-reporting about these phenomena, I felt fairly assured that I was not suggesting (Glover, 1931; Brenneis, 1994) this to her. And, since they were finally being acknowledged, I added that free association included not only saying what comes to mind and what one senses in the body, but also *what one hears inside,* too (see chapter 4, section on technique). Ms. G looked a bit sheepish but did acknowledge her growing curiosity about the ice-encased youngster. Once again, I might have been concerned about reifying her metaphor if I had suggested that this dream character was anymore than that, but she made repeated references to it on her own. Failure to acknowledge or empathize with her subjective inner reality that the girl in the glacier seemed to have a life of her own would have been an error, in my view. And, by now I had a working formulation to help understand how the dream ego could represent changes in states of consciousness by creation of personifications (see chapter 5 on dream ego), so I was listening very carefully for "her" presence. Ms. G nodded vigorously when I pointed out to her in her own metaphorical language that we might be in for some challenging times if she were to try to defrost this trapped young girl and hear what she had to say. I had come to understand that a child lapsing into a defensive altered state during a traumatic episode might have symbolic dreams not only about her experience but also about how her ego had undergone a profound change at the time. I, therefore, wondered if the girl in the glacier was a vestige of her childhood, waiting to be discovered, learned about, and set free. But, like any delicate relic that had been wonderfully preserved in either a glacier, the desert, or the ocean depths, when suddenly being exposed to the elements runs the risk of deterioration and disintegration. Its handling required the greatest of care, and I hypothesized that Ms. G "on a deep level" was trying to make sure conditions would be

safe enough for this to happen. So, after building up momentum, she felt
ready to resume the analysis.

DISCUSSION

Ms. G's resumption of analysis was marked by an elaborate dream in which
she lost and found me several times. There were convoluted twists, turns,
and blind alleys on a road she was driving, along with several dangerous men
whom she thought she could trust but who betrayed her sexually. She likened
the dream to her transference dilemma in analysis, where both the preoedipal
separation issues as well as her victorious oedipal entrapment were being
played out. She lost no time in rededicating herself once she began in earnest,
valuing the analysis in a way that was impossible before. She was courageous,
intellectually honest, and determined to find out the "truth" (Schimek, 1975)
about her relationship with her adopted father and how her mother could have
"slept" through it all. Early on, she requested double sessions, intuitively
sensing that as much as she was relieved to get up and go at the end of the
hour, in many ways she was just getting started on getting the glacier to melt.
I had my doubts about the value of her idea (see chapter 4, section on technique), wondering if whatever advantage that would possibly be accrued by
two sessions in one day would be offset by the decreased frequency per week,
i.e., going from four sessions per week to two double sessions or one double
session and two regular sessions per week. I expressed my concerns about
unwittingly playing into her resistance, but eventually decided to accede to
her idea on a trial basis when my schedule permitted it. This modification
lasted about six months, in which we averaged a double session about every
two to three weeks. Several observations were made: (1) the scheduling of
the double session and the processing of it afterward were major events which
in and of themselves introduced an artifact through the element of excitement,
anticipation, performance anxiety, and hope; (2) my willingness to listen to
her and go along with it was an important reflection of our collaboration and
mutual efforts on her behalf; (3) there seemed to be no harm done; (4) the
longer time enabled her to more easily let her guard down and lapse into
reveries which facilitated an experiential session in which multisensory bridges to the past (Brenner, 1988b) and somatic memories (Kramer, 1990)
seemed to emerge. At such times, for example, she often experienced great
bladder pressure due to an urge to urinate which had been easily avoided in
the usual forty-five minute session. Ms. G was obviously free to excuse
herself, but masochistically "held it in" instead, to avoid the bathroom. These
painful sensations then legitimized her attention being drawn to the urogenital
and rectal areas, which then gave her "permission" to associate to this part

of the body which had been totally ignored in the first phase of her analysis. Associations to the ladies room at the office then gave way to memories of the bathroom in her childhood house. She was able to visually reconstruct every detail of this previously forgotten part of her house and reported that she "saw" herself crying in fear and in pain. With the help of the inner voice of the girl in the glacier who indeed seemed to represent her being not only frozen with fear but also her autohypnotic dissociated state during repeated sodomous acts, she became able to reconstruct an utterly terrifying, lonely, and traumatic childhood.

It was a profound insight that Ms. G became conscious of the times when she would be feeling intensely in the transference but actually visualizing her father's menacing countenance, like a flashback from long ago (Blank, 1985). At times she also hallucinated his pajamas, the smell of his cologne, his heavy breathing, and his sighing. Eventually, the nightmares of his hunting her down relentlessly became replaced by more manageable dreams in which he shrunk in size and became a pesty nuisance which she could shoo away, or dreams in which he was not seated at the head of the table anymore. Elements of his own traumatic past very possibly were transmitted and contributed to her psychopathology, also (see chapter 6 on Intergenerational Transmission). A reflection of her increased mastery, Ms. G's daytime fears greatly diminished also, and as her analysis continued, it became known and felt "on all levels" that the girl in the glacier was really Ms. G after all.

SUMMARY

Aspects of the analysis of a woman with obsessional and masochistic tendencies are presented. She had extreme isolation of affect and lack of access to her inner psychological life. Her analysis was essentially conducted in two phases due to an interruption associated with enormous resistance over confronting her traumatic past. Evidence of a dissociative or "It's not me!" self (see chapter 9) first manifested itself in the form of a dream of a girl encased in a glacier. Defensive altered states of severe trauma may have been represented in and contributed to the formation of her dreams (chapter 5). This organizing influence was hypothesized to be a factor in the perception that there is a separate self in the mind, in this case, a frozen girl who had a life of her own. This dissociated self was perceived as "her and not her" and contributed to an almost unanalyzable disturbance of memory. Recognition and acknowledgment of these aspects, as well as the use of intersubjectivity (chapter 9) and technical modifications were helpful in salvaging the analysis. It was clinically useful for the analyst to conceptualize that the nature of the patient's problem was on a continuum of "multiple personality" which in this case was thought to be an upper level dissociative character.

Chapter 2

THE DISSOCIATIVE CHARACTER

How didst thou make division of Thyself? [Shakespeare, *Twelfth Night*].

The revival of interest in "multiple personality," now officially known as Dissociative Identity Disorder (DID), and the advent of specialized inpatient units (Kluft, 1991) is a phenomenon that has generally bypassed psychoanalysts.

Many have not seen any cases of DID, so it is an uneasy topic, which, in some circles, may even be regarded with scorn (Abse, personal communication). After all, the conclusion reached by Taylor and Martin (1944) was that there are two types of believers—the naive and those with actual experience with multiple personality. Kramer (1990) states, "I, for one, have never encountered an adult who has fabricated a story of incest" (p. 167). Given the prevalence of such reports by these patients (Braun, 1984; Kluft, 1984; Putnam, Guroff, Silberman, Baraban, and Post, 1986), a review of the history of psychoanalytic thought regarding incest (Simon, 1992) may offer a clue as to why this correlation was not recognized earlier in what was thought to be such a rare disorder.

In my role as an inpatient administrator, consultant, supervisor, and private practitioner, I have had the unusual opportunity of treating, interviewing, and reviewing the cases of several hundred patients with a suspected diagnosis of DID. This condition seems to generate more controversy, confusion, and schisms in the staff than any other disorder. Reminiscent of what

This chapter is a revised and expanded version of a paper published in *The Journal of the American Psychoanalytic Association*, "The Dissociative Character: A Reconsideration of 'Multiple Personality'" (1994), 42:819–846.

occurs with other primitive characters, this split is unique because the credibility of the patient and subsequently the diagnosis are often the issue. Survivors of incest may grow up not believing themselves (Kramer, 1985), or feeling that they will not be believed by others (Sachs, 1967), and such patterns can be enacted in the hospital. The dramatic quality of "switching" to other personalities, and the obvious secondary gain of disowning one's behavior, especially when criminal charges are involved (Orne, Dinges, and Orne, 1984), add to the controversy. Furthermore, the role of iatrogenic hypnotic influences has long aroused suspicion that such patients have been created or at least further fragmented by treatment (James, 1890; McDougall, 1926). Yet, interestingly, there is not a single documented case of iatrogenic "multiple personality" to my knowledge, despite claims that it could be intentionally created in order to carry out covert missions in the name of national security (Estabrooks, 1945).[1]

It has been said that many refractory patients with borderline pathology, eating disorders, and some in very long analyses, may suffer from unrecognized dissociative problems, also (Kluft, 1987a). Some cases of transsexualism (Schwartz, 1988), bestiality (Shengold, 1967), pedophilia, drug addition, prostitution, and striptease dancing may also be linked to dissociative pathology (Socarides, 1992). If these findings are to be taken seriously, it might be useful to apply and synthesize the wealth of knowledge accrued by psychoanalysis to further our understanding of DID and the related but less dramatic situations in daily psychoanalytic work.

But, it has been unclear where multiple personality fits in. For example, Kernberg's (1975) classification of character pathology, as determined by the centrality of repression versus splitting, falls short of including those conditions in which "altered ego states . . . may be incorporated, in part, into the character structure of the individual" (Arlow, 1992, p. 75). It would seem that DID is one of those conditions. I am suggesting, therefore, a continuum of character pathology in which defensive altered states predominate. At one end of this continuum, I would consider multiple personality a lower-level "dissociative character," and a more consolidated ego using such altered states at the upper level. After a brief historical review, I shall present four vignettes to illustrate my hypothesis.

HISTORICAL PERSPECTIVE ON DISSOCIATION

The "lure" (Pruyser, 1975) of Janet's (1889) concept of "disaggregation" or dissociation has continued, tempting analysts from Freud on to incorporate

---

[1] Such assertions and the subsequent release of previously classified documents about government sponsored mind control research (*Project MK ULTRA*, 1977; Scheflin and Optin, 1978;

some version of his model of the mind. Janet believed that a split existed in the psyche of constitutionally predisposed people who were traumatized. As in hysteria, the development of autonomous aspects of the personality, sometimes discovered and treated by hypnosis, was seen as the etiology of multiple personality. Though organic in origin and attributed to a passive disintegration of the mind, the appeal of his spatial model has lingered, as his influence persists to this day.

Jung also theorized a split psyche composed of "personified autonomous complexes" (1902). Though not always recognized because of his break with psychoanalysis and the use of his own terminology, Jung's influence has persisted (Satinover, 1986).

Freud's attempts to incorporate the notion of a split in the psyche continued throughout his life. Initially, Breuer and he (1893–1895) described "splitting of consciousness" in hysteria and incorporated these ideas into the hypnoid state. In these traumatically induced trances, they observed that memories were unavailable to normal consciousness, and thoughts in the *condition seconde* could form their own groups of ideas. Even as Freud's thinking shifted away from this French tradition, to repression and the structural theory, he nevertheless continued to wrestle with the notion of splitting. Obviously, however, he posited an active, defensive, unconscious process in order to ward off anxiety.

Ultimately his describing various types of splitting in hysteria, dissociation, perversion (1923b), neurosis (1940a), and psychosis (1940b), resulted in some of the ambiguity over terms which has plagued psychoanalytic theory since (Lichtenberg and Slap, 1973; Pruyser, 1975). Then, as "splitting of the ego" was elaborated upon by the object-relations theorists (Klein, 1946; Fairbairn, 1952; Kernberg, 1975; Volkan, 1976), his earliest views were deemed obsolete, after which the study of hypnosis, hypnoticlike states, dissociation, and DID declined and diverged.

The interrelatedness of these phenomena (Frankel, 1990) has important implications, because I believe it was assumed that since the free associative psychoanalytic method replaced hypnosis (A. Freud, 1936), it was able to "reach" all the areas of the mind that hypnosis could. But is that really so? While Freud (1891) recognized the importance of spontaneous self-hypnosis in very suggestible people, subsequent theory and technique did not fully address this phenomenon. This oversight is significant because unrecognized, spontaneous, autohypnotic states may, in fact, remain quite elusive to analytic treatment.

Lewin (1954) observed that:

Marks, 1979; Weinstein, 1990) add a bizarre twist to this very misunderstood mental disturbance which fuels the controversy. Further discussion of this facet is beyond the scope of this volume.

> [W]e may have some resistance to the idea that analytic therapy and technique are related to sleep . . . we may be denying or ignoring the fact that when it was still growing up, its technique consisted of putting the patient into a sleeplike state and that it encouraged the dreamlike productions of the talking cure. . . . If we have, we may not be aware of all the traces of hypnotism and anesthesia we have unwittingly carried along with us [pp. 500–503].

A number of other writers have made important contributions in this area despite the thrust in other directions. Fliess (1953), for example, described the "hypnotic evasion," and Dickes (1965) redefined the hypnoid state as a primitive defensive alteration of alertness for "protecting the ego against unacceptable instinctual demands" (pp. 400–401). (He also compared and contrasted these states to classic hypnosis and sleep.) Shengold (1967, 1989) subsequently studied the autohypnotic defenses against the devastating effects of early trauma, describing "hypnotic facilitation" and "hypnotic vigilance." While Anna Freud omitted the term *dissociation* in her mechanisms of defense, she, too, reported on a patient who warded off sexual anxiety by a trancelike sleep (1954). Her emphasis on making the distinction between defenses against inner versus outer dangers through, for example, repression and denial in fantasy are pertinent here also (1936). There is no listing of the term *dissociation* by Laplanche and Pontalis (1973) or in the American Psychoanalytic Association glossary (Moore and Fine, 1990), although other well-studied, altered states, such as déjà vu (Arlow, 1959), déjà raconte (Boesky, 1969), derealization, and depersonalization (Arlow, 1966; Renik, 1978) are listed.

Glover's enthusiasm for the use of the term *dissociation* was obviously not shared by others. Considering the problems with the term *splitting,* it is no wonder that an even more nebulous and historically problematic word would not be further accepted. Instead, it quite often lost its original connotation and has been used as a qualitative description or as a synonym for splitting. Despite its "chequered" history (Glover, 1943), though, the term persists, and the dialectic between Janet and Freud continues a century later. A redefinition of this term, therefore, may be useful in the understanding of multiple personality.

PSYCHOANALYTIC THEORIES OF "MULTIPLE PERSONALITY"

Just as the theory of a split in the psyche has been applied to most types of psychopathology, so have most theories been applied to explain DID. Sensationalized in fiction (Garcia, 1990) and reviewed extensively elsewhere (Ellenberger, 1970; Berman, 1981; Kluft, 1984; Greaves, 1993), it is defined in DSM-IV (APA, 1994) as "the presence of two or more distinct identities or personality states (each with its own relatively enduring pattern of perceiving, relating to, and thinking about the environments and self)"(p. 230). This disturbance, not due to any organic or medical condition, is also characterized by an extensive memory problem during which time at least two of these personality states recurrently take control of the individual's behavior.

Freud's (1923b) theory that different identifications could take over consciousness at different times relied on repression and did not include autohypnotic phenomena or trauma. Jones (1953) noted almost offhandedly that Breuer's case of Anna O was one of a double personality, and the implication was that Freud's views were sufficient to explain her symptoms. However, Ferenczi came the closest to understanding this condition, but interestingly did not apply his formulation to this legendary case. Ferenczi's observations about children who became automatons in order to comply with their parents' sexual demands linked incest trauma with trance states. He described "various kinds of splits in the personality" and "all the different fragments, each of which behaves as a separate personality" (Ferenczi, 1933, p. 165). His findings are in keeping with contemporary views, but his early death and the discrediting of his ideas delayed an appreciation of his work. Other theories followed suit, but they did not address the issue of trauma until decades later. For example, Erickson and Kubie (1939) described a vertical division of the mind which contained two relatively complete mental groupings.

Fairbairn (1952), of the British Middle School, was also interested in "multiple personality," and he thought that Freud's tripartite model was just one example of the possible "functioning structural units" of the mind, and that "multiple personality" was another. In addition, he described a layering and fusion of internal objects which varied in complexity from person to person.

Federn, whose contribution to the understanding of ego states and fluctuating ego boundaries in psychosis and dream states is better known, thought that "multiple personality" could be explained on the basis of the reactivation of different repressed ego states (1952). Watkins and Watkins (1979–1980, 1993) have elaborated on Federn's ideas and conceptualize a continuum of dividedness in the mind, from normal adaptive differentiation to pathological maladaptive dissociation, which would be epitomized by "multiple personality."

Abse (1974, 1983) postulated that both an altered state of consciousness and splitting of the ego were necessary for the dissociation central in DID. Such a defensive solution was at the expense of repression and clear continuous consciousness, resulting in a type of identity diffusion maintained by amnestic dissociated "personalities" (Akhtar, 1992).

"Multiple personality" has also been considered a variant of borderline personality (Buck, 1983; Clarey, Burstin, and Carpenter, 1984), a type of transitional object (Marmer, 1980), and to be caused by developmental arrest (Lasky, 1978).

It has even been thought to be a variant of the narcissistic character (Gruenwald, 1977; Greaves, 1980) using Kohut's (1971) model of the "vertical split." Undoubtedly, such severely traumatized people have narcissistic issues (Kestenberg and Brenner, 1988), but, according to Goldberg (personal communication, 1991), Kohut did not intend for his theory to explain this condition.

Kluft's (1984) view is that it depends on dissociation proneness and overwhelming life experiences, especially sexual abuse, which result in whatever propensity for dividedness exists at the level of development at the time of the trauma. This developmental perspective grafted onto Janet's ideas led him to conclude that DID is a posttraumatic disorder of childhood.

Finally, Arlow (1992), who builds on Freud's theory, speculates that it is "the alternating conscious representation of highly organized fantasy systems, each of which coalesces into a particular idiosyncratic identity. These identities are not compatible with each other and . . . can dramatize internal conflicts" (p. 75).

Levine (1992) concludes that "there is something out there . . . I'm not sure, however, that we have settled on the best way to formulate it" (p. 2).

I find it helpful to think of "multiple personality" as part of a spectrum.

CASE 1. A HYPNOID STATE: DISSOCIATION AS A DEFENSE

Paul reported that he had just run a red light, narrowly avoiding a major collision. "I just don't know where my mind went . . . ," he confessed in a shaken and bewildered way. He then said that he often fantasized about an accident on the way to analysis and wondered what would happen. He went on to comment on how his competitiveness was being enacted by putting his belongings on the desk and then smiling triumphantly as he approached the couch. He then expressed his deep love and hatred, hesitated, became quiet, and seemed to get lost in thought. He said he knew there was much more on his mind but was unable to say what. It was brought to his attention that he was getting lost in thought again, alluding to his near auto accident. He brightened and immediately responded, realizing that it was, in fact, the same issue. He recalled that during the previous hour he was very critical about the uncertainty of not starting exactly on time every time. It was pointed out to him that his need to have a perfectly attuned analyst was necessary to keep him from feeling severely hurt and rejected. He was thankful for the tactful comments and, crying quietly, he acknowledged his narcissistic fragility very briefly. He then felt a powerful urge to retaliate. He felt very wounded, and his unacceptable wish for murderous revenge was on his mind when he ran the red light.

CASE 2. CHARACTEROLOGICAL DISSOCIATION: UPPER-LEVEL DISSOCIATIVE CHARACTER

Samantha had made significant strides in her personal and professional life but still was unable to reconstruct her childhood after years of analysis. She remained sexually inhibited, feeling disgust and revulsion during encounters with her idealized lovers, who would inevitably disappoint her, leaving her feeling trapped in a sadomasochistic dyad. Repeating a pattern from childhood, her analysis was notable for her tendency toward tiredness, which often progressed to falling asleep for an entire session. Her sleep seemed blissful and satisfying. During times where erotic transference issues were in ascendancy, she slept for months.

Earlier efforts at interrupting her somnolence (Dickes, 1965) and interrupting her hypnotic evasion were unsuccessful, so, following Ferenczi's (1914a) advice, she was "permitted" to sleep and dream as long and as often as she needed to. Samantha experienced hypnogogic hallucinations (Isakower, 1938), sleep paralysis, and cataplexy, essentially developing narcolepsy. The situation became a source of great curiosity to the analyst, who soon realized that countertransference issues were operative when he found himself becoming sleepy also (McLaughlin, 1975) and fantasizing about research grants to study the effects of analysis on narcolepsy! He, too, evidently questioned the wisdom of analysis where there was a full-blown sleep disorder as a flight from intolerable sexual anxiety.

Samantha's sleep, however, gradually became ego dystonic after a long period of waking up disoriented and tripping over her feet as she exited the office. She became more aware of the sexual nature of her associations, developing the capacity to observe herself drifting off to sleep. She also recognized the defensive nature of her slumber and would comment on it as she helplessly drifted off. Eventually, she began to talk during these altered states, her voice sounding distant, stilted, and hollow.

Samantha had amnesia for what she would discuss during these times, but it was not recognized until efforts to tie in material from a previous session revealed that she had no recollection of it and even less curiosity. The subtle changes in her speech became easier to recognize, and the behavioral manifestations of her confusion following long periods of silence seemed to be consistent indicators of her dissociation. She had no observing ego during these times and would startle easily. The analyst continued to listen, essentially becoming an auxiliary memory bank and assuming that one day she would become curious about what was being said. She would utter unrelated phrases or blurt out what seemed like memories, and then return to her usual consciousness totally bewildered by her comments.

Not unlike someone becoming aware of an embarrassing parapraxis but unable to stop, Samantha did indeed begin to wonder what it was that she was trying to say. She felt very "crazy" and out of control, terrified that there was another part of herself, or worse yet, another self, locked inside, struggling to burst forth. She seemed convinced of something very real, even structural, going on in her mind (Singer, 1988) and had urges to run from analysis. It was pointed out to her that if she could not escape through "sleeping," then she might feel the need to run in a literal sense. She calmed down temporarily but felt as though she were entering a new phase of analysis when she realized what might be bothering her. One day, Samantha saw a television program about sexual abuse of children, and she flushed with embarrassment, feeling that it was actually her life being discussed. She felt utterly transparent and "found out."

This extreme overidentification left Samantha feeling very strange and unreal when she arrived for her next hour. As she recalled the events, she spoke in a detached manner, observing herself in a depersonalized state (Arlow, 1966). She then became drowsy, fearing that the other self was coming out again.

Memories eventually emerged in her sleeplike state. "Bad things" had actually occurred, but it felt like it was to someone else. What she described was a time in elementary school when an uncle moved in with the family for an extended period of time. "It was a though he needed a sex object ... ," Samantha lamented. He would get into bed with her and sing her songs while she relaxed into a blissful state. When his sexualized touching excited and overstimulated her, she would become agitated and enraged. Memories of his explosive orgasms were verbalized and enacted daily in this state. The use of repetitive hypnogogic images and dreams of these events were very important in the therapeutic process. Gradually, she developed some awareness of what she was describing, getting a sense of continuity about her childhood. She also wondered about her mother's role. She was puzzled over the contradiction of mother's anxious overprotectiveness and her allowing such things to happen.

Through countless repetitions of reliving genital sensations, smothering feelings, and nausea, Samantha was then able to believe that it was indeed she and not some other version of herself who had actually experienced the trauma. Her sleepiness diminished dramatically afterwards. The reconstruction process, which was quite lengthy, ultimately enabled her to more fully understand that her sexual inhibition was linked to trauma. It was a repetition, in an altered state, of her attempts to reduce her and her uncle's excitement during his nighttime visits to her bed. Through her own hypnotic facilitation (Shengold, 1967) she engaged this scenario regularly on the couch, as she tried to elicit and control a feared sexual response in the transference. Her long-standing learning problems (Ferenczi, 1933; Kramer, 1990) improved considerably.

CASE 3. DID: LOWER-LEVEL DISSOCIATIVE CHARACTER (A PSYCHOTHERAPY HOUR)

Rhonda was not sitting in her usual chair nor wearing her usual glasses in the waiting room. She had an uncharacteristically wide grin as she sprang from the chair and sidled into the office, appearing very light on her feet and secretly amused. She then looked around, stating that it seemed like a very long time since she had been there. In fact, it was the day before. She announced that she was instructed by Rhonda to mention that she had taken a red pill. Her unusually youthful and cheerful behavior, along with referring to herself in the third person, suggested that "another personality was out." Several years into treatment and having developed a therapeutic alliance in this state of mind, she proceeded. She said that Rhonda would not be returning and that she, "Lana," was the one who woke up that morning and came to the appointment. Recently, Rhonda had been tormented by recurrent dreams of lying on a bed in an all-white room while something was being done to her. When asked what else she needed to say, since it was assumed that her "appearance" was dynamically determined, she appeared puzzled and then became silent. Then her eyes darted back and forth, her face contorted, and she became terrified. She cried in a shaky voice and said she wanted to come back to the office. She appeared lost and disoriented, thinking she was in another doctor's office. She protested being tied down, screaming about her legs being pulled apart and placed in stirrups. She writhed in pain, crying that she was not a bad girl. Doubled over, she begged that she be allowed to return. She was empathically told that it seemed as if she were reliving a trauma from long ago, that, indeed, she had never left the office. She eventually stopped sobbing, and her eyes started to flutter for about ten seconds.

Her eyes then deviated to the left, and she started to twirl her hair in an infantile manner. Her face appeared to change, her expression becoming softer and more quizzical, as she spoke like a little girl. She then asked for her crayons. When asked to whom her therapist was talking, she exclaimed, "Violet!" in a surprised and exasperated way, as if to say, "Don't you recognize me, you silly man?" She had said that she was 3 years old and liked to draw. Utilizing play therapy techniques, an alliance with her was developing through drawing. She was handed the crayons and a pad of paper, which she eagerly, but warily, took. She then hopped off the chair and sat on the floor, scribbling a drawing of her aunt. Unlike most of the "others," "Violet" was left-handed. "Violet" went on to say that this "old aunt" was not there anymore. "She was died," "Violet" said and then went on talking about losing her in a very sad and forlorn way, as the end of the hour was approaching rapidly.

"Violet" and the other child alters never wanted to leave the office and would cry incessantly in terror at the prospect of being all alone. The therapist employed a very modest hypnotic technique of asking her to close her eyes for the count of three while requesting "Lana" to return. This approach seemed to help focus her own autohypnotic efforts. With this patient, he used the strategy of having "whoever" started the session to end the session so there would be less confusion and disorientation afterwards, allowing her to return to her very demanding teaching job. "Lana," however, did not ree-merge, and the patient became more regressed and mute in a dissociated state of limbo. He, therefore, suggested that Rhonda return, which she eventually did. However, she was horrified and completely bereft to discover herself in a session. She was disoriented as to day and time, having "switched" the night before. From her perspective, she had been in a fuguelike state. She became reoriented, but she continued to feel agitated and tearful about not only her confusion, but also about the content of the session which was seemingly disconnected from her current state of consciousness.

CASE 4. DID: LOWER-LEVEL DISSOCIATIVE CHARACTER

Cindy was unclear about her reasons for analysis, but she conveyed a look of someone hopelessly trapped and pleading for help. She complained of depression, feelings of detachment, and inability to sustain intimate relations. Despite her history of severe physical deprivation and being raised by alco-holic relatives, she overcame considerable adversity to become a successful architect. She was not psychologically minded, had great difficulty verbalizing her inner experience, but was utterly committed to treatment. Occasionally, however, she would miss an appointment and seem uncharacteristically blasé or even oblivious to it. It was also not unusual for her to be mute for two or three successive hours, after which time she felt so apologetic and pressured that she forced herself to talk, only to repeat this pattern over and over. Appropriately, she questioned whether she were able to do analysis but was determined to try harder.

Several years into treatment, she reported a nightmare in which she was happily sitting with her uncle, who was transformed into a hideous assailant.

She ran out of her house screaming for her life. Shortly afterward, she reported another dream in which her uncle was so drunk that she lovingly helped him to bed. The bed then became a bare mattress on the floor on which he was lying naked, and he grabbed her. She felt very troubled by these dreams and began to open up about her chaotic childhood in which she was required to do "what the women were supposed to do."

A real situation arose in her life which threatened to interrupt treatment, and she felt she had no choice but to terminate. While she was in the midst of contemplating her fate, her house was burglarized while her husband was away. She fully expected to be raped and killed, describing a detached feeling of observing herself, a depersonalization, followed by a blanking-out sensation in which she acted automatically. She recounted her ordeal with eerie, mechanical affect. Several days later, she experienced a hypnagogic state in which she saw a "picture" of a young girl being molested in an empty house. As she described the hallucination, she began to whimper and cry in a little girl's voice. She then became agitated and acted as if she were struggling to break free, lying disoriented and frightened on the couch. She identified herself as "Tina," an 8-year-old-girl, and sobbed quietly until she entered a sleeplike state. Several minutes later, Cindy looked at her watch in a startled way, wondering what happened to the time, and vaguely feeling she had missed something.

Over the next two weeks, a series of "alters" entered the office, identifying themselves, their functions, and leaving on their own at the end of the session. Each had a different version of the burglary. "Clara," for example, the sexual one, thought that if she could satisfy the man's lust, her life would be spared. "Judy," on the other hand, tried to outsmart him and get the attention of a neighbor. An internal disagreement ensued, but "Judy" ultimately prevailed, sustaining a minor wound before the man fled. She also said that many of the others had waited a long time to make themselves fully known to Cindy because she needed to know about the many terrible things that had happened to them. She was grateful for help and knew how essential treatment was.

Cindy had amnesia for these days. Essentially, she was in a fugue. She confessed, "It was happening again, the way it used to, a long time ago." She sheepishly admitted hearing voices intermittently for most of her life and being secretive about them for fear of being thought totally crazy (Kluft, 1987b). She further acknowledged that during her mysterious absences and long silences on the couch, she often had no memory of her actions or thoughts. She hoped that over time things would settle down again so she would not have to think so much, but the analyst pointed out that he was informed there was a lot she needed to know. He also wondered about the timing of these dramatic revelations, but she could offer no explanation.

The next hour, Cindy stopped suddenly just outside the office door, cringing in fear as she seemed to go into a trancelike state. She cautiously entered the office, standing by the door looking in horror at the couch. She apparently had switched to "Tina" again, who was confused and frightened over being back in the office. "Tina" said she was supposed to say that she was the one who was molested in the empty house. She then described, in considerable detail, a childhood of ongoing exploitation, sadistic sexual assaults, and terror at the hands of various adults in her life. She was sobbing, cowering, and in enormous emotional pain, most unlike Cindy. The analyst was deeply moved by her anguish.

The following hour, Cindy returned, bewildered and sad. She reported amnesia from the time she walked down the hall prior to the session until many hours afterward, when she found herself huddled in a corner at home, with her eyes red and swollen from crying. She did not return to work that day. She became rigid and silent for several minutes. When she spoke again, her voice was slower, distant, and commanding, while the cadence of her speech became slower and forced. She identified herself as "Judy" again and scolded me in a most direct fashion. "How could you let her leave like that? Didn't you know how upset she was? We want to trust you to keep things like that from happening! She has to be able to go back to work! How could you let her go?"

The analyst was initially taken aback by her surprising rebuke, which he thought alluded not only to her wish to pull herself together before she left the office, but also to her deep fears of abandonment in the transference. It seemed as if she were pleading with him, in an altered state of consciousness, not to let her break treatment in her current condition. The analytic challenge at that point was to help her recognize this conflict before it was too late.

DISCUSSION

The essence of Paul's hypnoid state seemed to be contained in Samantha's characterological defense and in the alters created by Rhonda and Cindy. The transient lapse of attention, the persistent somnolence, and the appearance of other selves with separate identities served to keep intolerable affective states and instinctual strivings from awareness. In other words, these four patients used various manifestations of altered states of consciousness as defensive maneuvers of the ego. The nature of these states, their origins, their meanings, how they were utilized, or whether they were incorporated into the character had implications for the therapeutic process.

For example, Paul's disorientation and brief loss of awareness almost ended in catastrophe. He reported the experience in the past tense, with an observing ego, and had no loss of identity. Such lapses of consciousness, like sleeplike disturbances, were thought to be widely used defenses (Winnicott, 1945) but difficult to study because of their fleeting nature (Fenichel, 1942). Furthermore, distinguishing this state from the ubiquitous daydream or withdrawal of attention cathexis (Freud, 1915), which often occurs during automatic behaviors such as driving (Hilgard, 1977), may be difficult because it is a multiply determined compromise formation.

One could formulate this defense in terms of a regressive ego state, repression, and isolation of affect (Loewald, 1955), but equating it to the emergence of an infantile state of mind might be reductionistic. What is fairly clear is Paul's conscious wish for sympathy, an unconscious narcissistically tinged oedipal wish for murderous revenge, an unconscious wish for punishment, and the partial gratification of a near accident. What is less apparent, owing to the dearth of historical data and the nature of dissociation, is the significance of the altered state itself.

Several years before, Paul sustained a sudden object loss, at which time he described going into a dreamlike state. He could not grieve or fully accept the reality of this death (Volkan, 1981) because he did not express his feelings or fully absorb his perception of that trauma. Whatever memories he had of the unexpected, sudden impact of the tragic news and of the funeral were kept out of consciousness, very deeply repressed, with the aid of his altered state, i.e., "in dissociation." As a result, he could not tolerate surprises and would become enraged at the slightest change in his routine. As Paul was driving to his analytic hour, his murderous transference impulse threatened to emerge. In an effort to keep it out of his consciousness, a defensive, altered state was reactivated. In other words, this time he warded off an internal danger with a defense that was originally employed to protect against the external danger of the sudden object loss. In so doing, dissociation seemed to change in its function by becoming a neurotic defense, augmenting repression. Despite Paul's essentially obsessional character, he experienced these states. In contrast to Melanie Klein's (1921) view that dissociation could trigger repression, in this case faulty repression apparently triggered dissociation.

The mental content in dissociation was quite resistant to the analytic process, however. The meaning of his altered states remained inaccessible until later in the analysis when, catalyzed by a series of surrealistic dreams of himself at the funeral, he could finally begin the grieving process. It is noted that all four patients experienced recurrent dreams and/or hypnogogic hallucinations which helped bring their trauma into awareness. The manifest content of this imagery resembled the trauma itself (Pulver, 1987), and the surreal, or split, representations of the patients seemed to symbolize their own fragmented psyches (Freud, 1900; Silberer, 1909; Silber, 1970; Kohut, 1977). The elusive associations in these states, which may be accessed by hypnosis, as with Rhonda, are as potentially analyzable as the defensive function they currently serve.

In Samantha's case, illustrating an upper-level dissociative character, she apparently lapsed into autohypnotic states during the time she was sexually abused. This trauma was extensive and repetitive. That it was time-limited and did not occur until latency probably prevented her from being more disturbed. During and after this time, she became overly preoccupied with her body and would regularly retreat into confusion, chronic forgetfulness, and dreamlike states. She would appear "spacey" and intermittently inaccessible, which became her predominant mode of adaptation as she negotiated adolescence and sexual maturity. As such, it became habitual, automatic, ego syntonic, and "characterological," persisting until her analysis.

Significantly, Samantha was already troubled prior to the incest, as she struggled with abandonment fears and anal conflicts, which complicated her oedipal phase. A perfectionistic child who masochistically internalized her aggression, she eventually became aware of her rage at her mother for failing to be a "protective shield." Evidence subsequently emerged of possible earlier overstimulation. This strain trauma (Kris, 1956) may have predisposed and perhaps prepared her to become her uncle's victim. In addition, she felt that her body was not her own, that it belonged to anyone who desired it. Although traumatically reinforced, there was probably an early body ego disturbance as a result of her troubled relationship with her mother (Khan, 1963). Her obedience to others, even when they exploited her, reflected a lack of cohesion in her superego, seen in traumatized children (Kestenberg and Brenner, 1986).

It is speculated that during her sexual trauma, she dissociated along her own psychic "line of cleavage" (Freud, 1933). She appeared to have a libidinally and aggressively derived altered state. The former was an idealized land of make-believe and singing, where everyone was happy all the time. The latter was a concentration camp (Shengold, 1967) of pain, torture, suffocation, and stifled excitation, which she relived in the analysis on a regular basis. Such patients may induce these autohypnotic states by rhythmic movements, repetitive mantralike sounds, humming, singing, fixating on objects in the room, using imagery, sleep deprivation, or substance abuse (Dickes, 1965; Dickes and Papernik, 1977; Silber, 1979). Samantha began to verbalize while she dissociated. She feared that a developed other self would emerge, but it never did, as her ego was apparently integrated well enough. When traumatized and subject to powerful instinctual pressures, however, she regressed. She experienced a disturbance in the continuity of her sense of self, due to her problems in object constancy (Jacobson, 1964). In contrast to depersonalization, she lost her sense of connectedness to her participating self (Arlow,

1966). It was described as "not me," or "someone else" but was not organized into another full identity or given a name as in "multiple personality." A necessary part of her work was, therefore, a "mending of her split" (Volkan, 1976) which seemed to be maintained through autohypnosis.

Along the continuum, it would seem that intermediate-level dissociative characters could exist, in which there might be several recurrent altered states, greater disturbances in object constancy, and greater problems in maintaining the continuity of identity. They would not, however, have the highly organized fantasy system, the formed alters, or the complete disavowal of parts of the psyche one often sees in DID. These cases may be what Ellenberger (1970) referred to as attenuated multiple personality or Dissociative Disorder Not Otherwise Specified (DD-NOS in DSM-IV parlance). Earlier, more extensive trauma and longer periods of childhood in defensive altered states could be expected in these individuals whose object relations would be even more disturbed but less so than in DID.

Regarding the two patients with DID, the enactments (Shengold, 1989) in the treatment of both were convincing that they experienced severe preoedipal sexual trauma, which continued into late adolescence. Rhonda, apparently more traumatized and experiencing more early unpleasure, was especially prone to hostile destructiveness (Parens, 1979), turned against herself. She required active interventions to save her life. For her to have reached a point where she became ready and able to examine not only her altered states but the minute details of her intrapsychic activity (Gray, 1973) was a profound change for her. When treatment began, she sat for over a year, experiencing amnestic periods, fluctuating consciousness, mood changes, severe headaches, and moments of profound psychic agony. It was not until she reported fuguelike symptoms (Fisher and Joseph, 1949; Akhtar and Brenner, 1979) and referred to herself in the third person that the true nature of her problem became clear. When the ever growing multitude of her alters became known, it felt like trying to facilitate a group therapy with an unknown number of members who initially had no knowledge of the existence of each other. In order to remain empathic, it seemed necessary to suspend disbelief, despite Freud's (1915) conclusion that it was incorrect to accept "the existence in us not only of a second consciousness, but of a third, fourth, perhaps of an unlimited number of states of consciousness, all unknown to us and to one another" (p. 170). Her conviction to the contrary was particularly compelling when she experienced auditory hallucinations of her alters fighting with each other over whether to pull her "inside" and who would "take over the body."

The therapeutic task following the described hour was to reconstruct and analyze what had taken place and why. The amnesia, the altered states with different identities, and the profound regression required special attention. If not specifically addressed, they would have been overlooked by her. After a number of years of intensive outpatient and inpatient therapy, Rhonda began to see that her dissociation was, indeed, a psychologically motivated defense. It might even be protecting her from frank psychosis. Though she believed that a number of different people actually inhabited her body, over time she had come to recognize the interrelatedness of the "others." This quasidelusional thinking persisted throughout her life, yet she was intellectually gifted, able to raise a family, and could function in a very demanding job. This type of hidden ego strength, in contrast to schizophrenia, was described by Jung (1939) as a guiding spirit or "rector animus." When overwhelmed about her childhood in therapy, she would automatically "switch" to an alter who seemingly had no knowledge of the conversation. Switching to alters was her predominant defense, occurring as a protection against anxiety in the transference, also.

It came to be understood that the switching during the hour in question was a reaction to an impending surgery to determine the cause of vaginal bleeding. It began when she started dreaming about and reliving an abortion as a teenager due to impregnation by one of her brothers. The conscious pain of such an intense somatic memory (Brenner, 1988b; Kramer, 1990; Levine, 1990) was apparently warded off through an autohypnotic state and a division of her ego occurring along her own psychic line of cleavage. Rhonda created a series of such alters, using denial in fantasy and displacement, who maintained their own mind–body units, in contrast to the "false self" (Winnicott, 1960), in which the mind is disconnected from psychosomatic functioning. She created "Lana," who had a highly organized sense of self with memories, continuity, and a seeming tripartite structure of her own. "Lana" 's function seemed to be related to the abortion. When "Lana" became overwhelmed in the session, she then "switched" to an infantile alter called "Violet." "Violet" was apparently created as a defensive response to earlier trauma, loss, and abandonment. Reminiscent of the "little-man" phenomenon, she did not age and seemed frozen in time (Niederland, 1956). Her inner world was populated by perpetrators, bad girls who deserved punishment, and indifferent or helpless bystanders. Anyone or anything that was good, was short-lived. It was ultimately determined that "Violet" 's appearance in the session defended Rhonda against her terror of abandonment in the transference due to an upcoming vacation. Overall, twenty-seven alters were discovered to comprise the mosaic of form and function in Rhonda's character.

The not uncommon finding of different handedness and different ocular refractions among Rhonda's alters raises questions about the effect of severe, early trauma on interhemispheric communication and other neurophysiologic mechanisms (Sperry, 1968; Jaynes, 1976; Nasrallah, 1985; Kluft, 1987b; Levin, 1991; Putnam, 1984). While such answers may not necessarily be gotten in the analyst's consultation room, further understanding of any underlying biological substrates could determine if we are merely reifying our metaphors or if, indeed, there is an organic contribution to such notions as "alters."

In Cindy's situation, the emergence of her alters occurred during analysis, a not unheard-of situation (Kluft, 1987b). Her prolonged trancelike silences and lack of psychological mindedness were powerful resistances, similar to those of Samantha, who slept. Had it not been for the fortuitous occurrence of a perceived need to terminate and being burglarized, she may have indeed broken off treatment. At the very least, it would have taken much longer for her secret to have been revealed because Cindy's self-contained privacy did not allow her to confide in anyone. She, like Rhonda, was terrorized and brainwashed (Shengold, 1967) by her abusers never to tell. The atmosphere in the analytic situation was conducive to the reemergence of her defensive altered states, but she was not sure she could trust. People were bad. She apparently, however, felt she had no choice under the circumstances, and the forces in her mind took over. Once the other "parts" made themselves known, it became much clearer that she was not able to articulate her conflicts because they were experienced as interpersonal disagreements by a group of unknown internalized others. "Judy" 's rebuke, "How could you let her leave like that?" provided an opportunity to examine her deep wish to be cared for and protected in the transference which Cindy could not tolerate or accept.

For her to own this conflict, it became necessary to explore why "Judy" was created and what purpose she was serving in the "system." Her role as an internal protector who knew about many of the others and their own memories of trauma needed to be explored. The reconstruction of her childhood began in this context. Cindy's gradual but painful realization that their experiences were actually hers, enabled her to eventually own her feelings and drives. This type of "integration of alters" through analysis of the transference may be possible for such patients whose enactments and regressions can be managed in the analytic situation. Ongoing self-analysis of the countertransference is essential in order to maintain the therapeutic position in light of the alterations of consciousness one may feel and the need to tolerate the patient's pain from seemingly unbelievable atrocities.

CONCLUSION

I do not think that a full theoretical understanding of DID can occur until Freud's goal of uniting dream psychology and psychopathology is realized (Lewin, 1954). Nevertheless, it may be useful, clinically, to think of DID as a disturbance in character formation in which dissociation is the predominant defensive operation, resulting in seemingly autonomous alters. Through analytic exploration, it may be demonstrated that these alters are the defensive creation of severely traumatized individuals whose psychic and perhaps physical survival may have depended on the development and maintenance of such states of consciousness. A continuum of the dissociative characters may exist in which DID is at the lower level and a more consolidated ego is at the upper level.

Dissociation is described here as a defensive altered state of consciousness due to autohypnosis, augmenting repression or splitting. It develops as a primitive, adaptive response of the ego to the overstimulation and pain of external trauma, which, depending on its degree of integration, may result in a broad range of disturbances of alertness, awareness, memory, and identity. Dissociation apparently may change in its function and be employed later on as a defense against the perceived internal danger of intolerable affects and instinctual strivings. Thus, it may be a transient neurotic defense or become characterological and may even be the predominant defense. The content of associations in dissociation is as important as the defensive purpose it serves and may be accessible through hypnosis but very resistant to psychoanalysis unless the analyst is aware of its presence.

It is recommended that the extent and depth to which dissociation is part of the patient's defensive armamentarium, resulting in autohypnotic states which may complicate treatment, be considered in assessments for analyzability. Analysis of the transference may be possible in dissociative character pathology which provides an opportunity for integration of the ego. Engaging these patients in treatment may be difficult, and the art of working with them is in finding a way to help them transform their depersonalized self-observation into analytic self-observation.

Chapter 3

THE CHARACTEROLOGICAL BASIS OF
"MULTIPLE PERSONALITY"

> If each, I told myself, could but be housed in separate identi-
> ties, life would be relieved of all that was unbearable. . .
> [Robert Louis Stevenson, 1886, p. 515].

Freud's goal of integrating dream psychology with psychopathology has yet
to be reached. Historically, when his interest in dreamlike states seemed to
wane, he pursued repression theory, structural theory, and ego psychology,
bypassing these phenomena. And, since the diagnostic system that has dominated American psychiatry is essentially based on phenomenology, it by-
passes psychodynamics. As a result, there have been gaps in our deeper
understanding of certain mental conditions, most notably, that area of dreamlike altered states known as the dissociative disorders (Brenner, 1994).

Once known as Gmelin's Syndrome, exchanged personality, multiplex
personality, double existences, dual consciousness, dual personality, double
personality, plural personality, dissociated personality, alternating personal-
ity, multiple personality, split personality, multiple personality disorder, and,
most recently, dissociative identity disorder (Ellenberger, 1970; Greaves,
1993), this condition seems to be experiencing an identity crisis of its own.
It is probably the most controversial entity in psychiatric history, as skeptics
adhere to iatrogenic, factitious, and sociological theories of causation rather
than consider the role of profound trauma in childhood.

This chapter is a revised and expanded version of a paper published in the *American Journal
of Psychotherapy* (1996), 50:154–166.

Adding to its mystique is the delay in making the diagnosis, often taking six to eight years of treatment before this condition is recognized (Coons, Bowen, and Milstein, 1988). Furthermore, the revised diagnostic criteria of the DSM-IV does not greatly help the average clinician: (1) the presence of two or more distinct identities or personality states which recurrently take control of the person's behavior; (2) an inability to recall important personal information that is too extensive to be explained by ordinary forgetfulness, and is not due to the effects of a substance or a general medical condition (APA, 1994).

Once properly diagnosed, however, even if specific therapy is initiated, there are great debates on the value of hypnotherapy versus more traditional forms of treatment. The lack of reliable published outcome studies and the rapid expansion of the "growth industry" of dissociative disorders has further left a cloud of uncertainty over the "multiples" and their therapists (Piper, 1995). And finally, the highly publicized malpractice suits by relatives of patients alleging abuse, the politicizing of the False Memory Syndrome movement, and the advent of managed care, have complicated efforts to work with these patients. As a result, we have reached the new millennium, having revived, but not resolved, the century-old dialectic between Janet and Freud.

In reviewing the history of dissociation and "multiple personality," two observations emerge: that some kind of a "split" in the psyche has been invoked as the reason for most types of psychopathology, and that "multiple personality" has been thought to be a variant of virtually every known disorder. Attempts to satisfactorily explain this condition may result in heated debates or schisms into believers and nonbelievers, degenerating into squabbles detrimental to scientific thinking.

Of the many controversies currently surrounding DID, the one most pertinent to this report is the so-called "state versus trait" debate (Exetein and Bowers, 1979). In other words, is this entity best considered a "condition" or a personality problem? Should it be categorized, as it is in the DSM-IV, as an Axis I condition or, would it more accurately be an Axis II personality disorder? Or, does this entity defy categorization at all? I will examine the importance of characterological factors and describe contemporary theories that compare it to the narcissistic personality and the borderline personality. This background will help to put the idea into context that it might best be considered a unique characterological entity, i.e., the dissociative character.

TRAUMA AND CHARACTER FORMATION

Rangell's (1967) classic psychoanalytic definition describes a traumatic occurrence as:

[T]he intrusion into the psychic apparatus of a stimulus or series of stimuli (the traumatic event), varying in their qualitative manifest contents, in their quantitative characteristics, and in their time relationship, which set off an unconscious train of intrapsychic events (the traumatic process) beyond the capacity of the ego to master at that particular time. The dynamics of the traumatic intrapsychic process which ensue lead to the rupture, partial or complete, of the ego's barrier or defensive capacities against stimuli, without a corresponding subsequent ability of the ego to adequately repair the damage in sufficient time to maintain mastery and a state of security. The resulting state (the traumatic state) is a feeling of psychic helplessness, in a series of gradations from brief, transitory, and relative to more complete and long lasting. As a result of insufficient resources on the part of the ego, there is a feeling of lack of control and a vulnerability to further stimuli, without the expectation of adequate containment, mastery, and adaptations. In relatively mild or transitory degree, this state is as much a part of the human condition as is anxiety or intrapsychic content, from both of which, though contiguous, it is different. In moderate or severe degree, either in quantity or duration, it itself is a pathological state, comparable to an anxiety state that is substantial or long lasting. The traumatic state can be followed by recovery or can go on to resolution or to a further elaboration into symptom formation. In itself, it is characteristically an unstable and transient psychoeconomic condition, which in the course of mental functioning goes on to a state of greater stability, in the direction of either favorable adaptation or a more pathological psychic product [p. 80].

One of these "more pathological psychic end-products" is the incorporation of the response to trauma into character formation. Freud, in *Moses and Monotheism* (1939), reemphasized that trauma plays a very large part in the formation of neurotic symptoms. Specifically, the determinants include those overwhelming events such as perceptions or bodily symptoms during the first five years of life, especially between the ages of 2 and 4, which are forgotten and which involve the sexual and aggressive instincts. A fixation to the trauma results in a compulsion to repeat whereas a negative, defensive reaction is manifested by avoidance, inhibitions, or phobias. And, if mastery is at one end of a continuum and symptoms are at the other end, it would follow that character traits are somewhere in between because they reflect fixation to trauma, yet are ego syntonic.

Nunberg (1956) elaborated on Freud's ideas by stating that such character traits could develop which would either repeat or avoid the trauma. Trauma would result in retardation of libido development or regression from a genital to a pregenital phase. In either case, the development of the traits would be in reaction to pregenital impulses. Of significance here, also, is Glover's notion of the screening function of trauma (1929) in that a memory of one trauma can mask another or be the condensation of many repetitive similar traumatic experiences. So, severe character pathology with the screening of trauma and preoedipal fixations can result from the ego's attempt to resolve overwhelming early experiences.

CHARACTEROLOGICAL ASPECTS OF DID

Ross and Lowenstein (1992) observe that:

> [T]he new paradigm of M.P.D. (D.I.D.) is a complex, chronic form of developmental posttraumatic dissociative disorder, primarily related to severe, repetitive childhood abuse or trauma, usually beginning before the age of five. [As a result] . . . the traumatically-induced dissociated states of consciousness lead to the development of multiple ''personalities'' [p. 7].

Thus they conclude that personality development goes awry, resulting in many personalities instead of one.

There is much research on the incidence of personality disorders in this population. For example, Coons et al. (1988) revealed that 86 percent of a sample of fifty patients met diagnostic criteria for at least one disorder; 56 percent of that group met criteria for borderline personality. What is unclear, however, is whether these findings reflect comorbidity, as is commonly thought, or whether they pick up on a pervasive characterological foundation of DID. Armstrong (1991), who studied the Rorschach profiles of fourteen patients with a dissociative disorder diagnosis, concluded that this sample was not psychotic but did have difficulty in affect regulation. She also observed a tendency toward introversion, internalization, an appreciation of subtlety, and a capacity for empathy. Although these patients exhibited borderline type vulnerabilities, they also had unusual areas of strength, which suggested ''an atypical developmental pathway'' (p. 544).

In a study of ninety-one patients whose ''personalities'' were therapeutically blended into ''unification,'' Kluft (1988) observed that almost 95 percent required much additional therapy. Failure to work ''with the problematic character traits of the unified individual'' (p. 220) resulted in a very high relapse rate back into dividedness. He then concludes that ''the cure of multiple personality disorder leaves the patient afflicted with single personality disorder . . . '' (p. 225). Kluft's prophetic recognition of the enormous characterological problems in this population has been confirmed by many clinicians who have observed that the ''psychic welding'' of alters through hypnosis does not hold. Despite their high hypnotizability and the centrality of autohypnosis in dissociation (Bliss, 1986), the underlying nature of the condition requires a more sophisticated treatment. It is now generally felt that a long-term psychodynamically informed approach with a variable amalgam of hypnotherapeutic techniques is the treatment of choice (Marmer, 1991). Such psychotherapeutic recommendations, along with the absence of specific pharmacologic agents, make this treatment quite different from the major Axis I conditions such as schizophrenia and the affective illnesses.

DID versus Narcissistic Personality

It has been theorized that DID is a variant of the narcissistic personality disorder (Gruenwald, 1977; Greaves, 1980). Schwartz (1994), however, feels that it is essential to consider it "both a chronic post-traumatic stress disorder and a complex, mixed-character disorder syndrome" (p. 194). Summarizing the work of Smith (1989) and Ferguson (1990), he describes "parallel narcissistic self-organizations, involving elaborate layering of false self-constructions and an overreliance on omnipotent defenses" (p. 196). He feels that the acting out and splitting seen in borderline personality may be prominent in the early part of treatment, whereas narcissistic features are more evident later. In contrast to Marmer's (1980) theory that alter personalities are "transitional objects forced inward" (p. 458), it has been postulated here that these patients have not developed nor can use transitional objects. Preferring a relational psychoanalytic model, which he feels is especially well suited to chronic trauma victims who have known domination and abuse, Schwartz (1994) notes that the paradigm shift from drive and defense to intersubjectivity could allow a better understanding of this condition. He concludes, therefore, that it is "a variation of narcissistic personality disorder involving the collapse of intersubjective experiencing and significant derailments of the developmental lines of aggression, fantasy, and use of transitional phenomena" (p. 224).

This formulation is controversial, not only because of the question of transitional phenomena[1] but also because it seems to minimize the importance of amnesia and altered states. In addition, it draws on Winnicott's well-known concept of the false self, which by definition is a mental construct disconnected from the psychosomatic functions. Clinical work with DID reveals that many alter personalities have intimate, albeit disturbed, relationships with their bodies, experiencing somatic memories, tactile hallucinations,

---

[1] Indirect evidence that these patients in fact do use transitional objects is easily gotten by a casual inspection of patient rooms on a dissociative disorder inpatient program, which reveal more stuffed animals per capita than anywhere else in the hospital!

conversion reactions, body-image distortions, and psychophysiologic reactions. Often, these symptoms are seemingly unique to certain altered states. These findings, therefore, suggest an important mind–body relationship which is not present in the false self. Finally, the use of the Kohutian model of the mind with its vertical splitting hypothesis is problematic because it was not intended to be applied to the understanding of "multiple personality" (see chapter 2). Even though these patients may have a narcissistic investment in their dividedness (Kluft, 1988) and severely traumatized individuals may have narcissistic problems (Kestenberg and Brenner, 1995), it does not necessarily follow that they have a narcissistic personality, per se.

DID versus Borderline Personality

Berzoff and Darwin (1995), in their work with DID, have also focused on characterological aspects and posttraumatic symptoms. The issue, as they see it, is whether DID is a variant of borderline personality disorder (Buck, 1983; Clarey, Burstin, and Carpenter, 1984) or whether there is comorbidity. After a review of a patient's fifteen-year course of treatment with both authors, they conclude "that an integrative diagnosis that included altered ego states, object relations, dissociation, and a trauma etiology would have made the most sense . . . " (p. 464).

Herman (1992) has labeled such a diagnostic entity a "complex posttraumatic stress disorder," but she views DID and BPD as part of a continuum, modern-day variants of what was once called "hysteria": "patients with borderline personality lack the dissociative capacity to form fragmented alters, but they have similar difficulty developing an integrated identity" (p. 127). Such individuals suffer from disturbances in consciousness, affect tolerance, trust in relationships, and the sense of self.

Fink and Golinkoff (1990) studied the differences between sixteen DID and eleven borderline personality patients, using structured interviews and psychological testing. Despite similarities in the high incidence of mood disorders in both, anxiety disorders were seen almost three times as often in DID. In addition, the presence of Schneiderian first rank symptoms of schizophrenia was significantly higher in DID. They concluded that the similarities of "an extremely high degree of internal disorganization, a high level of affective instability, and extreme distress" represent a lack of specificity of the testing "in differentiating severe character pathology from post-traumatic disturbances" (p. 133). Rather than invoking the issues of comorbidity or variants, they see a blurring of two distinct entities from improper interpretation of psychological testing.

Marmer (1991), in contrasting DID with borderline personality disorder, believes that in the former the self is more split than the object; in the latter, he contends that the object is more split and that there is a greater tendency toward idealization and devaluation. Metapsychologically, the area of greatest importance and complexity in comparing these two conditions is this exploration of dissociation and splitting, the latter being the hallmark of the borderline personality. Although studied widely, there still is no consensus and confusion continues.

The DSM-IV (APA, 1994) describes a dissociative symptom as "a disruption in the usually integrated functions of consciousness, memory, identity, or perception of the environment" (p. 231). Once again, such a definition is useful, but it is limited because of the exclusive emphasis on phenomenology. In an effort to explore dissociation in more depth, Davies and Frawley (1994) also apply an object relations model, seeing it as "a completely separate organization of self and object representations" (p. 64). They contend that "events become incorporated and ultimately understood vis-à-vis the particular matrices of self and object experience within which they are ensconced, and that they are bound together and organized with particular regard to the intense emotional experiences that accompany them" (p. 64). They share the view that the original traumatic experience reemerges in unmodified form in such states. Stressing the relational aspects of this organization also, the dissociated child "exists only in the context of a perpetually abusive object relationship" (p. 71). Furthermore, they see "multiple personality" at the bottom of a continuum of dissociative *disorders,* in those who have suffered more sadistic abuse from perpetrators with whom they have had a close relationship. The notion of some type of a continuum is appealing to many therapists, but, here too, there is a lack of consensus.

Marmer and Fink (1994), in their comprehensive comparison of the borderline personality disorder with DID, conclude that despite similarities in disturbances in identity, affect regulation, interpersonal relations, and impulse control, especially regarding self-injury, there are crucial differences between the two. They feel that while splitting occurs in both, it results in polarization in the former versus identity division in the latter. In addition, they consider dissociation to be different from splitting and occurring in both also. They describe dissociation in the former as a "low tech" spaced out state, as opposed to a more symbolized sophisticated "waking dream" in DID. Furthermore, they consider trauma as an important precursor in both, but note a developmental disturbance resulting in a lack of repression in BPD. They conclude that DID, "by use of primary process-linked symbolic dissociation, is able to continue development to the repression hierarchy, although at a profound cost of simultaneous suspension of reality testing" (p. 765).

With regard to aggression, they see those with BPD as coming from families with overt aggression as opposed to covert or secret aggression in DID. As mentioned earlier, psychological testing, especially if one uses newer specialized instruments like the Dissociative Experiences Scales (DES) or SCID-D, and if one considers the element of trauma in the interpretation of projective materials, apparently distinguishes these two entities. And finally, manifestations in relationships and in the transference are seen as different. BPD patients may develop an intense chaotic rapprochement-style transference, characterized by clinging and idealization alternating with flight, rage, and devaluation. In contrast, DID patients are described as being continually distrustful and wary about relationships, yet inwardly are desperately searching for someone who will listen to and believe them. Although abandonment issues are present in both conditions, they are handled differently. The BPD patient is extroverted, being prone to externalize intrapsychic conflict by actively polarizing people into "good" and bad" part objects; the DID patient tends to be cautious, wary, and introverted, relying on their inner world, i.e., their alters, for soothing and comfort. Having convincingly contrasted the two, they leave us with the original question. How is this entity best described? After all, a posttraumatic disorder of childhood occurs during the time of personality development.

DID as a Unique Character

To my knowledge, only two writers, including myself, have expressed the explicit view that it is a unique characterological entity. These theories overlap in important ways, but are at variance with each other also. In a case of parallel development, McWilliams (1994) describes the "dissociative personality," while I prefer the "dissociative character." In both, DID is seen as a personality disorder whose predominant defense mechanism is dissociation. McWilliams envisions a continuum of DID itself, with some patients operating on a neurotic level while the more disturbed subpopulation would be organized at a borderline or psychotic level. A schema like this might seem to be supported by Kluft's (1986c) notion of "high functioning multiples," a designation given to those patients who elude hospitalization, do not seriously self-mutilate, achieve considerable stability and success in their lives, and do well in therapy; i.e., they integrate easily. Unfortunately, Kluft's description of three patients does not lend itself to anything other than data about *functioning* and does not address the deeper issues of whether these patients actually have a different psychic structure from the "lower functioning" DID patients. Certainly, those individuals with concurrent substance abuse or eating disorders, for example, would have additional problems which predispose them to further regression and require special attention.

Critics of McWilliams' (1994) model question how someone could be so seriously traumatized at such an early age, have such a profound disturbance in identity and reality testing, yet be a "neurotic." The juxtaposition of a neurotic, oedipal level of intrapsychic development with such a catastrophic illness could further strain the credibility of the "multiple personality" diagnosis, but some patients apparently appear this way. McWilliams did not elaborate on how this contradiction could be reconciled, but it may be that this subgroup is either "reaching up," as it were, to use neurotic defenses to mask a more primitive organization, or has, in fact, freed up some ego to reach this level of development (chapter 4). But even if the latter were so, many writers still feel that the predominant fixations in DID are preoedipal in nature, associated with profound separation and abandonment anxiety. More work is needed in this area to further understand the various levels of development observed in these patients.

In an effort to address such issues, I, too, describe a continuum, but it is a continuum of dissociative *character* pathology. As such, I consider the true "multiple personality" a lower level dissociative character. I also postulate that there is an intermediate level dissociative character with a more integrated psyche which could correspond to the DSM-IV category of Dissociative Disorder, Not Otherwise Specified (DD-NOS), and the so-called attenuated multiple personality. In addition, I consider the existence of a higher level dissociative character, in which the altered states of consciousness would result in minimal disturbance of identity.

The cornerstone of this model is the notion that dissociation itself is on a continuum, which is redefined as follows:

A defensive altered state of consciousness due to autohypnosis, augmenting repression or splitting. It develops as a primitive, adaptive response of the ego to the overstimulation and pain of external trauma, which, depending on its degree of integration, may result in a broad range of disturbances of alertness, awareness, memory, and identity. Dissociation apparently may change in its function and be employed later on as a defense against the perceived internal danger of intolerable affects and instinctual strivings [p. 841].

Such a conceptualization incorporates self-hypnosis with the object relations theory of mental development, which organizes character development around defensive operations based on splitting or repression. In so doing, dissociation is seen as a two-step defense mechanism which results in an enhanced separation of mental contents. The psychic cost of such a seeming disconnectedness is at the very least, a loss of continuity of consciousness, and at the most, the development of multiple personality. These phenomena are observable signs and symptoms, which the clinician, if open minded and properly trained, can then recognize.

Ironically, one of the criticisms of this attempt to bridge the ever widening chasm between descriptive psychiatry and psychoanalysis, was that the definition was too narrow and restrictive (Brenneis, 1995). It was intended, however, to streamline many disparate theories by describing a mechanism which defended against anxiety due to here-and-now intrapsychic conflict through the reactivation of altered states from past trauma. The redeployment of these altered states for a new purpose could be attributed to the development of secondary autonomy of these dissociated states. This relative autonomy could then explain how these states may, at times, be willed on by the patient or accessed through hypnosis, yet at other times occur spontaneously to ward off anxiety from intrapsychic conflict (Ross, Ball, Sullivan, and Caroff, 1989). An appreciation of the dual nature of dissociation could then help therapists work psychodynamically on both the reconstruction of one's past, and on present day or transferential issues.

PERVERSE SEXUALITY

Further exploration of the characterological basis of multiple personality then led to the rediscovery of the importance of perverse sexuality as an organizing influence in this entity (see chapter 4 for more information). Sexual dysfunction has been reported in 84 percent of this population (Coons et al., 1988), but in-depth psychodynamic exploration of the significance of this pathology has been quite difficult. Beginning with an informal survey, I noted that in a sample of inpatients admitted with a dissociative identity disorder diagnosis, over 50 percent reported feared or actual loss of sexual impulses ranging from heterosexual and homosexual promiscuity to sadomasochism, pedophilia, bestiality, exhibitionism, menage à trois, and erotic asphyxia. Significantly, the history and symptoms of one who develops a "classical" perversion may be quite similar to one who develops DID: early trauma, precocious, repeated exposure to genitals of the opposite sex, severe anxiety, excessive aggression, body image disturbances, and an impaired relationship to reality. In addition, therapists who see large numbers of DID patients almost universally agree that it is commonplace to see a female patient have a least one male alter who is very unhappy or angry about being trapped in the body of a woman. However, the rage and resulting self-mutilation that accompanies this particular grievance is often obscured by the chaos, turmoil, pain, and drama related to the scenarios of abuse that are being reconstructed or apparently relived from childhood. As a result, the significance of this transsexual conflict may easily be overlooked, especially because it, too, is dissociated. Nevertheless, psychotherapeutic exploration into this sexual identity issue and other related conflicts provide a crucial avenue to follow in treatment of these patients.

To illustrate this point, a case will be described in chapter 4, of a woman in treatment for almost a decade, which evolved into a five times per week analytic experience. The nature of the therapeutic alliance was such that analysis of the transference was possible, allowing the emergence of her major states of consciousness to become fully involved in the therapeutic process. In so doing, three predominant alters, organized around three different sexual pathways (i.e., sadomasochistic heterosexuality, homosexuality, and transsexualism), came to be understood as providing the important functions of encapsulating and disowning her aggression, anxiety, pain, traumatic memories, and sexual gratification. It appeared that through this mode of character formation some healthy ego became freed up for more advanced development. As mentioned earlier, the capacity for empathy and for abstract, symbolic thinking, for example, a surprising achievement in such a seemingly disturbed patient population, might be explained by this mechanism.

It became evident that intrapsychic conflict was experienced as an internalized interpersonal conflict and that it was necessary to appreciate the defensive quality of "switching" from one alter to another as a way of reducing anxiety. For example, the patient warded off the anxiety of emerging heterosexual transference feelings by spontaneous switching to her homosexual alter in the course of therapy hours. But, this alter also had her own memories of abuse which needed to be contended with. By appreciating the dual nature of dissociation, it could then be analyzed within the therapy as a defense against here-and-now anxiety which utilized altered states from previous trauma. The content of these altered states then formed the basis for her piecing together the shattered remains of her childhood.

MEMORY AND DREAMS

Exactly what the significance of such contents are, and how this material might correlate with the past, is at the crux of the problem of "multiple personality" (see chapter 5). Consequently, another perplexing criticism of my theory was based on the mistaken idea that I thought the manifest content of what is "in dissociation" is always a replica of the original trauma (Brenneis, 1995). Such a controversial position would assume a video replay quality of dissociation, which would not take into account the possibility of perceptual distortion or elaboration in fantasy. While it may be that trauma is registered and stored in unmodified form in some cases, one needs to consider a variety of other factors such as the theoretical problem of distinguishing repressed memories from unconscious fantasy, a perverse and negotiable attitude toward reality, the role of suggestion, a disturbance in the barrier between wakefulness and REM sleep in traumatized individuals (Ross et al., 1984), and the dreamlike secondary revision quality to dissociative content (Marmer, 1991; Brenner, 1995).

The psychic reworking of such material was illustrated (Brenner, 1995) by a patient who was describing the death of a childhood friend, an accident which was confirmed by outside sources. The patient had no recollection of this horror in her usual state of consciousness, but three different alters had three slightly different versions of the incident based on the patient's various conflicted *feelings* about her girl friend. Further evidence of the dual nature of dissociation was that these altered states with memories emerged amidst a suicidal crisis over an intense homosexual transference to her female therapist.

The striking relationship of dreams to dissociated states was then demonstrated by the vignette of a DID patient, who, in her usual state of consciousness, reported a very distressing dream: she was watching a young girl being sexually abused by an unknown man while an unknown woman was holding her down. A number of days later, a young girl alter spontaneously emerged in a session, who described an eerily similar experience first hand. There were, however, several minor, but important differences in this rendition, such as her having a clear idea of who her perpetrators were. Interestingly, this alter had no awareness that the dream had been reported, and the patient had amnesia for the time her alter was "out" giving her report of the trauma.

These mental events were initially felt by the patient to be quite disconnected from each other, and it appeared as though dream work was operative in both states. Furthermore, such clinical events, which are not unusual in psychodynamically oriented treatment of these patients, were eventually recognized to have a common origin. In the dream, the patient was watching someone other than herself be abused. Everyone's identity was apparently disguised, whereas in her dissociated state, she narrated the experience in the first person and knew who her abusers were. It appeared, however, that the price she paid for that knowledge was to convince herself that it happened, but to a separate self, or part of the mind, who shared the same body. Whatever forces in the mind created the young girl in the dream seemed to have contributed to the creation of the dissociated young girl alter, also. Understanding how "the stuff of dreams" is related to the formation of these quasi-identities will require more research and intensive treatment of these cases. This knowledge, which could expand our overall perspective on identity and character development, is further discussed in chapter 5.

SUMMARY AND CONCLUSION

This review has focused on the characterological features of DID, extending the "state versus trait" debate to the realm of the dissociative disorders. Aspects of DID have been studied in regard to the narcissistic personality and to the borderline personality disorder. A number of different theories are presented which describe DID as a variant of, on a continuum with, or being comorbid with each of these two personality disorders. It is then hypothesized that DID is best considered a distinct characterological entity. Two theories are put forth, which describe a personality disorder whose predominant defense is dissociation.

Of the two models, the one which is more developed and possibly has more explanatory value is the "dissociative character." In this schema, DID would be considered a lower level dissociative character, utilizing primitive forms of dissociation in which splitting is enhanced by an autohypnotic defensive altered state of consciousness. These altered states originate in response to the overstimulation of external trauma, but get reactivated in the service of here-and-now intrapsychic conflicts. Recognition of this dual quality of dissociation seems helpful in psychodynamic treatment, which allows for analysis of the defense and analysis of the content of these states. The nature of the content of what is "in dissociation" appears to have a dreamlike quality to it which may correspond to previous trauma but also be subject to some secondary revision. There is also clinical evidence to support a common origin to the representation of a separate self in both dreams and alter personalities.

Within this lower level dissociative character (DID), one of the other influences around which seemingly separate identities develop, is the effect of perverse sexuality. It appears that a number of dissociated sexual pathways may be followed in the same individual, which encapsulate aggression, childhood trauma, and anxiety. When this exceedingly complex psychic structure is successful, it may be that some ego is then freed up to proceed with healthy development. If there is validity to these speculations, then further advances in our understanding of "multiple personality" will help us realize one of Freud's own dreams, that of uniting dream psychology with psychopathology into a more coherent understanding of mental functioning.

PART II

PATHOGENIC ORGANIZING INFLUENCES

Chapter 4

TRAUMA AND PERVERSE SEXUALITY

> Perversion – n. 1) The action of perverting someone or something; the state of being perverted; turning aside from truth or right; diversion to an improper use; (a) corruption, (b) distortion; a perverted or corrupted form of something. 2) Preference for an abnormal form of sexual activity; sexual deviance. Also, (an) abnormal or deviant sexual activity or behavior [*New Shorter Oxford English Dictionary*, 1993, p. 2174].

The role of perverse sexuality as an organizing influence is explored in this chapter. Following a brief review of psychoanalytic thinking on sexual trauma, perversion, and dissociation, I will describe a clinical case in which transsexualism, homosexuality, and sadomasochistic heterosexual practices were manifested during altered ego states. Analysis of the transference revealed the centrality of sadomasochism in this patient. It is hypothesized that various perverse structures may be formed within these seemingly autonomous, amnestic states, in order to contain anxiety and encapsulate the aggression which resulted from early psychic trauma. Issues relating to diagnosis, countertransference, reconstruction, and psychoanalytic technique are discussed also.

The pejorative use of the word *perversion* and the reluctance some analysts feel about using this term scientifically, especially in relation to homosexuality, may result in losing sight of the relevance of definition number (1)

This chapter is a revised and expanded version of a paper published in the *Journal of the American Psychoanalytic Association,* "On Trauma, Perversion and 'Multiple Personality.' " (1996), 44:785–814.

above, i.e., the element of victimization in the development of a sexual deviation.

The defensive and organizing influence of perverse sexuality, one of Freud's first discoveries (1905), may play an important role in "multiple personality" (Stoller, 1975). Though sexual conflict and masochistic behavior occur frequently (Kluft, 1984; Putnam, Guroff, Silberman, Barban, and Post, 1986; Brenner, 1994), the controversy surrounding the diagnosis and the dearth of such cases in analysis (Lasky, 1978; Marmer, 1980) has left this area unexplored. An informal review of the presenting complaints of a six-month sample of inpatients with this diagnosis revealed that more than 50 percent feared or actually lost control of ego dystonic sexual impulses. The behavior ranged from heterosexual and homosexual promiscuity to sadomasochism, pedophilia, bestiality, exhibitionism, menage à trois, erotic asphyxia, and kleptomania. (A link between kleptomania and fetishism has been previously described [Zavitzianos, 1971].)

Classically, in perversions, childhood trauma during the phallic phase, in those with constitutional "weakness of the sexual apparatus" (1905), intensified the castration complex to such a degree, that instead of being repressed it was warded off by ritualized behavior and fantasy (H. Sachs, 1923). In order to deny the anatomical differences between the sexes and to perpetuate the illusion that the mother also had a penis, a fetish might then be employed as a "token of triumph over the threat of castration" (Freud, 1927, p. 154). But with the expansion of knowledge of earlier, prephallic development, a high risk time at the end of the second year was also identified as heightened genital sensitivity accompanied by maturation of the anal sphincter (Greenacre, 1968; Galenson and Roiphe, 1972). Bodily trauma at that time could disturb anal phase development (Chasseguet-Smirgel, 1978, 1981), separation-individuation (Mahler, 1968; Socarides, 1960, 1989), and object relations (Kernberg, 1975; Volkan, 1976) not only due to an intensification of castration anxiety but also a physiologically grounded aggression (Gillespie, 1940, 1952; Greenacre, 1968; Parens, 1979). In addition, if there were repeated exposure to the genitals of the opposite sex, the child's developing body ego would be distorted in that area. Resulting confusion over the anatomical differences and a persistent phallic woman fantasy (Bak, 1968) would betray deeper defects in the psyche, such as splitting of the ego (Freud, 1940b) and disturbances in one's sense of reality (Glover, 1933; Chasseguet-Smirgel, 1981; Adair, 1993; L. Grossman, 1993).

Interestingly, the clinician may see a similar history of early trauma, severe anxiety, excessive aggression, body image disturbances, and an impaired relationship to reality in "multiple personality." I hypothesize that it is at the lower end of a continuum of "dissociative character" pathology in which dissociation is the predominant defensive operation. I have redefined dissociation as a defense originating in response to the overstimulation of external trauma, using autohypnotic altered states of consciousness which augment repression or splitting. Depending on factors such as the level of development and integration of the psyche at the time of the trauma, there may be variable disturbances of awareness, alertness, memory, and identity, due to dissociation. This defense then changes in its function, becoming relatively autonomous (Brenner, 1994) and warding off anxiety due to the inner danger of intrapsychic conflict. Awareness of the dual nature of dissociation then enables analysis of this defense in a psychoanalytic context. Such an approach is complicated, however, because of the apparent presence of a cadre of personifications (Fairbairn, 1952) which appear to take over consciousness. While a history of childhood physical and sexual abuse is reported in a very high percentage of these cases (Kluft, 1984), it is unclear just how this trauma is related to the formation and function of these dissociated "selves." Furthermore, the use of jargon, terms such as *alters, switching, coconsciousness, abreactive pain,* and *hypnotic integration of personalities,* suggests a different model of the mind and a radical treatment. My experience, to the contrary, has led me to conclude that psychoanalysis has very much to offer regarding not only an understanding of these terms but of treatment itself.

Regarding the significance of deviant sexuality in such cases, I am quite familiar with the long-term treatment of a woman, in which three of her personifications had distinctively different sexual proclivities, namely transsexualism, homosexuality, and sadomasochistic heterosexual practices. Such a constellation is surprisingly not unusual based on the over three-hundred patients I have either evaluated or treated myself. This patient's sexuality during her altered states were deeply concealed, abhorrent secrets which, when revealed, allowed the treatment to progress. In the transference, the sadomasochistic issues predominated which, when brought into the realm of interpretability, became a turning point. As the supervisor of this case, I will offer the following clinical material disguised as per Clifft's guidelines (1986), to illustrate how sexualized solutions became the organizers for her "alters."

CASE REPORT

History

The history was elicited from the patient in the early weeks of treatment. Hannah, a divorced mother of three in her midtwenties, was referred for treatment of recurrent depression. In spite of what sounded like a history of a rather debilitating "biologic" illness, she had succeeded in the developmental tasks of young adulthood by having both a family and a career, thus suggesting some underlying strengths.

Growing up, her mother was an alcoholic who, because of her fear of germs, did not allow young Hannah near her. Her mother seemed unapproachable and untouchable. An only child, Hannah was lonely and isolated, with no ally except for an older female cousin living with the family, who did much of the loving caretaking but could not really protect her. Her cousin moved away suddenly when Hannah was an adolescent, and she grieved bitterly for her.

Hannah's parents separated before her birth and mother remarried immediately. She described her stepfather as a man of contradictions. A religious churchgoer and very charming he spent much of his free time with her, which Hannah craved. But, he had a dark side, in that he was given to violent rages which absolutely terrified her, resulting in Hannah being totally obedient to him at all times. She recalled, mournfully, how, as a young girl, he viciously grabbed her favorite doll from her arms, throwing it against the wall and crushing it.

As a teenager, her parents had peculiar attitudes about her dating. Her mother accused her of being a slut, while her stepfather seemed overprotective and perhaps a bit jealous. She got pregnant, moved out, quit school, and got married when she was 17. While she could not wait to leave, she felt strangely under her parents' power and would be visited by them regularly. Hannah eventually became suicidal, developing a postpartum depression, and was hospitalized. Her follow-up was limited, as she would try to wean herself from therapy as soon as she felt better, only to repeat the cycle. At the time of her referral, she was going through a divorce and was quite sad over her loss.

The "Preanalytic" Phase of Treatment

Hannah had a wide-eyed, timid, childlike manner. Despite her clearly hinting at a disturbing history of sexual abuse,[1] she was puzzled that weekly psychotherapy was initially recommended instead of monthly medication checks. She was conflicted over developing a therapeutic relationship, testing limits, and expressing her contempt for psychiatry. Several months into treatment, she began to feel very self-destructive, and, as a sign of her growing trust, handed over a very sharp knife, an ominous foreshadowing of things to come.

---

[1] Many years later she admitted that sexual involvement with her stepfather was ongoing until shortly before starting therapy. She had known it all along, but had forgotten specifics from childhood which emerged during treatment.

She revealed that since she was young, she would cut herself regularly, having devised a way to bleed profusely, yet not leave obvious marks. Her willpower faded, and she was briefly hospitalized.

During therapy at this time, Hannah would intermittently become silent, looking very deep in thought and easily startled. Her expression could change abruptly or she would start to cry without obvious reason. One time she left a session so distraught that she became catatonic outside the office door. In time, Hannah began to describe the mysterious disappearance of certain items, and she seemed convinced that her house was haunted. Her sleep soon deteriorated and she began to feel self-destructive again. She tried to displace her aggression by destroying some of her possessions, but to no avail. Then, in a moment of desperation, she slipped while describing her plight, referring to herself as "we" instead of "I." Rehospitalization was necessary then, and again at such times when she was unable to control herself.

The diagnosis of multiple personality was made at this time. Hannah spent her days in bed, crying, sucking her thumb, clinging to her teddy bear, and insisting she was 5 years old. She spoke like a child, was amnestic about therapy, and drew primitive pictures of being attacked by monsters while in bed. She said that "the others" inside had been mean to her by doing bad things to her teddy bear, like hiding and cutting it. This explained the mysterious disappearances at home. But, when asked about "the others," she froze and hallucinated, blurting out that she was not allowed to talk about it under the threat of death.

Hannah, however, had no memory of the times she behaved like a little girl who insisted her name was "Lucy," but accepted the observations that were shared with her. Over time, the little girl, "Lucy," revealed the name of her main persecutor, "Vera," a very angry, self-destructive teenager whom she believed shared the body with her. "Vera" had no interest in participating in treatment and through "Lucy" 's hallucinations tried to scare her doctor away with threats of inner violence. Furthermore, unbeknownst to him at the time, "Vera" would leave her home at night and pick up men in bars, a secret she kept well-hidden from Hannah. In other words, the patient would venture out for sexual interludes in an altered state, for which she had amnesia. However, "Vera" 's dramatic entry into the therapeutic situation did not occur until months later. In the meantime, an alliance was forged with "Lucy," the little one, who, apparently lacking object constancy,[2] was terrified of abandonment and needed constant reassurance from the older ones, inside.

---

[2] It is unclear whether some alters actually have different levels of development, or whether the lack of object constancy is part of the basic underlying disturbance.

After a period of restabilization, numerous "others" emerged, and unable to be trusted, she almost died from several suicide attempts. It was an extremely chaotic time for her, as she, in altered states, apparently relived memories of profound sexual abuse. Overwhelmed by shame, guilt, and intense self-hatred, she resorted to self-destruction as her salvation. It was during this time that "Vera" emerged, after Hannah started having flashbacks and dreams of having an abortion as a teen. "Vera" suffered greatly then and in the present as she gradually let her story be known.[3] She endured a period of enormous sadness, agitation, dissociation, and suicidality requiring restraints, seclusion, and high doses of medication. In the midst of her greatest despair, feeling trapped in the hospital, she began to hallucinate a man's voice, someone who was even more threatening than "Vera."

The man's voice "belonged" to "Marshall," who was enraged because he was trapped in the body of a woman. "He" seemed to be in a paranoid rage and could erupt at any moment. Indeed, the patient's aggressivity was so intense that it was only safe to speak to "Marshall" when physical precautions were taken. He was suspicious of everyone's motives, wondering why and how his doctor wanted to help. Shortly thereafter, the patient became assaultive, which resulted in Hannah's internal protectors devising a way to prevent future violence. Through some type of autohypnotic jail, "Marshall" was allowed to communicate by writing without completely "taking over the body." Hannah, too, went into some type of confinement, as it was felt that the knowledge of her abuse and the transsexual alter would result in further suicide attempts. As a result, "Vera" and two "others" became the prominent states of consciousness.

One of these other alters was "Carla," a lesbian, who had bad memories of being forced to perform fellatio. She was afraid of all men and wanted to have nothing to do with her therapist. She felt ostracized and discriminated against by the rest of the inner people because of her sexual preference. Little more was known about this state of mind until a friend died in an auto accident, triggering off a nearly fatal suicide attempt. Another secret, discovered almost too late, was that "Carla" and this woman were lovers with a suicide pact. The patient was found in a comatose state and reported a near-death experience. But by this time there was an almost complete rupture of trust, and her doctor told her that he could not work with her anymore if she continued to deceive him and act on her suicidal wishes. She was transferred

---

[3] In one poignant moment "Vera" revealed that she was hiding a blade. The analyst reflexively offered his outstretched hand, realizing that in her rage she could have very easily cut him. He decided, however, that he needed to demonstrate some trust in her before she could trust him, so he kept it outstretched. After a menacing look she carefully placed the blade in his hand and started to well up. This incident became a nodal point in treatment.

to another facility and helplessly realized that she was enacting her worst fears of being sent away from home.

Hannah went through a critical period of self-reflection, concluding that she really wanted to live, that she was terribly sorry for all that she had done, and that she wanted to continue treatment with him after she was released. Her doctor sensed the depth of her agony, the genuineness of her plea, and his own sorrow for the seeming disintegration of this woman's life over the two years she had been in treatment. He told her that he believed her sincerity but needed time to digest all that had happened. He then concluded that if indeed she survived her next ordeal, he would see her in consultation and would decide from there. A number of weeks later they met again and her treatment entered a new phase.

The "Analytic" Phase of Treatment

Hannah did not know why, but she had resolved to live after her near-death experience. Following a thorough discussion with her and her various personifications, it was agreed upon to meet five times per week. It was quite evident that Hannah had developed a complex attachment which manifested itself in the various reactions that she and the "others" had toward her doctor. It appeared as though each personification was developing "his or her" own unique troubled relationship, which tended to support the notion of their separateness. However, it became clear that there was great tension *between* these states, and that these conflicts seemed to be a major source of anxiety, also. Taken as a composite, therefore, she developed a deeply ambivalent transference which was experienced as an internalized, interpersonal conflict. Specifically, the child part, "Lucy," felt so loving and needy that she wished he would literally adopt her, while "Carla" was terrified, "Vera" was enraged, but aloof, and "Marshall" felt hateful toward him. In their own ways, they punished "Lucy" for her frustrated longings.

Overall, at this point, the patient seemed to be manifesting a diffuse rapprochement type of transference, her efforts at clinging, holding, and longing fluctuating with rejection, withdrawal, and flight. "Vera," for example, still insisted she had no feelings for the analyst and never would. Instead, she would go to bars picking up older men who reminded her of her stepfather and performing whatever sadomasochistic sex they demanded. Then, when the men were off-guard, she would get revenge by hurting their genitals. She would try to escape in time before they retaliated. Afterwards she would feel thoroughly contaminated, disgusted, and evil, resulting in an irresistible urge to cleanse herself through burning or bloodletting.

Eventually, "Vera" started "coming to therapy" more often and was "out" much more than the "others" in the sessions. But, her shame became so profound that she could not continue to talk face to face, so she asked to use the couch, as it was the lesser of two evils. Although suspicious about its purpose and terrified about not being able to keep her eye on the analyst, the intolerance of her shame prevailed. He tried to follow not only the ebb and flow of her feelings, but also her desperate efforts to ward them off, so he tried not to interfere with her fluctuations of consciousness. Instead, he expressed his curiosity and shared his observations with her, when she was amenable. For example, he would point out long silences, changes in her speech pattern, or atypical behavior such as sucking her thumb. He acknowledged "Vera" 's determination to talk to him, empathically noting that "she" was the one now recognizing her need for help.

Lying on her back, talking about her recent exploits, the patient was constantly interrupted by the emergence of altered states, apparently reliving of memories of being raped. She would become quite disoriented and amnestic, behaviorally expressing what was done to her in a very graphic way. At times it would become so real for her that she needed time at the end of an hour to reorient herself as she came out of these states. If not, she often would forget where she parked her car, wandering the area in a fuguelike state until she found it. Interestingly, the emergence of these vivid sexualized demonstrations corresponded with her protests about not wanting to become dependent upon the analyst. Under these circumstances, her autohypnotic flight into the past was seen as a defensive retreat from her here-and-now feelings in the emerging transference. When these observations were first brought to the patient's attention, she vehemently rejected them, responding with a bout of cutting which almost required rehospitalization. It took several more years before she could tolerate and acknowledge any such feelings, which always needed to be discussed with the utmost sensitivity. It was important to recognize, therefore, that not only was the content of these abreactive states thought to be potentially useful in the reconstruction, but the timing of their appearance in a given hour was crucial also.

"Vera" eventually became preoccupied with her curiosity about the analyst. She desperately tried to suppress her interest, but over the next two years began to report a series of dreams in which she was being chased or attacked by men with weapons, while the analyst stood by passively. The dreams evolved, in which her stepfather was raping her while the analyst watched, took notes, and let it all happen. The dreams seemed very real and sometimes continued while awake. As disturbing as this imagery already was, she became frankly suicidal once again after dreaming that her stepfather's face transformed into the analyst's face during such an assault. Although she could not bear the thought, she had ruefully confessed that she even contemplated trying to seduce the analyst into a compromising position. At this point, any fantasy about him still felt extremely dangerous, which had to be cut out of her mind by cutting her genitals.

The seriousness of her promiscuity literally hit her in the face several weeks later, when the patient showed up for a session with a swollen black eye after one of her nights out. Apparently, she had succeeded in living out her fantasy of being beaten (Freud, 1919a) and dramatically became conscious of "Vera's" forays afterward. Until that time, the patient was unwilling and unable to own that a part of her mind had the power to "take over" and turn her into a woman of the night. She had refused to question the extra money she often found in her wallet. Crying with shame and helplessness over this life-threatening compulsion, she felt mortified because she had fantasized that she was with her analyst that night. Gradually, however, she became able to talk about the necessity of pain and danger for her arousal, the connection between her perversion and her incest, and intensity of her eroticized longings in the transference. When these strivings peaked, she would cut herself again, a ritual which could arouse her to orgasm, serve as a punishment, and also cleanse her.

She writhed in pain as she soon afterward recalled trying to fall asleep as a young girl, with her nightgown and sheets soaked in semen and blood. As they tried to reconstruct her tragic life, it appeared that "Vera" was created back then in order to contain, disown, and survive such regular incestuous assaults by her stepfather. Starved for attention and love, she initially submitted to his demands not knowing right from wrong. She relived his painful penetrations, crying and screaming, although she had been regularly told that it really did not hurt her. She renounced her own senses for her stepfather's reality. "Vera" tearfully confessed that at times she was even willing, knowing that since it was inevitable, she could at least control when it happened. The sooner it was over, the sooner he would leave her alone so she could sleep. When she reached puberty and experienced orgasm with him, her stepfather became delighted, insisting that she had wanted it all along. She was terribly confused about her longings for the analyst who became the embodiment of her stepfather. She could usually make a distinction between the two but often needed to look around the room to remind herself where she was.

Her shame and self-hatred reached a new high when she disclosed this information. She expected visits from her stepfather several nights a week and was especially tormented, starting in latency, when her mother conveniently left when his male friends would visit. The men reportedly would first engage in homosexual sex and then would sadistically assault her, saying that they wanted her to be a boy. "Marshall" was apparently created to help the patient deal with this trauma. This conclusion helped her realize why she would have flashbacks and hallucinate the inner screams of "Marshall" 's agony during her relived assaults. It was no wonder that "Marshall" was explosive when he emerged, experiencing what seemed like a homosexual panic. This type of adaptation to the perverse reality of her childhood seemed to have survival value for the patient, as "Marshall" protected "Vera" who was protecting Hannah. This defensive sequence was then replicated in the transference.

But, as "Vera" 's life became more known, it seemed that she was the major state of consciousness who experienced much of the early sexual abuse. She recalled, how as a young teen, she would sell her sexual services to men, who often abused her further. The patient then reported vaginal bleeding in the here-and-now, as she pieced together a hideous memory of an illegal abortion where she almost bled to death. The patient grieved bitterly for her lost baby and linked the memory of fetal tissue from this abortion to the screen memory of her stepfather crushing the head of her doll when she was 5. She doubted she could ever live with herself having learned some of the things she had done.

Her need for reality testing, reassurance, and softening of her savage superego was so great while her impulse control was so tenuous it was necessary that the analyst tell her that he did not share her view of herself. He told her at such a critical juncture that she was acting as judge, jury, and executioner, determined to carry out her sentence of capital punishment for her crimes. Rather than hating her and thinking that she was the most despicable person in the world, he told her that he felt sad for her instead. He then said he thought she grew up brainwashed and terrorized, having to do bad things in order to feel like a good girl in her father's eyes. She then sobbed for the rest of the hour, an expression of affect so profound that it seemed to come from all of her. Indeed, she recounted that "everyone" inside was grieving over the abortion. She then went to her lover's grave, after which "Carla" became more involved in treatment.

"Carla" was terrified of men and of the couch. She, like "Vera," had a wish to get rid of the "others," to take exclusive possession of the body, and she was not interested in any joint effort on behalf of the patient. Here too, Hannah had little awareness of her sexuality as it was expressed through "Carla." A considerable amnestic barrier remained between "Carla" and the others, but her elusive, standoffish veneer was shattered by the death of her lover. She had never loved another so much and felt utterly cursed by this loss. The analyst told her that his not knowing the nature of their relationship was a reflection of the secrets she kept from herself, as a whole person. As a result, it made it impossible for him to have anticipated the intensity of her suicidal reaction. He then told her that he could not help Hannah unless "everyone," including her, was able to open up. But "Carla," too, insisted upon her separateness from Hannah, and too vigorous attempts to help her realize that she was just one person merely increased her defensiveness, having the same effect as a premature interpretation. So, the analyst did not challenge her perception any further at this time and listened to "her" associations also. She sobbed quietly over the succeeding hours, expressing her shame and ultimately her apology for this nearly fatal omission. Over time, an empathic connection enabled her to begin to trust and talk to him.

"Carla" revealed that she felt an attraction to women as far back as she could remember. The comfort, nurturing, and mothering from her cousin and certain teachers showed her that contact with females could be safer than with males. When girl friends would sleep over they cuddled each other and, as preadolescents, began mutual exploring of each other's bodies. During her teens, the patient met a prostitute who befriended her and would have sex *with her* after "Vera" finished on the streets with the men. This pattern continued and had implications for treatment as the patient, in one state, became secretly involved with a woman while, in another state, was desperately trying to eradicate her sadomasochistic longings for her stepfather in the transference. The lover's death and the uncovering of the suicide pact brought her complex sexuality further into focus where it remained the major theme from then on. "Carla" 's emergence and need to remain aloof then came to be understood as the patient's attempt to keep her distance, through a homosexual ego state, for fear of losing control of her erotic feelings for the analyst. The defensive function of "Carla" 's presence was supported by her eventual acknowledgment that even she, a lesbian, was starting to have erotic feelings. Her confusion over such "unnatural" feelings was then explored as any other transference fantasy material.

The defensive altered states gradually diminished over several years, as she accepted and became conscious of the "Vera," "Carla," and "Marshall" parts of her psyche. A more continuous consciousness emerged, while the behavioral and verbal differences between these personifications lessened. A greater observing ego developed as she had more "coconsciousness with her alters." Her overall functioning improved, but a major problem remained—she wanted to be just one person. Hannah, the "original" patient, went "deep inside" several years previously, and it was felt that she needed to reemerge if everyone were to blend into one. Ultimately, the patient began to feel an unusual sense of inner cooperation, as her personifications learned to communicate with each other, working to prevent any other part from acting on her destructive, instinctual strivings. The patient then knew that she was on the road to recovery when she became able to acknowledge and safely tolerate her wish for the analyst's baby, her forbidden pregnancy in the transference, which helped her further reconstruct her past.

Hannah, "herself," gradually reemerged in the sessions for brief periods, very tentatively seeing how much she could tolerate "being out." She

was easily overwhelmed by the challenge of assimilating the construction of
her life, which her other "parts" had been working on in her absence. Paral-
leling her life, Hannah needed to experience her treatment while in altered
ego states, also, periodically checking the waters of the transference, as it
were, to see if she could stand the temperature. There was a resurgence of
self-destructive impulses during this time, as Hannah finally confessed to
feeling the same way toward her analyst that "Vera" did. Owning her sadomasochistic self was an enormous integrative challenge, which required ongoing caution and tact. Her susceptibility to self-punishment at even the slightest
hint of feeling judged or criticized required constant clarification of "who
said what to whom and why" in order to help her further distinguish between
her inner dialogue and her outer dialogue with her analyst. In so doing, she
learned to recognize the intrapsychic origin of her guilt.

Hannah preferred to "listen inside" rather than have the analyst review
and construct the treatment process for her, as it helped her own her thoughts
better. When she felt frustrated with her forgetting, the analyst, at this point,
could then easily interpret her defensive flight. Similarly, her "switching" in
the sessions was more readily recognized as an unconscious effort to change
the subject through the emergence of a personification who had no idea of
what was being discussed. For example, he pointed out to her that her wish
not to know about her sexual feelings resulted in the sudden appearance of
her dissociated child state, "Lucy," who "was not listening and did not
understand grown-up feelings." The regressive aspect of this defense was
eventually recognized by the patient as something that she, as just one person,
had to own. Over time, these modes of forgetting greatly diminished and
shortened in duration, seeming less like her former disorienting, amnestic
dissociation and more like repression. Interestingly, she went through a period
of weeks in which she constantly made parapraxes, a phenomenon which
was very rare until then. In addition, as she became less intentionally self-
destructive, she went through a phase of accident proneness. She berated
herself for her clumsiness and felt the pain of her injuries deeply with minimal
autohypnotic retreat. Hannah was then able to analyze these accidents, examining the contributions of her unconscious conflicts which manifested themselves in a more typically "neurotic" fashion at this point.

The patient began to feel hope as she experienced a type of bittersweet
reunion with herself. She started to talk about a life after treatment, imagining
a time in the future where she could live without the analyst. Interestingly,
she renewed a relationship with a man who was decent and stable, looking
to the future with him. She wondered when she would be ready to terminate.
At this time, Hannah appeared to be working through a myriad of fantasies,
memories, and experiences, stopping each step along the way to incorporate
and own what belonged to her. The analyst essentially interpreted that

"Vera" was Hannah and Hannah was "Vera." Similarly, with each personification, Hannah needed to remind herself or be reminded that they were
really her own creations, i.e., altered ego states which had names. During
this first phase of termination, which lasted about a year, Hannah's hope was
regularly interrupted by renewed grief as she finally come to realize that all
the thoughts, feelings, urges, and memories belonged to just one person. But
just who was that person? She was not quite sure, as yet. The termination
process was full of regressive episodes, and a time of further integration as
she really got to know herself. She came to the realization that she was
actually quite a likeable woman whose friends truly cared about and admired
her. Her mourning for the analyst seemed to promote this self-understanding
and strengthening of her ego.

When Hannah entered the second phase of termination, she set a date
to terminate in six months, knowing that she was free to return if or whenever
she felt the need. Much of the remaining time was devoted to an extended
catharsis in which "all" of her wailed over her inconsolable love and hatred
for her stepfather. This process seemed to further consolidate her integration.
(See chapter 8 for more discussion about integration and the dissolution of
the dissociative self.)

DISCUSSION

Hannah's situation, though by no means unique, was noteworthy because of
her working in the transference during her more than eight years of treatment.
As a result, it became possible to experience and recognize the intensity
and centrality of her sadomasochistic relatedness. In so doing, the dazzling
kaleidoscope of her phenomenology, with her shifting personifications, variable sexuality, and constantly changing clinical picture became more stabilized and eventually made sense.

Hannah's initial presentation of a timid, obsequious, depressive, gave
way to a picture of a mysteriously tortured woman. Her lapses of memory
and consciousness increased as she was given standard psychiatric care for
her serious depression. She was unable to verbalize her affects or describe
her inner experience (Krystal, 1978), and characterological factors seemed to
predominate over "biological" factors. Psychotherapy was intensified but
she again regressed, manifesting catatoniclike symptoms and histrionic mood
changes. In retrospect, she acted like many different people who were joining
in on a conversation already in progress. Such patients' lifelong practices of
hiding their amnesia from others and becoming expert at piecing together the
fragments of their daily lives, may be a factor in the difficulty of making
the diagnosis of multiple personality (Kluft, 1987a). Her thought-blocking,

fuguelike symptoms, supernatural fears, and seemingly autistic preoccupation
could have been confused with a schizophreniform decompensation (Kluft,
1987b). However, when she slipped and called herself "we," there was
mounting evidence for a dissociative disorder, and it was essential to be open
to such a diagnosis.

This patient, to my knowledge, did not read about DID, was not exposed
to patients with this diagnosis, and was horrified to acknowledge her inner
experience to anyone. Indeed, with a little discouragement or redirection, she
would have tried to keep her secret even longer, as she grew up doubting her
senses and being told that no one would believe her anyway (O. Sachs, 1967).
Her disturbed and fluctuating sense of body and mind had a hallucinatory
quality to it (Adair, 1993), in that she could believe herself to be a young
girl, a teenager, or a violent male. She shunned close relationships, feeling
bewildered that anyone could like her, or see any goodness in her. In her
mind she was despicable, contaminated, and ruined for life.

Her suicide attempts and near-death experience not only attested to the
gravity of her situation, but also seemed to result in a profound emotional or
"spiritual" awakening (Moody, 1975). It has been reported that such an out-
of-body experience may be a dissociative phenomenon also (Serdahely, 1992,
1993), and perhaps it is the penultimate dissociation before death (see chapter
9 for further discussion of these issues). Hannah not only felt she left her
body to observe the resuscitation efforts, she also reported hearing the pessimistic words of a physician who predicted serious brain damage if she were
to recover. In reflecting on her inexorable pull toward death, this dramatic
shift in her outlook, although multiply determined, seemed to have been
catalyzed by the near-death experience. It was as though she had a taste of
death which helped her see her life as more real and more valued.[4] In addition,
she became courageously oriented toward learning the truth about herself, a
superego aspiration and value (Calef, 1972; Calef, Weinshel, Renik, and
Mayer, 1980) which is essential to the process.

The period of time she spent at another facility was crucial not only for
the patient but also for the analyst, who, through his own countertransference
self-analysis, carefully considered the prospect of continuing with her. He
felt depletion, anger, bewilderment, sadness, self-doubt, and an enormous
sense of responsibility. The patient was incredulous that the analyst could
still stand to work with her. He said that it would be difficult and told her
that he might need some ongoing consultation with a senior colleague and
that it might also help him and others if they, at some point, could write

---

[4] While it is not entirely clear what accounts for this phenomenon, there may be some
similarities here to what has been described as an enhancement of narcissism in the service of
survival in children who experienced close to death experiences during the Holocaust (Kestenberg
and Brenner, 1995).

about his work with her. She agreed to both requests. But Lasky has cautioned against the upsurge of messianic rescue fantasies while working with such patients (1978), so the analyst had to cautiously evaluate the patient's belief that he was the only person in the world who could help her. A review of the tumultuous course of treatment led to the conclusion that analysis of the intense, but seemingly diffuse transference was the only course left. (I will discuss this issue further in the section on technique.) It seemed as though the patient had reached "rock bottom," an expression borrowed from the treatment of addicts, referring to the lowest point in their lives, when they have no choice but to give up and die, or get serious about getting help. As a result, when they met again in consultation, she accepted the conditions of treatment—maintaining a safety contract not to kill herself, saying everything that comes to mind, and meeting five times per week.

Hannah survived her worst fear of being sent into exile, and learned that her analyst, although committed to helping her, was not an unconditionally loving object. This experience seemed necessary for the patient, who worried that her all-powerful aggression and badness would contaminate or destroy all those to whom she got close. By acknowledging his limits, the analyst showed the patient he could protect himself from a potentially deadly masochistic collusion with her, yet care enough to give her another chance.

The analyst's willingness to send the patient away was in contrast to an earlier intervention, when he intuitively extended his hand to confiscate a blade she was wielding. At that time, it seemed as though he risked bodily injury in order to foster an alliance with her when she was in her violent "Vera" state of mind. Under those circumstances, "Vera" was first emerging in treatment and seemed to be testing her doctor's courage. She was in the larger holding environment of a secure inpatient setting and had not manifested any outwardly directed aggression. Though she easily could have cut him, he apparently surprised her by trusting her, sensing that her threatening behavior belied an underlying fear of closeness and wish for acceptance. Her hostility seemed to be melted by her tears of disbelief, as she, for the moment, let herself feel that someone could care enough about her to endanger himself.

Later on in treatment, he told "Vera" that he did not hate her, but rather felt sad for her, as he conveyed compassion instead of enacting a projective identification. He then followed up this response with a superego interpretation, in an effort to undo her brainwashing by her father (Shengold, 1989), by stating that she was acting as judge, jury, and executioner for her sexual sins and pregnancy. As she internalized the analyst as a new object (Loewald, 1960) who would help tame her vicious superego, she then experienced a more continuous consciousness. Owning more and more of her psyche felt like a long awaited reunion with herself. As she began to contemplate termination, her dissociation was lessening, seemingly replaced by more typical repression, as evidenced by a period of parapraxes and unconscious accident-proneness, instead of suicidality. The termination phase, lasting about one and a half years, enabled her to further consolidate her identity. She appeared to become more individuated as she mourned for the analyst. Intermittent follow-up for several years revealed not only the difficulty in initial posttermination adjustment, but also the progressive consolidation of her identity, the reduction of anxiety, and an increase in sublimatory capacities (see chapter 11 for discussion of termination issues).

Perverse Sexuality

In this case of "multiple personality," the modulation and containment of aggression seemed to be the central task of the patient's psyche. Her life experience and mental condition support the three hypotheses regarding the pathogenesis of sadomasochism (W. Grossman, 1991): (1) "that pain and painful affects are the 'sources' of aggression" (p. 25); (2) that the development of mental structure, along with repetitive compulsive or impulsive behavior, is a result of conflicts and defenses against aggression; (3) and that the capacity for fantasy formation, which is necessary to master trauma, may, in some cases, be damaged by the experience itself, "leading to a failure to transform the traumatic experience through mental activity" (p. 26). Hannah apparently encapsulated her trauma and her extreme hostile destructiveness (Parens, 1979) through three channels of perverse sexuality, in three dissociated amnestic states. In so doing, some of her ego appeared to be spared (Wholley, 1925) allowing her to function and to proceed with development, which was a remarkable feat. As a result, there were times when she was quite capable of symbolic abstract thinking and sublimatory behavior, a marked contrast to her other states of mind.

It appeared that Hannah was not only subjected to repeated exposure to the genitals of the opposite sex, but also to painful, overstimulating sexual experiences during and after her prephallic phase. Over time, these violations became pleasurable for her. She engaged in repetitive, obligatory enactments of these painful sexual experiences, her oedipal victory, as both the aggressor and the victim, as "Vera." "Vera" 's self-mutilation was highly eroticized and was not given up until many years into treatment. It seemed that the nature of her dissociative states, which resulted in her reliving trauma in such a real, but seemingly disconnected way, encapsulated those aspects of her experience which could not be symbolized or transformed in the service of mastery. It was not until she articulated and tolerated her fantasies in the transference, after much preparatory work, that she could make use of an analytic process which enabled her to consolidate her ego and metabolize her trauma.

The "alterations" in her ego (Freud, 1937) were complex fantasy and identificatory systems, organized into different sexualized personifications. In keeping with Arlow's conclusion that "perversions constitute problems of gender identity, of male–female difficulties" (Panel, 1986, p. 248), one of these personifications was "Marshall," the transsexual. He identified with the aggressor and was violent to others before they could be violent to him. This entity was sadistic, paranoid, and unstable. "Carla," on the other hand, was a more functional masochistic organization. As a lesbian, she avoided men completely and internalized her aggression, becoming suicidal when her lover died. In contrast, "Vera" externalized and eroticized her aggression, repetitively living out her sadomasochistic oedipal scenarios. "Vera" became the predominant form of relatedness in the transference and, as such, this sadomasochistic perversion seemed to be the core organization in her psyche. But, in order for the patient to have survived and to have been so successful in her life as she was, she developed an extraordinary capability to keep things separate. As a result, these three dissociated selves seemed to have "lives" of their own since childhood. They also appeared to have different levels of ego organization and object relations, a variability known to occur in perversions (Kernberg, 1992). As a result, Hannah's inner world was quite populated, always keeping her company and also seeming to serve a transitional function (Marmer, 1980; Fink, 1993).

These personifications partially succeeded in warding off not only separation anxiety but also castration and penetration anxiety. Apparently through self-hypnosis, as described in fetishism by Greenacre (1969), she maintained the illusion of the maternal phallus by creating "Marshall," the transsexual. "Marshall" seemed to be a condensation of the patient's enraged, desperate search for both her mother and her missing penis (Volkan, 1979), while attempting to serve as a defensive retreat from heterosexuality, also. The violent rage that "Marshall" experienced was mitigated at times when he could believe that something could be done about his missing appendage. Sex with a man intensified the patient's anxiety over penetration, which was defended against with rage. Sex with a woman was more tolerable, permissible, and less frightening. As a result, the transsexual state helped rationalize "Carla" 's homosexuality, also. The patient's lesbianism appeared to be a reflection of her inability to move forward and give up the primary attachment to a maternal object. She made narcissistic object choices which she thought were safe, but drew her into suicidal despair. By living in a world of all women, she regressively obliterated the difference between the sexes by renouncing the existence of men and the incestuous danger they posed for "Vera."

The powerful neurosogenic effect of the oedipal victory through incest, as emphasized by Parens (1993), repelled the patient back to safer ground.

However, she could not escape the original danger posed by the women in her life, namely neglect, abandonment, and loss. An understanding of the meaning of this sexuality required not only analysis of the states themselves, but also the relationship between them as intrapsychic conflict was experienced as an internalized, interpersonal conflict. A whole range of psychosexual and developmental anxieties appeared to be defended against by the tension between and the shifting from one personification to the other. Clearly, more cases are needed to further delineate this process.

Reconstruction and Memory

The extent of the trauma and the accuracy of the reconstruction of her childhood, which was based on never forgotten memories, on dissociated memories (Brenner, 1995), and on enactments in the transference, raise thorny questions which go to the heart of psychoanalysis. Over time, her overpowering narratives (Laub and Auerhahn, 1993) which transported her back in time and had her reliving atrocities in altered states of consciousness, were replaced by a more coherent, chronological account of her life. She became able to own the experiences as hers and became able to distinguish the past from the present. In addition, she became able to reassemble her disjointed somatic memories (Kramer, 1990) and memories of sensory experiences (Brenner, 1988b). As convincing as this was for the analyst and the supervisor, when the patient corroborated memories of her abortion through relatives and confirmed the long-standing incest by her stepfather himself, it further reinforced the authenticity of her saga.

But analysts have been backed into a theoretical corner as there is no easy distinction between repressed memories and unconscious fantasy, a problem reviewed by Person and Klar (1994). This situation may be complicated where one's relationship to reality is negotiable and perverse (L. Grossman, 1993). In such cases, fantasies and dreams may be more important than reality, which may be devalued or disregarded at will. As a result, sorting out what is real in the here-and-now is difficult enough, let alone confronting the past. The role of suggestion (Brenneis, 1994), even if exaggerated (Brenner, 1995), also needs to be taken into consideration. (Interestingly, however, there has been, to my knowledge, no documented case of iatrogenic "multiple personality.") To add yet another level of complexity to this conundrum, victims of trauma who are known to experience flashbacks and repetitive dreams may not have the usual barriers between REM sleep and wakefulness (Ross, Ball, Sullivan, and Caroff, 1989), resulting in the feeling that they are living in their dreams, like Hannah. Consequently, there may be a neurophysiologic substrate underlying some of the problems in distinguishing dreams from reality (see chapter 5 for more discussion about dreams). Recalled events that were originally experienced in altered states of consciousness simply may not be readily identified as memories. With all these factors, it would then seem to many that approaching any sense of what may have "really" happened in childhood is so fraught with uncertainty that it would be impossible and probably not worthwhile to even try.

But Shengold (1979, 1989) and others disagree, however, repeatedly illustrating that manifestations in the transference, such as the preoccupation with boundary violations, are regularly experienced by incest victims. This was the case with Hannah, who not only reported some never forgotten memories of incest, but who had also dissociated. In this vein, van der Kolk and Kadish have concluded that "except for brain injury, dissociation always seems to be a response to traumatic life events" (1987, p. 185). The intensity of affect, along with the repetitive nature and the timing of her dissociations in sessions, were convincing of both their traumatic origin and their defensive quality in warding off anxiety in the here-and-now (chapter 2). Acknowledgment of incest by the stepfather further supported this formulation. Nevertheless, the controversy continues, as recent analytic cases in which memories of abuse were ultimately determined to be fabrications (Raphling, 1994; Good, 1994) illustrate the complexity of memory and learning "the truth" about one's self.

Technique

It would be an interesting, but ultimately fruitless debate to argue whether Hannah was actually "in analysis" or not. However, the decision to even consider analysis in such a catastrophic situation, though well described (Glover, 1954; Ticho, 1970), is worthy of further comment. It was felt that if there were any way to make sense of her chaos, to help her understand and get control of her mind, then analysis of the transference was the route. But having been chastened by the potential lethality of her internalized aggression, and having been quite active in her psychiatric management, it was not clear how much exploration and resolution of the transference might be possible. The analyst realized that the "decision" to offer Hannah an analytic experience might be seen as controversial, but it felt like an evolution to him.

There were obvious reasons to question her suitability for analysis, such as her suicidality, her hospitalizations, and the use of psychotropic medication. Yet, there was a strong alliance which was forged over the years with blood, sweat, and tears as she was very engaged in the treatment. In addition, she showed curiosity and a determination to understand how her mind worked. Her life depended on it. Furthermore, she was slowly developing an observing ego which could be used in the service of therapy. Despite her weaknesses and vulnerabilities, she clearly manifested a hidden ego strength, which has been previously described in "multiple personality" (Jung, 1939).

Unfortunately, the analytic literature was sparse regarding technique (Lasky, 1978; Marmer, 1980; Berman, 1981), and most psychiatrists who were working with such patients at the time tended to control or avoid the transference. Instead, they sought a melding of the psyche through suggestion, a "hypnotic integration of personalities" as it were. The analyst, therefore, proceeded with caution, bolstered by his observation that Hannah's dissociative "switching to different alters" could be seen in response to anxiety in the transference. It often felt like playing a game of three-dimensional chess, needing to be attuned to his relationship with each personification, to the meaning of the tension between them, and to the overall patient herself. As the treatment progressed, all of the personifications became intensely consumed by their relationship with the analyst. In particular, "Vera" 's predominance might be seen as an unusual manifestation of the transference neurosis.

Interesting, Richards (1988) reports a curative result in a woman with strikingly similar features. This patient, also a victim of paternal incest, had a history of hospitalization, a disturbed early maternal relationship, self-mutilation, promiscuity, and depersonalization. Furthermore, she used her opposite hand for cutting and masturbation, a phenomenon seen in "multiple personality" (see chapter 2). Central to her successful outcome was the recovery of memories of the incest, the veracity of which was apparently not even in question. Though very little is mentioned regarding his technique, we are told that the patient was asked to sit up at one point when she became suicidal. Further discussion of other technical considerations and modifications can be found in part III of this volume which illustrates that whether treatment evolves into an analytic process, as with Hannah, or whether a dissociative character diagnosis unexpectedly emerges during the course of treatment, it presents a great challenge.

Some of the implications which I will address here pertain to the fundamental rule, the duration and ending of the hour, reality, and the analysis of defense. Many of these patients who experience auditory and tactile hallucinations (Kluft, 1987b) feel reluctant to report these phenomena, for fear of being labeled crazy and untreatable. As a result, it may be helpful to specify in the instructions for free association, that whatever comes to mind also includes these sensations. Although self-observation was not part of Freud's original instructions, most analysts today, according to Bush (1994), value this capacity and see it as an essential part of the analysis. It is especially important that this population be encouraged to self-observe by listening inwardly (Kluft, 1994) to what is heard "in the mind" and by tuning into what is being felt "in the body," as these sensations may be somatic memories (Kramer, 1990) or some sensory bridge to the past (Brenner, 1988b). Such patients are often in various degrees of depersonalization and need to learn to apply their inherent capacity for detached self-observation to the treatment situation.

These individuals can also experience disorientation, overpowering narratives (Laub and Auerhahn, 1993), and intense affective states rendering them unable to simply get up and leave at the end of a session. In Hannah's case, her defensive regressions into her child states left her feeling lost, ignorant, inept, and too terrified to leave. At other times she was too dazed and headachy to drive. At these times, she seemed no better prepared to exit the office than someone emerging from postsurgical anesthesia. As a result, she was occasionally informed that the end of the hour was approaching, which helped her get mentally prepared to leave. While there was undoubtedly unconscious meaning to being unable to part, it was generally not amenable to interpretation early on. Mutually agreed upon longer sessions may have had value also (see chapter 1), but in Hannah's case, one would encounter the same issue at the end of the hour. Consequently, the transference and countertransference problems which may have arisen from frequently running over time until the patient felt ready to go seemed to be offset by the use of a parameter, the "two-minute warning." In so doing, the patient's observing ego was summoned and gently reminded of the demands waiting just outside the door. It appeared that the ego's synthetic functioning was suspended and it needed time to be reestablished. When the treatment progressed, these states became blended and continuous, allowing the patient to feel more "whole," and to have an ongoing capacity for self-observation. This achievement in DID jargon is "coconsciousness." As a result, there became less need for the warnings, a development which could then be pointed out to the patient and analyzed.

Patients with severe dissociative pathology pose a constant threat to the continuity of the therapeutic alliance, so certain noninterpretive interventions may be helpful to anticipate problems and to maintain what, at times, is a fragile connection (Bibring, 1954). Dickes' (1967) work with the regressive ego, for example, considers the importance of not only addressing the transference and the working alliance, but also reality. Therefore, a telephone call or a clear statement about the patient's health or safety may be indicated at crucial junctures in treatment. As with Hannah, when she became suicidal, it precluded free association because her safety contract needed to be reaffirmed. The patient's perverse relationship to reality was a major problem, and in order to have utilized the couch most effectively, it was imperative to develop and maintain a therapeutic alliance throughout all the major ego states. In so doing, the analyst became better able to analyze the dual nature of dissociation, which defended against current intrapsychic anxiety through the activation of altered states from the past.

Summary and Conclusion

The treatment of a patient with a history of paternal incest and dissociated sexuality in the forms of homosexuality, transsexualism, and sadomasochistic heterosexual practices is described. Associated with her sexual problems were disturbances in separation-individuation, object constancy, body image, sexual identity, regulation of self-esteem, anxiety about genital injury, and reality sense. Three perverse pathways seemed to have been traversed in order to encapsulate and contain her extensive childhood trauma, anxiety, and aggression. They became organizing influences for the formation of personifications in her multiple personality, which seemed to free up some ego to allow a degree of healthy development. With considerable preparatory psychotherapy and work with her dissociative defenses, the patient became able to tolerate a profound "mosaic transference" (see chapter 10 for more discussion) which could then be worked through. A sadomasochistic perversion which symbolically enacted her incestuous oedipal victory in a dissociated state, emerged as the central organization of her psyche.

In order to analyze the defense of dissociation, it was necessary to observe how and when the patient lapsed into altered states, find a way to make her aware of it, examine what mental contents were kept apart in the here-and-now, and explore the genetic origin of the states. In this case of multiple personality or lower level dissociative character, such defensive altered ego states seemed to augment primitive splitting by promoting greater disconnectedness between aggressively and libidinally derived self and object representations (see chapter 2). The patient further disowned these mental contents as they coalesced into personifications. One of the forces in the formation of these structures appeared to be the erotization of aggression in perverse sexuality. An appreciation of these vicissitudes was needed in order to facilitate movement toward the unification of her mind, which was accompanied by the cessation of self-destructive behavior, and the capacity for healthier relationships.

Despite the limitations of generalizing from a case report, it seems significant that more than 50 percent of a sample of inpatients with a diagnosis of DID reported similar dissociated sexual impulses. These findings, along with the recognized importance of early sexual trauma and a disturbed mother–child relationship both here and in perversions, suggest a more important link between the two than has been recognized heretofore. This area warrants further research to help improve treatment of dissociative disorders and to study refractory cases of perversion which may be due to unrecognized dissociative character pathology.

Chapter 5

TRAUMA AND THE DREAM EGO

> We are such stuff as dreams are made on and our little life
> is rounded with a sleep [Shakespeare, *Tempest*, Act IV,
> Scene 1].
>
> [T]he dreamer's ego can appear two or more times in the
> manifest dream, once as himself and again disguised behind
> the figures of other people.... In itself, this multiplicity is
> no more remarkable than the multiple appearances of the
> ego in the waking state... [Freud, 1923a, pp. 120–121].

The long-standing quest to understand recurrent posttraumatic dreams continues to challenge and polarize psychoanalysts. The original controversy centered around Freud's theory of the death instinct (1920a), postulated as the opposing force to Eros, and the source of the repetition compulsion. The death instinct was supposed to explain the recurrent, painful nature of mental phenomena such as recurrent nightmares, but it has all but been replaced by more contemporary theories of aggression. Although some writers, notably Kleinian theorists, have not quite let Thanatos rest in peace, this debate is much less heated now, and, for many, seems only of historic interest (Akhtar, 1995).

The current controversy over traumatic dreams relates to a different aspect, the extent to which manifest content accurately depicts the traumatic experiences themselves (Brenneis, 1994). This question is less esoteric and

An earlier version of this chapter, "On Trauma, the Dream-Ego, and 'Multiple Personality,'" was presented to the Northwest Alliance for Psychoanalytic Study on April 12, 1997, Seattle, Washington, and at the annual meeting of the American Academy of Psychoanalysis, January 10, 1998, New York.

has received widespread media attention, having gotten caught up in the sociolegal tidal wave surrounding allegations of childhood sexual abuse. For these reasons, it, too, has gone beyond the pleasure principle, but it has also gone beyond the psychoanalytic realm. While this debate rages on and further research is needed, other analytic concerns can get overlooked. For example, the link between shame, disintegration of the self, and the wish to reconstitute, has been recently studied and thought to be a crucial part of the dream work (Lansky, 1995).

Nightmares which disturb sleep are generally considered clinical evidence that the dream work mechanism has been flooded. What other repercussions might there be when the ego's usual means of processing through dream work is overwhelmed in patients who have experienced severe early trauma (Person and Klar, 1994)? Specifically, what is the relationship between posttraumatic dreams and those clinical entities known as dissociative disorders in which dreamlike, altered states of consciousness and variable disturbance in identity may be seen (Kluft, 1984)? Can we further Freud's unattained goal of integrating dream psychology with psychopathology (Freud, 1917) by pursuing that direction in this population? "The wishful fantasy and its regression to hallucinations are the most essential parts of the dream-work, which . . . are also found in two morbid states" (1917, p. 229) has not been reviewed in light of trauma.

I have maintained the position that the accumulated analytic knowledge over the last century has much to offer the sophisticated clinician working with these patients, despite the new terminology, different models of the mind, and the use of hypnosis that has been employed by many. Furthermore, to review for a moment, I have found it clinically valuable to consider a continuum of dissociative character pathology, in which dissociation is the predominant defense. In this hierarchy "multiple personality" would be considered a lower level dissociative character, whereas a more integrated psyche which employs autohypnotic defensive altered states would be at the higher end of the continuum (chapter 2). Recognition of the dual nature of dissociation, which defends against here-and-now anxiety due to intrapsychic conflict through the reactivation of defensive altered states from past trauma, facilitates a psychodynamic understanding of these very complex patients.

One of the perennial questions regarding "multiple personality" pertains to the genesis of the personifications themselves, which Fairbairn (1952) attributed to the fusion and layering of introjects and Arlow attributed to a coalescence of fantasy systems (1992). I have pursued the study of such organizing influences in the formation of these personifications, by rediscovering the importance of perverse sexuality, which may encapsulate aggression, anxiety, and traumatic memories. Some patients appear to traverse more than one sexual pathway in different amnestic altered states with seemingly separate identities. Interestingly, this perverse solution may then free up some ego for healthy development (chapter 4).

Of particular importance in this chapter is the well-known finding that such patients also appear to be in a "waking dream" (Marmer, 1980, 1991) during their dissociative episodes. In my own observations of this dreamlike state (see chapter 2; Brenner, 1995), I have considered the importance of the so-called "functional phenomenon" (Silberer, 1909) as a facet of it and another organizing influence, contributing to the patient's sense of separateness. Although mentioned by Freud (1900), developed by Rapaport (1949), and later revived by Silber (1970, 1979), this aspect of dreams has been largely overshadowed by the classical theory of wish fulfillment. This phenomenon refers to the ego's capacity to symbolically represent its own various states of consciousness or functioning, in metaphorical, somatic, and anthropomorphic terms. In other words, the mind has a natural tendency to create people to represent its own different levels of alertness or awareness. Somewhat elusive and not always recognized, Kohut (1977) apparently incorporated this concept into his notion of self-state dreams in narcissistic patients, positing a dream which represented the reaction of healthy segments of the psyche to threats of loss of cohesion. For a number of reasons, both the functional phenomenon and the self-state dream have received limited attention in the literature (Slap and Trunnell, 1987).

My experience with hundreds of patients with severe dissociative pathology has shown that there is clinical value in viewing their dreams and their altered ego states from this perspective. In a number of cases, I have even observed striking similarities between the manifest content of traumatic dreams and the first-hand accounts of the personifications themselves, which suggest a common mental origin to both (see chapters 2 and 3; Barrett, 1995). I hypothesize that these findings reflect the psychical elaboration of altered states of consciousness, which originally occurred in response to severe early trauma and have spilled over from the posttraumatic dream. The massively traumatized child who has recurrent dreams at night of his defensive altered states during the day may thus become further confused by the mutual influences of one or the other. The result may be the formation of dissociated quasi-identities which attempt to keep mental contents separate.

In order to illustrate the functional phenomenon itself, how dreams and personifications may be related, and the clinical implications of their common origin, I will begin with a hypnopompic experience of my own, followed by three clinical vignettes. This material describes: (1) a hypnogogic experience on the couch; (2) a nightly dream journal of a decompensated patient; and (3) the resolution of a regressive impasse in a case of "multiple personality" which emerged during analysis. Then, there will be a discussion on the importance of interpretive work which addresses not only *what* is kept from consciousness, but *how* it is kept away, i.e., dissociation in the service of negation.

CASE 1. HYPNOPOMPIC DREAMLIKE STATE

My alarm goes off. I am struggling to wake up but want to go back to sleep for five more minutes. I'm afraid I'll oversleep if I do and not wake up on time. Suddenly, I'm in my car in a cramped parking lot of a college, in a hurry to leave and go home at the end of the day. I start to back up and realize that two other cars want to leave also. I have to wait because I am blocked by one car and put on the brake. I look to my right and see a younger bearded man smiling at me waiting to see if I go next. He does not seem to be in as much of a hurry. I still decide to wait for him, but my brakes give out and my car goes backward involuntarily. I look to the younger man, somewhat amused and helplessly shrugging my shoulders, as I try to direct the car out, which seems to have a mind of its own. I drive the car out of the lot, but it goes out the entrance instead of the exit and I turn right instead of left which I think would have been the shorter direction back home. I end up on a highway going in the opposite direction in the face of a lot of oncoming traffic. The cars do not seem to slow down, but there are not many and we easily avoid a crash. I weave in and out to avoid a collision, thinking that if I cannot reverse my direction, then I should at least cross the highway to go with the flow. Traffic begins to build and it gets scary. With great difficulty I steer the car to the other side but still find myself going against the traffic. I get alarmed and decide the only thing I can do is try to pull over to the shoulder so I can think about what to do. Next, I manage to drift over to the shoulder, momentarily relieved, and suddenly I am completely awake! In fact, I did not oversleep and my symbolic ordeal could have lasted only moments.

Discussion

Going out of control in the opposite direction seems to symbolize my inexorable pull back to sleep, which I cannot overcome: my brakes gave way, I went out the entrance instead of the exit, I turned in the opposite direction, and I went against the ever increasing flow of rush hour traffic in a car that had a mind of its own.

The car theme seems to be from the day residue, since the night before I had heard that a colleague's car was rear-ended in a multicar pile up on the highway. The left–right directional confusion is a long-standing issue, perhaps related to ambidexterity ("selection themes pertaining to the Holocaust"; Kestenberg and Brenner [1996]). My own near miss on the highway the week before due to skidding from an unexpected icing is probably a factor, too. The smiling bearded man in the parking lot was the only other clearly defined person, and he was like a younger version of myself. He was carefully watching me in order to gauge his own actions to see what I did. He was an academic type who was not caught up in the pressures of the workaday world and I envied him. We looked at each other in a bemused fashion, tacitly but knowingly communicating with each other. In my hypno-pompic state, my conflict over waking up and the struggle to regain conscious-ness seemed to get personified by the creation of an idealized academic, younger self who could make his own hours, take his time getting out of the lot or bed, and not be constrained by such mundane concerns as rush hour traffic.

CASE 2. A HYPNOGOGIC EXPERIENCE ON THE COUCH

After many years of analysis, Samantha was working through the complica-tions of an incestuous oedipal victory which apparently consisted of regular sexual contact throughout latency. Her uncle never denied her claims. Her memories, which originally emerged during altered states, were experienced as belonging to someone else, who just happened to share her body. Over time these psychic contents were gradually tolerated and became fully owned by her. During a session where her longings in the transference were felt with exquisite poignancy, she began to get drowsy and caught herself falling asleep as she narrated a dreamlike image: "The soccer team is lining up on the field to kick the ball. . . . " She immediately became conscious of her words, which "woke" her up in puzzled amazement. Although she criticized herself for being unable to remain completely alert throughout every hour, she did give herself credit for catching herself very quickly and for remember-ing the image, although she was unable to remember what she was originally talking about. She began to associate to this hypnogogic image, repeating a familiar series of memories about a sexual encounter with an old boyfriend during a coed soccer game, but her thoughts took her further away from the immediacy of her flight from the transference. I, therefore, intervened with an alternative perspective, an interpretative remark about the functioning of her mind, as it had become increasingly important for her to understand how her mind worked (Gray, 1973). I commented that even though she still drifted off after so much hard work on trying to develop a sense of continuity of consciousness, at least this time "everyone" was out on the field working together. She brightened and responded by saying that indeed, her "goal" was a unification of her mind. As though this awareness helped her recognize something, she suddenly recalled that before becoming somnolent, she was experiencing sexual arousal on the couch, associated with alternating fantasies of her stepfather and the analyst making love to her. She became aroused again but could tolerate it this time. She was too overwhelmed earlier in the hour, and her old defenses took over. Had she continued to associate to her old boyfriend, she may have eventually arrived at the same point but, in my experience with her, it most probably would have been in a removed, intellectualized, and highly defended manner.

Discussion

Silberer's (1909) descriptions of the symbolism his own mind created, as he struggled against drowsiness in order to continue to think, included images of other people also. Representing his struggle to maintain his concentration, in one example he envisioned an unfriendly secretary in a library who ignored him, whereas, another time, a helpful assistant awaited his orders. Despite such "personification of drowsiness," Rapaport (1949) reports that in normative circumstances, as in my own case, "distinguishing between I and not I is presumed . . . [Whereas] in other states of consciousness parts of the self may not be as presumed. Multiple personalities . . . are commonly known examples" (p. 200). Under certain circumstances, therefore, this universal phenomenon may contribute to or reinforce a sense of multiple selves. Samantha, however, was at a point in treatment whereby these defensive altered states did not result in further fragmentation.

CASE 3. A NIGHTLY DREAM JOURNAL OF A DECOMPENSATED PATIENT

Barbara, a successful but erratic woman, had become quite regressed over the preceding year after a public confrontation with her stepfather whom she had always suspected abused her as a child. Her suspicions were corroborated by her older sister. Her dissociated accounts were becoming fuller and more extensive, as different personifications emerged and reported them in her diary. She did not discuss these things with her therapist, who thought she was schizophrenic. Barbara also had amnesia for many episodes as an adult which were accompanied by inner or outer directed violence and polymorphous perverse sexuality. Prior to definitive treatment (see chapter 8), it was revealed through her voluminous journals written in distinctly different handwriting, that one of her alter personalities was a feisty teenaged lesbian, who was prone to wrist-cutting and was enraged at the stepfather for what he did to a 5-year-old personification, "Baby." There was also a monstrous older male personification who seemed to be an inner representation of the stepfather, and was convinced that his fate did not depend on the life or death of the body (see chapter 7). He wanted to kill all "the others" for revealing secrets of the abuse. "He" also hated the female qualities of the body and felt trapped, expressing a transsexual conflict (see chapter 4) by severely lacerating the breasts in an effort to remove them through a self-inflicted mastectomy. The patient was becoming depleted and imminently suicidal so she was hospitalized.

The patient's exhaustion, it was discovered, was due to severe insomnia, nightmares, and somnambulism, during which times she threw furniture, wandered around, and hid in a fetal position in her closet. While it was potentially dangerous for me, over time it became possible to communicate with her in her different altered states. Her nocturnal behavior, however, remained an intractable mystery despite constant nursing intervention and high doses of medication. Out of desperation, and because our therapeutic alliance permitted it, I decided to ask her to extend her journal writing to include a nighttime log of "who" went to bed, "who" dreamed what, and "who" awoke each time. Barbara had no interest in reviewing the data with me, but dutifully allowed me to read her nightly account. A review of this data over an eight-week period revealed a strikingly consistent pattern in which Barbara would typically go to bed and sleep for one to two hours. She would then awake and record a fragment of her nightmare that a little girl was being physically assaulted or sodomized in a certain way. There were characteristic sensory accompaniments, such as the smell of alcohol, the sound of the radio, and a yucky, sticky, tactile feeling. Shortly afterward, the young girl personification would sign in and wander around looking for would-be assailants, calm herself down by eating ice cream, and fall back to sleep. The cycle would repeat itself one or two more times until "Baby," the 5-year-old, convinced that the stepfather would return and snatch her from the bed again, would hide in the closet. Before that happened, the scrappy teenage lesbian would have a tantrum and throw furniture in a rage. Barbara would then awake in the closet in a fetal position, terrified, confused, and very tired.

Discussion

It appeared that what the patient experienced in her defensive altered states during the day continued to plague her at night in the form of a sleep disorder. There was blurring of the boundary between dreams and wakefulness (Ross, Ball, Sullivan, and Caroff, 1989) as her dissociative symptoms seemed to meld into one continuous nightmare. During her fitful sleep, she had recurrent dreams of an unknown little girl being sexually violated. Then, when she awoke, she "switched" into her little girl personification, who seemed to live out the dream scenario in her nighttime wanderings. Significantly, "Baby" 's first-hand account of her stepfather's abuse was identical to the description of the unknown little girl's ordeal in the patient's nightmares. For

Barbara, her need to disown her mental contents was so great that analyzing her dreams was only a preliminary step in helping her to own the contents of her mind. Eventually viewing videotapes of herself in altered states, in conjunction with dream work, helped her "integrate" (see chapter 8). During this agonizing process, the patient's reconstruction enabled her to conclude that she went into an altered state during her painful and overstimulating abuse. She then had recurrent dreams of her mental aberrations which seemed to reinforce a sense of separateness, resulting in a conviction that bad things had happened to someone else and not her.

Case 3. Resolving an Impasse

Cindy's treatment was reaching an impasse due to frequent absences over a six-month period for a variety of medical symptoms which could have been alleviated by an operation. Her analysis of many years duration had already taken a surprising turn when her diagnosis of multiple personality emerged after several years. At that time, she became traumatized after a foiled burglary at her house and developed dissociative symptoms of amnesia, fugue, and alter personalities coming forth (see chapter 2). Despite her success in the professional world, she lived a very private life, avoiding intimacy and breaking off with potential suitors lest her secret be found out. Her evasiveness was appreciated in retrospect as she originally sought help for depression and low self-esteem, claiming that the awards she received were not deserved since she did not really do the work herself. At that time, I did not realize that she meant it literally. Her history of growing up in poverty and being sent to live with alcoholic relatives on a farm was similarly vague, as she emphasized hunger, cold winters, and having to assume adult responsibilities at a young age. As treatment unfolded, it then became clear that what she was implying when she said she had to "do what the women did" was that she was expected to perform sexually. Her older brother independently also reported being exploited as a child.

Cindy was horrified to acknowledge that her dissociative symptoms, quiescent since late adolescence, had returned. She was also convinced that "the inside people" were separate entities who inhabited her body. She saw it being analogous to time sharing and simply did not want to think about it. While I knew nothing of this initially, her inability to express feelings and her reluctance to reflect on her inner life made me question her suitability for psychodynamic treatment at the outset, but her desperate pleading look and her profound unspoken wish for help offset her lack of psychological mindedness. Consequently, I agreed to see her in twice weekly psychotherapy, which as one might expect, was an arduous process. As a result, when treatment did not progress after a year, I was quite ambivalent about recommending analysis to better enable work with her characterological resistances and may have given in to a countertransference rescue fantasy. She was completely devoted to therapy as she tried to "get it right," and despite lack of obvious progress, seemed to be functioning better in her life. I felt sadness and compassion for her, also, and agreed to increase to four sessions a week.

When her true diagnosis became clear in her second year on the couch, her various personifications would arrive at the sessions on time, as Cindy did, introducing themselves and reporting horrendous stories of deprivation, torture, and sadistic sexual abuse. She was quite different and uncharacteristically affect-laden in each state. Cindy had no memory of these sessions and was curiously disinterested, giving new meaning to her initial lack of access to her inner world. Her need not to know was a source of frustration to "the inside people," as one of her parts made an impassioned plea for me to help as "they" had waited so long to find somebody whom they trusted enough to help "her." Having already had some experience in the treatment of multiple personality by the time her personfications emerged, I was nonetheless surprised, as I did not suspect it in this patient, at least consciously. All I sensed was that she felt very trapped inside and was trying desperately to tell me something.

I continued treatment in the analytic mode, essentially trying to extend the therapeutic alliance with her by including these altered states of consciousness in the process. I then reviewed the fundamental rule, informing her that saying what comes to mind included what she heard when she listened inside. This elaboration seemed necessary (see chapters 4, 8, and 10), after she reluctantly admitted hearing voices. Although I made it clear to the patient that all parts of the mind were not only welcome but essential, her fear of losing total control to "them" and never regaining it gave her a very stiff, rigid, and proper demeanor. Indeed, her fears were not unwarranted, as it was discovered that in her altered states she was prone to excessive drinking, flight, cutting, overdosing, and getting beaten up. This behavior became known when it started to occur during the time of our scheduled sessions and was brought to my attention in unusual ways.

In one particularly dramatic episode, instead of showing up for an appointment, she called in an absolute panic, having just "come to," finding herself naked in a strange hotel room in an unknown location. It took many months to understand what had happened that day as the interplay of her personifications was eventually teased out. It appeared that tremendous upheaval had resulted from Cindy's growing relationship and sexual interest in a man, a situation with obvious transference implications. She experienced this conflict as an internalized interpersonal struggle between herself and at least five of her personifications. It appeared that an alter who was known to be outgoing, flirtatious, and very interested in sex—the antithesis of Cindy—was furthering a relationship, again, which frightened the "little girls" inside who feared they would be violated and raped again. In addition to this fear, a volatile teenage alter became enraged as she too began reliving scenarios of abuse and torture. Her antidote was to punish and try to destroy the body before the bad people could get to her again. As a result, the patient started to cut her inner thighs and take a massive overdose. As a protective measure, a male personification whose rage was more externalized, inter- vened by drinking heavily to subdue the suicidal impulses, and took a bus to a distant city. "He" checked into a hotel and continued to drink until the patient passed out. When "he" awoke, somewhat grubby and hung over, "he" took his clothes off to take a shower. While on the way to the bathroom, "he" passed a full length mirror which horrified him to see the reality of his situation—a male identity trapped in a woman's body. The illusion of being a man was temporarily shattered and "he" went deeply "inside," feeling shocked, humiliated, and miserable. It was apparently at this point that Cindy experienced herself as having "come to," totally disoriented, lost, and naked. She then called me, which interestingly was during the time of our session. I then helped her calm down and get reoriented.

Similar to this fuguelike episode, Cindy's deepening transference was experienced and expressed through her personifications. Consequently, it was necessary to consider the feelings of each self, the dynamic tension between them, and the timing in sessions when she would shift to a given state, in order to appreciate what was happening with the patient overall. For example, Cindy was initially stoic and indifferent to vacations, but gradually I began to receive phone messages from her alters. She berated me for abandoning her and exclaiming that it was not possible to build trust if I were there one day and gone the next. When I brought these calls to her attention, she was disbelieving, and refused to consider that these complaints had anything at all to do with her. Her resistance to the awareness of transference (Gill, 1982) seemed directly proportional to her quasidelusion of separateness. At times I questioned the viability of any treatment, not to mention a modified analytic approach. But we persisted because there was no other choice, adopting a more supportive reality-based approach when she got most regressed.

Cindy wanted to continue on the couch, but when an anxiety-laden issue prompted a "switch," "others" would take over. They might continue to lie down, sit up, pace, check the door, huddle in a corner, or just glare at me. I, at times, served as an auxiliary ego and memory bank to help her fill in memory gaps when she became more amenable to hearing about what was discussed. However, she steadfastly maintained her conviction that whatever memories of past abuse might surface or whatever current exploits I might learn about did not really pertain to her. Her massive disavowal may have had survival value during a traumatic childhood, but as an adult with tremendous internalized aggression, it perpetuated an illusion that could have had lethal consequences (see chapter 7).

Cindy was slowly beginning to accept basic issues like psychic determinism, but to accept the possibility that the others were truly part of her mind would have meant owning the utterly degrading and relentless assaults reported by ''the children.'' She did not think she could live under those circumstances and was not sure she could go on in treatment. To have confronted her at this time that she was just one human being may have resulted in a painful, negative therapeutic reaction (Renik, 1991), so, I cautiously waited. Cindy was not a quitter, but only the flirtatious one could verbalize just how deep her attachment in the transference had become, so I accepted this dissociated form of expression and did not interpret this defense to Cindy. Her alter ego was beginning to be out more and more in the sessions, expanding her repertoire of ego functions in the hopes of ''taking over'' completely.

Several months later, the patient had a flare-up of a chronic digestive condition which incapacitated her for days at a time. It was not possible to consider with her that she might have had a psychosomatic regression to flee from dangerous transference feelings. While she could probably live without the recommended surgery, she would have been doomed to a life of intermittent episodes and progressive disability. She started missing sessions regularly and experiencing two recurrent nightmares. In one series, she was terrified, watching a naked teenage girl being held down on a table by an unknown woman while an unknown man savagely cut her body. The young girl was screaming in pain and the people either laughed or were indifferent to her plight. In the other series, once again she was terrified, watching a naked young girl being led to a barn, where she was blinded by bright lights and surrounded by farm animals. Cindy was quite shaken up by these relentless nightmares but had no idea what, if anything, they could mean to her. In the meantime, her physical condition worsened and she lost progressively more time as she reverted to defensive altered states to ward off the pain.

Sessions by telephone were tried, and while they helped by reinforcing her tenuous object constancy through the contact, they were not able to further the process. When she was feeling well enough to travel, the sense of discontinuity in the sessions was even greater than usual. Eventually, however, we were able to recognize the conflicting forces in her mind which resulted in her indecision: Cindy, herself, wanted the operation for pain relief, but the flirtatious one opposed it, fearing that she would be disfigured and not attractive to men anymore. In contrast, the transsexual was in favor, hoping to obliterate the female aspects of the body and get a sex change at the same

time. All of the younger personifications were morbidly afraid of the procedure, and the nature of the fears provided a window of understanding, which
eventually resulted in a breakthrough in her treatment. However, she proceeded with the operation without this understanding and became suicidal,
so she was subsequently hospitalized for a number of weeks. Interestingly,
this period of confinement allowed more continuity of treatment than if she
were to have convalesced at home.

The teenager was convinced almost to the point of paranoia, that the
operation was performed by the same bad people who had cut her open
before. It was the punishment they had always threatened if she were to tell
secrets about what they did to her. She was fixated on a scenario of being
held down by the girl friend of her cousin who inserted a knife in her vagina
and slashed her mercilessly while they laughed. Another alter, one of the
young girls, dreaded the operation for a different reason. She knew there
were bright lights in the operating room and it brought back bad memories
to her. She, too, was fixated on a memorylike scenario but in this one she
was tricked into going into an abandoned barn on her relative's farm. When
inside, she was blinded by lights and stripped of her clothing. Pornographic
pictures were then apparently taken while she was forced to perform sexual
acts with certain farm animals. Interestingly, Cindy's surgeon was affiliated
with a teaching hospital and asked her if she minded if photographs could be
taken during the procedure.

There were uncanny similarities between her two recurrent nightmares
and the images of abuse she described first hand and relived in two of her
dissociated states. I brought these observations to Cindy's attention in our
daily sessions, which, at this time, were conducted sitting up. She reacted
with astonishment and bewilderment. I then asked her how she could be
absolutely sure that the nightmares belonged to her but could so easily disown
the first-hand accounts of the two personifications, who with minor variations,
reported the same horror. She had no answer. Although not convinced at
first, Cindy did want to pursue the relationship between her dreams and her
personifications. In one particular session when the teenager was "out,"
reliving excruciating genital pain, I asked Cindy to listen in, which, for the
first time, had become possible for her.

After much work in this area, Cindy acquired "coconsciousness," which
reflected growing ego strength and a capacity to observe herself. This expanded awareness laid the groundwork for developing a continuity of consciousness with these seemingly disconnected and disowned identities, thus
providing the clinical proof to her that they were indeed part of her mind all
along. In a sense, Cindy was employing a complex form of negation, which
resulted in her conclusion that "it must be somebody else." It was an extraor-
dinarily painful realization that what the "inside people" were convinced

had happened appeared to be some version of Cindy's own childhood experience. She was more prepared this time to consider the unity of her mind, but the risk of acting on suicidal impulses was never far away until her aggression was neutralized. Cindy eventually concluded that the fear and pain of her early trauma were so intolerable at the time that she must have lapsed into an altered state, enabling her to feel like it was happening to someone else as she left her body. This disruption in her consciousness was apparently anthropomorphized, which was depicted in both her dreams and in the eventual creations of her personifications. This theme then became a central issue as she began to recognize how her shifting from state to state served as a most elusive defense in here-and-now anxiety situations. Once she developed this awareness she realized it would be easier to "take back" these memories without having to look at and be looked at by me, so she decided to resume the use of the couch.

Discussion

The sense of dividedness in this severely traumatized patient's mind appeared to be related to, but also extended beyond, the lack of integration of libidinally and aggressively derived self and object representations. It was enhanced by her subjective experience of separateness through the employment of dream-like and "hysterical" mechanisms. There was reciprocal amnesia between her personifications with their monoideic fugues (Janet, 1907) and her dreams which seemed to symbolize the anthropomorphization of her disturbance of consciousness (Silberer, 1909) during the original trauma. In other words, when Cindy switched into different alters, she had no memory of her dreams, while as Cindy she had no memory of what her alters knew, yet remembered her dreams. In addition, she seemed to utilize a pseudoexternalized displacement by attributing her impulses, affects, fantasies, and memories to her cadre of "inside people." In so doing, she could disown what was disagreeable or intolerable, and experienced her intrapsychic conflicts as interpersonal conflicts. Her narcissistic investment in her separate personifications (Kluft, 1987a) posed a most formidable resistance, which if challenged too soon could have had suicidal implications.

The onset of her medical symptoms, occurring at a time of increasing intensity in the transference, resulted in further dissociative symptoms, absences, and a regressive impasse. Her recurrent dreams at this time bore an irrefutable resemblance to the first-hand accounts of the childhood sexual trauma reported by two of her personifications. The internal consistency of those accounts enabled the patient to "feel it in her bones" and allowed her to be convinced that she was truly victimized. In order for this to happen, it seemed crucial to help the patient realize how her mind may have operated during such intolerable experiences. By doing so, she began to consider that the creation of her alters may indeed have been the spilling over, as it were, of what usually remains in the realm of posttraumatic dreams. The symbolic representation of her defensive altered states at the time of the original trauma took the form of other children being violated, while she left her body and went deep inside. There seemed to be reciprocal influences on the dreams and on her perception of herself, as this cycle apparently repeated itself for years. This phenomenon manifested itself, perhaps, through her "switching" to dissociated other selves. Interpretive work on how her mind functioned seemed to facilitate a movement toward a coalescence of her psyche and neutralization of aggression, which enabled her to proceed with analysis of the transference and a reconstruction of her childhood. There seemed to be an important interrelationship between dreams, defensive altered states, and this particular form of disturbed identity.

A SPECIAL FORM OF NEGATION

The essence of this defense accorded by the creation of different selves seems to be the ability to disown intolerable behavior and mental contents. These include not only dreams, but knowledge, memories, affects, instinctual strivings, somatic sensations, and bodily representations. The anthropomorphization of altered states appears to be an important substrate in the genesis of these selves. Such autohypnotically induced states may also result in transient conversionlike symptoms such as paralysis, anesthesia, and tactile hallucinations. At these times, the patient may experience the body differently at different times, further supporting the notion of separate selves. Pain threshold and psychosomatic phenomena may vary from state to state, also. Multiple perversions (see chapter 4) and transposition phenomenon (see chapter 6) contribute to identity confusion also. And, if the awareness of severe, repetitive early trauma is so overwhelming and needed to be kept secret from the outside world also, the creation of a socially compliant persona is also necessary. Cindy was such a socially conditioned self, which was perhaps a variation of the false self (Winnicott, 1960). In multiple personality or dissociative identity disorder (DID) jargon, Cindy would be described as a "host personality." In such a state of mind, patients, when discovering or being confronted with evidence of dissociation, quite often conclude, "It's not me! It can't be me! Either it didn't happen and it's my imagination or *it must be somebody else!*" A quasidelusional insight may then occur, of being possessed and having to share the body with others. Because of the fear of being labeled crazy, further mistreated, and perhaps being institutionalized indefinitely, this dreaded fear may become yet another horrible secret that must be kept hidden.

Not unrelated to Weinshel's (1977) formulation, these enormously complex characterological defenses are essentially in the service of negation, and Freud's (1925a) observations of this ubiquitous phenomenon have special relevance here. He noted that one can reject an image or an idea even after it comes into consciousness through negation: "indeed it is already a lifting of the repression, though not, of course, an acceptance of what is repressed" (pp. 236–237). But, because the intellectual is separated from the affective, a partial acceptance of the material may occur. But, even when a full intellectual acceptance of what is repressed finally does occur, the defensive process still is operative.

Freud also linked the process of negation to the origin of one's intellectual judgment, since one is confronted with the basic challenge of judging what is in the contents of one's mind. Thus the ego function of judgment must concern itself with two main decisions: determining whether something has a particular attribute and whether it exists in reality. And, because the original pleasure ego introjects everything that is good and keeps out everything that is bad, the ego equates bad with foreign and external. But, eventually the reality ego must then determine whether what has been perceived (and by definition internalized) can be found again in the outside world. This second aspect of judgment also concerns itself with what is external and internal, since what is real is both external and represented internally while what is not real is only inside the mind.

Inasmuch as the capacity for thought enables one to conjure up images of what is no longer present, Freud asserted that the underlying aim of reality testing is to refind the original lost object. Even though there may be distortions in the reproduced image, the exercising of one's judgment helps determine what action to finally take. This judgment is an interplay of both instincts, in that affirmation, a substitute for uniting, would be a derivative of Eros, whereas negation, as a result of expulsion, is derived from the destructive instinct (see chapter 7). Since making a judgment requires the capacity to symbolize disowning something in order to free up thinking from repression, when the ego does recognize what is unconscious, it does so symbolically through a negation, e.g., "I never thought that until you said it first." In such cases, Freud's (1913) advice about well-timed interpretations is especially important, in order to allow the patient adequate time for the gradual lifting of repressed material. In so doing, it is almost already "known" by the time the analyst makes the interpretation, having been preconscious for a period of time and, therefore, recognized by the analysand as her *own* wishes, fantasies, or memories. This ownership of one's mental contents is often problematic in traumatized dissociative patients, even though there may be other developmental evidence of early trauma (Blum, 1997). It is no surprise, therefore, that severely traumatized individuals who have not been able to come to terms with the truth of their pasts complain that they cannot trust their judgment about anything. Conversely, an indicator of progress in owning their dissociated mental contents is a growing confidence in exercising judgment.

Conclusion

In severe dissociative psychopathology, patients may appear to employ a pseudoexternalized displacement in the service of negation. In so doing, a quasidelusional insight could result in the conclusion, "*I* didn't think, say, do, feel, or dream that—someone else did!" The anthropomorphization of autohypnotic, dreamlike, and hypnogogic states, a reflection of the functional phenomenon, seems to be a contributing factor to this psychological state. A reciprocal amnesia between these dissociated states and posttraumatic dreams may further reinforce this process of disowning what is in the mind. As a result, this complex form of negation cannot be reversed by a mere lifting of repression through simple interpretation. And, the timing of any interpretive effort is crucial in helping the patient recognize and own these mental contents. An appreciation of these convoluted machinations of the mind in response to severe early trauma is necessary in the analysis of this defense, which may be catalyzed by the transference. When successfully handled, such patients, who initially report the absence of memory of severe early trauma may, over time, become able to own what "deep down inside" or in their "heart of hearts" they knew, but did not *really* know was in there all along (Brenner, 1997).

Chapter 6

INTERGENERATIONAL TRANSMISSION OF

TRAUMA

> Adaptation to reality was characterized by the simultaneous
> living in her present and in the past of her father [Kesten-
> berg, 1982, p. 148].

Growing up with a traumatized parent can leave its mark directly and indi-
rectly. But, while it has become a cliché that yesterday's abused children
become today's child abusers (Steele, 1970; Blum, 1987b), much less is
known about the subtle and indirect transmission that occurs even when
parents try to protect their offspring. The daily absorption of the adult's
traumatic past, taken in by the developing psyche of the child as a function
of mothering and/or fathering, may be overlooked (Kestenberg, 1972, 1982;
Klein, 1973; Bergmann and Jucovy, 1982; Jucovy, 1986). While this aspect
of intergenerational transmission may be considered strain trauma (Kris,
1956) or cumulative trauma (Khan, 1963), there are several reasons why it
may not even be recognized as a contribution. It is likely to be overlooked
if overt, gross abuse, deprivation, or shock trauma (Furst, 1967) overshadows
it, or if the parent's trauma history is not clear. In addition, countertransference issues may induce the analyst to unconsciously collude with the patient's
silence to avoid painful affects, such as grief, anxiety, shame, and guilt which

---

Earlier versions of this chapter, entitled "The Legacy of Trauma and Its Vicissitudes,"
were presented to the Houston-Galveston Psychoanalytic Society on October 11, 1996, Houston,
TX, and to the 2nd Annual Northwest Conference on Trauma and Dissociation on April 18,
1997, Seattle, WA.

may accompany the parent's past (Moses, 1978; Danieli, 1980). Then, if we consider the theoretical problems related to differentiating a repressed memory of trauma from an unconscious fantasy (Person and Klar, 1994) in just one person, we see that this dilemma is only confounded by the challenge of evaluating its impact across generations.

Nevertheless, it has been possible to examine transmission in cases where the history of parental trauma is not in doubt, when it was time limited prior to the child's birth, and where the child himself was not directly affected. Sadly, there has been no shortage of documented human tragedy, and the Holocaust, most notably, has provided most of the data on transmission.

TRANSMISSION OF HOLOCAUST TRAUMA

The genocidal destruction of two-thirds of the European Jewish population during World War II was the Holocaust. The term has been trivialized, commercialized, exploited for secondary gain, denied, and also applied to other recent mass atrocities, such as those in Cambodia, Rwanda, and Bosnia. It is not possible to assess the extent of an individual's suffering, based on the magnitude of the catastrophe or the number dead in any given event. And, as a result of many variables, including premorbid factors, the extent of traumatization may be different, not only amongst Holocaust survivors but also amongst survivors of other genocidal persecution. But, the Holocaust is by far the most widely studied, and more than fifty years after the liberation of the concentration camps, it is estimated that there are still roughly three hundred thousand survivors alive today worldwide. Their number is dwindling quickly, but they have produced a second, a third, and even a very young fourth generation. The lessons to be learned about politics, religion, and human nature are endless. Our understanding of the long-term effects of massive psychic trauma (Krystal, 1968; Grubrich-Simitis, 1981; Ornstein, 1986) on both adults and on the developing child (Kestenberg and Brenner, 1996) has also greatly increased. In addition, the passage of time has allowed us to examine intergenerational transmission.

CASE 1

Simon, an American-born man in his late twenties, refused to buy or even ride in German-made vehicles. His aversion to the German language was so strong that he would get nauseated to hear people speak it. He often dreamt of being chased or imprisoned, trying in vain to escape and rescue his family. He recoiled at the thought of trains, showers, and barbed wire. Simon also had contempt for policemen, distrusting any authority figure wearing a uniform. Both his mother and father were teenaged sole survivors of their families, having endured the inhuman conditions of slave labor and concentration camps during World War II. As the oldest of three children, Simon was named for his maternal grandfather who was gassed and cremated at Auschwitz. With the exception of his young and fit daughter, who became Simon's mother, the rest of the family perished along with the grandfather. Simon's mother was chronically depressed, and mute about her past, whereas the father could not stop talking about it, although he actually disclosed very little about his own ordeal. All of his friends, social activities, intellectual pursuits, and spare time had some connection to the Holocaust. Simon grew up feeling left out of this secretive and all-consuming past life of his parents, especially when his father would get lost in thought. It frequently seemed to Simon that he was more interested in his private world than in his own young son. As he got older, Simon tried to join in on the father's obsession, and they even developed a sardonic special greeting for each other, "Heil Hitler!" Simon sensed that he had a huge burden, in that he somehow was to make up for all of his parents' losses. His problems were felt to be insignificant compared to their suffering, and he felt he had no right to complain or to experience pleasure. He also felt he could never measure up to some idealized image of stoicism and imperviousness. Despite his adolescent rebellion, Simon was quite enmeshed with his parents, whose unresolved grief was unspoken but always present. His mother needed to know his whereabouts at all times and Simon complied. The most striking feature of all, however, was the sense he had, at times, that he was actually "there," living through the Holocaust. Without realizing it, he aspired to be a criminal, but it was out of an unconscious sense of guilt (Freud, 1916). He barely avoided being sent to jail a number of times for a series of minor infractions that could easily have been remedied. He derived a perverse sense of victory each time he escaped incarceration. He seemed to unwittingly bring on these sanctions and punishments through neglect, passivity, and a curious confusion over rules and laws. This confusion was exemplified during a hospital visit to a friend when he gave in to an overwhelming urge to help his buddy escape from the ICU. The friend was in a semidelirious postoperative state and was feeling trapped, scared, and helpless. But instead of rescuing a victim, Simon found himself participating in a destructive enactment. The friend urged Simon to take him to a woman's apartment for one last sexual experience just in case he were to die. Simon had doubts about this request, but could not say no, feeling too guilty about leaving his friend behind and not granting what might be his last request. In fact it almost did become his last request when the friend collapsed from the exertion, and a horrified Simon heard him crash to the floor during a violent coital episode. It created a true life and death situation. Simon then experienced an unremitting panic attack, as the failed rescue mission ended in disaster. Instead of becoming a hero, he felt like a perpetrator, a helpless bystander, and a guilt-ridden survivor, as his parents' traumatic past suddenly became superimposed on his own reality. Analytic exploration was necessary to help him eventually see his unconscious participation in recreating both a Holocaust scenario and a dangerous primal scene from his childhood. Interestingly, he later learned that his father's wartime experience included resistance activity and a series of near captures by the Gestapo. When he was finally caught and sent to a concentration camp, he was in the midst of trying to secure safe passage and escape for his family through his underground connections. Simon's father was perpetually tortured by guilt over not having been able to save his family.

Discussion

The phenomenon of living in two worlds simultaneously, borne of trauma and not of psychosis, was described by Kestenberg as a "time tunnel" (1982). She observed that in Holocaust survivors, there appeared to be a profound communication of their traumatic experience to their children, resulting in a transposition of the past, whereby they might feel that they too were living a Holocaust reality. Consequently, the developing ego in the second generation was confronted with not only the usual tasks of adaptation, but also with the integration of their parents' traumatic reliving of the Holocaust. As a result, there could be an intensification of developmental dangers and a characteristic preoccupation with survival, loss, persecution, and Jewish identity. The resulting feeling of almost "being there," can have a surreal, uncanny, or dissociative quality to it and has raised important metapsychological questions about the specificity of Holocaust trauma and the transmission of trauma in general.

At a most basic level, it may be that certain conditions merely accentuate and fixate the tendency in young children to assume they have always been part of their parents' earlier lives. For them to ask a question such as, "Where was I before I was born?" is not only a function of the separation–individuation process (Mahler, Pine, and Bergman, 1975), but also a cognitive milestone, for it requires a comprehension that there was a time in the world before their existence. As with other universal, anxiety-laden issues, this theme is depicted in popular literature and films and it is often in the form of time travel. Interestingly, the hero is frequently a child who goes back in time and gets caught up in the dilemma of changing the past in order to avenge a crime, correct an injustice, or prevent a tragedy.

The underlying oedipal component to this reparative fantasy was humorously depicted a number of years ago in the very popular movie *Back to the*

Future (1985). Here we see a young man who is very ashamed of his parents and seems to want to disown any relationship to them. He then travels back in time and lives out his prehistory with the help of a wild-eyed but affable scientist (who is not an analyst!). He becomes entangled in a love triangle with his parents when they were of high school age, but they do not know he is to become their son. He resists his future mother's amorous advances and helps his pathetic, defenseless, pushover of a father stand up to the class bully who humiliates him on a daily basis. In so doing, his future father gains strength, pride, respect, and most importantly, the love of the boy's future mother. The son, the hero, avenges his father's past victimization and rehabilitates him. He helps the father become the kind of man that he can look up to. In order to do so, he must renounce his own oedipal desires. In return, he creates a strong and successful father with whom he can develop a healthy male identification. And, as is the case in transpositions, there was an ambiguity between the past and the present. This ambiguity can progress to confusion and disorientation, when there is blurring between dream, fantasy, memory, and reality which accompanies severe early trauma (Brenner, 1995; see also chapters 2 and 4).

Simon, however, was quite aware of his hypersensitivity and repugnance toward German and Nazi symbolism. He intellectually "knew" it was related to his parents' past, but the deeper aspects of his living *as though* he were in the Holocaust were unconscious. Specifically, he was oblivious to the meaning of his bizarre "rescue" of the friend in the ICU, which, on one level, was a concretization of the father's Holocaust trauma (Bergmann and Jucovy, 1982). He enacted an unconscious reparative fantasy of rescuing a family member like his own father from the Nazis, which was also a feat his father was unable to do.

A related organizing fantasy frequently seen in children of survivors is one of "selection" (Brenner, 1988a). Woven into this Holocaust scenario, both oedipal and preoedipal conflicts may be played out with sickeningly real imagery from the parents' past. Here, too, this motif has emerged in popular literature with *Sophie's Choice,* by William Styron (1979). Ilany Kogan (1995), in the analytic literature, recently described such a woman with a "selection" fantasy whose mother was a survivor. She could neither escape the symbiotic engulfment of this perpetually grieving mother nor could she tolerate the anxiety and guilt of an oedipal victory. Consequently, she found refuge in a perverse solution, characterized by sadomasochism and a phallic woman fantasy (Bak, 1968), in which she became a female Doctor Mengele in an S.S. uniform wielding a deadly phallic baton. In her fantasy, she made the "selections" on the entry ramp to Auschwitz, deciding who would live or die by a casual wave of her powerful stick. People were used or discarded at will. Within her inner life, she could then maintain total control over her object world, being the omnipotent Nazi "angel of death" (Abraham, 1986).

The Holocaust "culture" (Kestenberg and Gampel, 1983) may completely saturate the mental life of children of survivors, *as though* they are transported back to a time when reality was worse than fantasy. Almost eerily, some would unconsciously recreate elements of the past when they reached the age their parents were during their ordeals. Such an internalization of the parent's past seems to extend beyond the symbolic or metaphorical world, suggesting a very deep, preverbal communication between parent and child (Herzog, 1982). Volkan (1981), in his work on pathological grief, described a depositing of the parent's traumatized self representation into the child. Faimberg (1988) has conceptualized a type of identification with a "telescoping of generations." She postulates an intergenerational narcissistic problem in which the parent appropriates the capacity for experiencing pleasure from the child and is internalized as a dominating and intruding object. It is similar to Bollas' notion of extractive introjection (1987). In this structure, a condensation of three generations may occur in which elements of a secret history not belonging to the patient gets incorporated. These identifications are unconscious, timeless, and may be uncovered in the transference. In such cases a pervasive anhedonia with a feeling of inner deadness is reported. As the child becomes the "container" (Kogan, 1995) for the parents to deposit their losses, fears, and hopes, the role of projective identification is considered to be a central mechanism here. Anna Freud (1936) had long since concluded that "identification with the aggressor" was often seen in trauma, recognizing that projection of guilt was at the core of it. Consequently, the projection of what was later to be coined as "survivor guilt" (Niederland, 1961), would be an essential part of the intolerable burden transmitted to the second generation. Blum (1986, 1987b), however, reminds us that identification with the rescuer and identification with the victim are other important outcomes in the resolution of trauma, which we see in Simon's case also.

The knowledge of these phenomena became widespread in the late 1970s and 1980s as the commonality of their experience spawned the Second Generation movement. Specialized group therapy (Fogelman and Savran, 1979), a proliferation of local organizations throughout North America, and autobiographical books, such as Helen Epstein's *Children of the Holocaust* (1979), marked a coming of age for this surprisingly resilient population whose prognosis was somewhat guarded in the earlier reports (Krystal, 1968). But, even before this time, in 1974 the New York based Group for the Psychoanalytic Study of the Effects of the Holocaust on the Second Generation (GPSEHSG) had been formed. Under the leadership of Judith Kestenberg, Martin Bergmann, and Milton Jucovy, it met monthly to study the issue of transmission of trauma. Analysts presented case material to the group which, over the years, probably had more collective knowledge of the subject than anywhere else in the world. They sought to tease out the so-called private pathology from Holocaust-related pathology and study the interaction of both as it emerged in the analytic process. In addition, they offered an annual discussion group at the winter meeting of the American Psychoanalytic Association in New York.

After attending this discussion group in 1980, I joined the monthly study group in 1981, and have been an active participant since then. Eventually, I had the good fortune of being offered the chairmanship of the annual discussion group when the senior leadership retired several years ago. In addition, my participation in Kestenberg's international study of child survivors produced a number of papers and presentations, culminating in our recently published book *The Last Witness* (Kestenberg and Brenner, 1996). In it, we present preliminary findings of the over fifteen hundred interviews that have been collected. Focusing on the effects of genocidal persecution on the developing psyche, we also looked for sequelae throughout the life cycle.

In our book Kestenberg and I examine the issue of transmission (of trauma) from the survivor's perspective. Our data suggest a wide polarity ranging from traumatic repetition to mastery and regeneration amongst survivor parents. Those who were primarily under the influence of the repetition compulsion endlessly repeated scenarios of survival, perhaps at times in defensive altered states of consciousness. They may include their children in their enactments, also. One man, for example, survived as a young adolescent by living in hiding with a series of lonely German gentile women whose husbands were off fighting at the front for the Fuhrer. This young man exchanged sex for protection, living in fear of certain death if he were to displease his benefactors and be turned over to the Gestapo. After the war, he continued as if he were still in danger, living a marginal life with a series of gentile wives and sending his children to be raised by others on the outskirts of town. When his son became a teenager himself, he joined a motorcycle gang, which sported Nazi helmets and insignias, and terrorized his father. As a result, the man felt persecuted by his antisocial son, a little Hitler, as he perpetuated and legitimized his life in hiding. He had no idea how such a seemingly cruel twist of fate could have been visited upon him after all his suffering, but after a number of years the two reconciled their differences. Interestingly, the son eventually sustained a number of work-related injuries, making a career living off workman's compensation and lawsuits. The survivor father apparently then felt a bit of perverse pride in his son, who stopped being a perpetrator and became a successful victim. Interestingly, the father was envious of older survivors who received a monthly restitution check from the German government and felt that his son had pulled a fast one on the authorities. Beating the system by outsmarting the one in charge has survival value in a world where one was being hunted down like a rabid animal, when being a Jew was a capital crime.

This type of superego seems to reflect a lack of cohesion, or a split (Kestenberg and Brenner, 1986), which developed in some young survivors who were caught between obeying their parents' precepts as opposed to following their own instincts for survival. Simon's disregard for certain rules, laws, and standards of behavior, although multidetermined, may have been an example of this survivor superego transmitted to the second generation. A similar phenomenon has been observed in other persecuted minorities, too (Apprey, 1993; Volkan, 1995, 1996).

TRANSMISSION OF TRAUMA AND DISSOCIATION

Transmission takes on a more pathogenic quality when it is associated with symptomatic disturbances of memory, awareness, consciousness, and identity. While most of the reported cases pertaining to the Holocaust emphasize transposition associated with defensive operations based on repression or splitting, one report does describe dissociative symptoms. Even though the etiology of dissociation itself remains somewhat of a debate, many authorities share the view put forth by Van der Kolk and Kadish (1987), that barring organicity, it is caused by psychic trauma. In this vignette (Gampel, 1982), a 7-year-old girl presented with amnesia, disorientation, learning difficulties, and "absences." Her father was the sole survivor of his family who, as a young boy, endured the Warsaw Ghetto and a concentration camp. He never spoke of his past, but his daughter was privately preoccupied with the fantasy of an electrified fence in a ghetto which could deliver a deadly charge to the children who were placed against it. Her parents were appalled and mystified to learn of the girl's knowledge of such things, a subject which had consumed her so intensely that it apparently made her ill. Her dissociative symptoms, which were thought to be almost psychotic in nature, reportedly resolved after several family meetings in which the father's Holocaust experience was openly discussed in front of the child. While it is unclear what, if any, other traumatogenic influences may have existed in this secretive family, it does appear that she identified with her father as a child victim.

Interestingly, an electrified fence became eroticized and incorporated into the masturbation fantasy of another patient, one with dissociative character pathology (chapter 2) who experienced incest.

CASE 2. COMBAT TRAUMA TRANSMITTED THROUGH INCEST IN A
DISSOCIATIVE CHARACTER

Harriet's father enlisted in the service as a teenager to fight in the Vietnam War. He survived a particularly bloody battle which resulted in thousands of deaths on both sides. In this well-documented inferno, there was incessant bombing, artillery fire, and hand-to-hand combat. The enemy was willing to take huge losses, so he was under constant threat of suicide attacks by guerilla soldiers. After a number of days of these relentless conditions, he killed a number of the enemy himself. He also witnessed the gruesome deaths of a number of his comrades, including several whose bodies literally blew apart in front of and all over him. What haunted him the most, however, was the memory of a mistake he made under these overwhelming conditions, which resulted in the death of one of his good buddies. He apparently detonated an explosive device before his comrade could get to safety, and they both realized it in those awful helpless few seconds before the explosion. Amidst the chaos and confusion of the battle, there was never any formal criticism or sanction of this event—indeed, Harriet's father was subsequently wounded himself and awarded a medal for his heroism. Harriet grew up with a vague awareness of her father's wartime past. His injury never healed and required several operations which she perceived to be life-threatening. She remembered and forgot the war stories numerous times as she grew up and had a seemingly disconnected understanding of the horror of it. She read a copy of his memoirs during analysis which described these experiences.

Father was reportedly quite symptomatic. He startled easily, could not tolerate any disobedience, yelled out orders in a barking fashion, and was prone to panic. He slept poorly and had nightmares of combat. He would lapse into moments of absent-minded reveries of which Harriet longed to be a part.

Harriet was convinced that he loved her more than her mother, a victorious feeling that left her both exalted and riddled with guilt. Her mother was described as overprotective, highly anxious, and emotionally frigid. As a child, she felt it her responsibility to keep her parents happy, sensing a great rift between them. She recalled a primal scene memory of her mother screaming in fear and anger at father to get off of her. Harriet had a recurrent nightmare of awakening to find herself surrounded by total destruction as the sole survivor of nuclear war. The panic of being totally alone and feeling vaguely responsible for it would haunt her all day. Coupled with a work inhibition, these symptoms eventually brought her to treatment.

In analysis, her restlessness, anxiety, and inability to think gave way, over time, to defensive altered states of consciousness. She lapsed into extended periods of silence, exhaustion, and verbal non sequiturs. During these amnestic states, she eventually expressed her emotional and physical reactions to sexual contact with her father, which was often accompanied by graphic anal posturing and pelvic thrusting. Through reconstruction after more than a decade of analysis, it seemed likely that there was regular anal and vaginal penetration throughout latency. In the transference, she begged for a sign of affection, seeming to have no understanding of the boundaries of the therapeutic relationship. After all, if her father would show his love through his genitals, why wouldn't her analyst? This erotized longing belied a deeper, concealed, and very demoralizing sexual inhibition in which her arousal would suddenly disappear as she approached orgastic excitement. Interestingly, she incorporated Holocaust imagery into a masturbation fantasy in which she was sadistically seducing and driving a man insane with sexual desire. He was forced to stand perfectly still up against an electrified fence in a concentration camp, and the moment his body moved during orgasm, he would be electrocuted. The identity of the man in her barbed wire fantasy fluctuated between her lover, her analyst, and then her father. Eventually recalling and owning her terrifying overstimulation with her father, she realized she had turned her passive helplessness into active, sadistic control with this fantasy. She alternated between being the good Nazi soldier just following her father's orders, to becoming the dictator, herself, demanding total obedience from me in response to her Nazi salute from the couch. She eventually realized that her profound guilt and fears of reprisal by her mother, coupled with her feelings of rejection when the incest eventually stopped, were condensed into the bleakness of the camps and her nightmare of being totally alone after nuclear war.

Such a burden would have been difficult enough to work through, but she felt there was yet another aspect that haunted her and we almost reached an impasse. We eventually discovered that she had a peculiar sense of almost having been "there," as her father's guardian angel, during combat. She wanted to be part of his anniversary commemorations and reunions, desperately seeking a souvenir from the battlefield.

When she was finally able to bring herself to find out more, with my encouragement, she learned how he and his buddies had to lie totally still night after night in their makeshift bunkers, knowing that the slightest movement could be heard by lurking enemy soldiers who were ready to make a deadly assault at the slightest noise. She recalled how she too would be living in mortal dread, being very quiet with her father, so as to avoid being caught by her mother and would panic at the slightest sound that might signal her approach. She then reremembered the story of her father blowing up his buddy, imagining their paralysis and horror when they realized that nothing could be done to stop the inevitable explosion. Harriet then became aware of an unconscious fantasy that her own body would totally self-destruct during orgasm and could not bear the thought that she might have climaxed with her father as a girl. She recalled how she would feel unreal while studying the facial expressions and bodily movements of her lovers during their helpless moments of orgastic surrender. She could never be sure if they experienced pain or pleasure and marveled that they survived each time. She then recalled with horror that her own father called out for his mother during his orgasms. Following this revelation, she remembered him telling her that dying soldiers used to cry out for their mothers on the battlefield. Her somatic memories of shortness of breath, burning genitals, and the smell of father's cologne, coupled with terror, confusion, forbidden pleasure, and subsequent revulsion left her feeling that any pelvic thrusting or bodily expression of sexual excitement could be lethal, so she must lie as still as possible.

Discussion

It was essential for Harriet to realize that being with her father seemed as if they were on the battlefield. There was tremendous resistance to this exploration, and she almost broke treatment along the way. There was always a deadly enemy lurking nearby and mortal dread of her body exploding with sexual overstimulation. In addition, she maintained a belief that she was keeping her father safe and alive by doing anything he asked. However, she feared that since he could kill his enemies and even his buddy, he could murder his own daughter, too. This split image of him as a murderer was in total contradiction to him as a wounded victim of war, as one who needed constant care and protection to stay alive. Similarly, she experienced herself as both a ruthless victor and a helpless victim of seduction in which Holocaust imagery and fantasy was incorporated. Her own murderous rage for being put in this no win situation between her parents was even more deeply concealed but eventually came to light as an important component to her transposition.

An even more obscured manifestation of transposition may be uncovered at the most severe end of the dissociative character spectrum, in the multiple personality, as a contribution to the creation of an identity for the "persecutionary father alter." As abusive or incestuous scenarios would get enacted between the various alters, it used to astound me as to how even the most profoundly traumatized patients would often have an alter who felt so tenderly and sympathetically about their parents' own miserable early lives. Quite often, this alter is especially removed from the others and hated by the others for betraying them and giving in.

CASE 3. TRANSMISSION OF CHILDHOOD AND COMBAT TRAUMA
THROUGH INCEST IN "MULTIPLE PERSONALITY"

Barbara was a profoundly tortured individual who had spent much of the last several years in and out of psychiatric hospitals. Despite her marriage of many years, raising three healthy children, and being competent in her chosen field, she would lapse into suicidal states associated with fugues, amnesia, and self-mutilation. On more than one occasion she had been beaten up, raped, and was found in a distant city in a fugue. She experienced a psychic reality in which numerous inside people inhabited her body. These included crying or self-destructive children, enraged teenagers, and a lesbian. She felt at the mercy of these forces and was especially terrified of a deadly man known as "the Admiral," whose function was multiply determined, including the personification of a transsexual conflict (chapter 4). The patient had a conviction in this male state of consciousness that nature made a serious mistake about "his" body. Out of anguish, despair, and rage, it had to be rectified by cutting or burning the female genitals and by bloody, self-inflicted attempts at mastectomy. Her overwhelming internalized aggression could only be kept in check through an elaborate, joint effort of her other "parts," but it was easily triggered by sexual arousal. Clinical contact with the patient in her "Admiral" state of consciousness put me at considerable risk of bodily injury, as she also had a history of violence toward others when feeling under attack. Consequently, safety precautions needed to be taken, and it took many months of alliance building with her in this state until we were finally able to sit relatively comfortably in the same room and talk. As I got to know "the Admiral" better, it became clearer that he also served as an internal persecutor whose perceived existence transcended the survival of the body (see chapter 7). "He" would inflict punishment, bodily injury, and enact abuse scenarios, but since the patient did not feel pain in this autohypnotic state until she reverted back to her usual self, her conviction of separateness was reinforced by transient anesthesia and amnesia. Furthermore, her rage in this state often masked prolonged orgasmic sensations which filled her with humiliating embarrassment and shame.

It appeared that "the Admiral" was a very complex compromise formation whose function and origin were multiply determined. Among these was an internalization of the stepfather, a brutal, sadistic tyrant given to uncontrollable, violent rage, who was a Vietnam veteran. But, in addition to the more obvious "identification with the aggressor," "the Admiral," whose relentless criticism and punishments served an archaic superego function, also seemed to have a life history of "his" own. Significantly, "he" reported "his" own traumatic boyhood, being mercilessly sodomized by "his" father. In addition, "he" described a wartime experience identical to Barbara's stepfather, as though "he" had actually been there. In this defensive altered ego state, the patient detailed a series of events, including a very bloody battle, the death of "his" comrade, and the killing of an enemy soldier in revenge. It was chilling to hear how "the Admiral" 's description of "his" kicking and beating the enemy soldier into unconsciousness paralleled Barbara's recovered memory of her father's savage attack of the mother during a drunken stupor. Significantly, such memories of childhood and of the stepfather's earlier life were independently corroborated by other family members.

Discussion

The patient's confusion over the past and present, her inner versus outer object world, as well as her difficulty in differentiating fantasy and dreams, reflected a disturbed reality sense which is often seen in multiple personality (chapter 4). In addition, her identity diffusion manifested itself in unusual ways, as she, at times, "became" an older man who believed "he" was sodomized by "his" own father as a child and who now was a career military officer. "His" punishments, which would consist of terrorizing an inner little girl who also shared the body, left the patient feeling totally unsafe and at "his" mercy. She would lose time and panic when she hallucinated the roar of "his" ship's engine approaching, fearing another bout of self-mutilation in an amnestic state.

A therapeutic breakthrough occurred after a suicidal regression, when the patient began to feel rivalry toward other patients and became very possessive in the transference. When I wondered aloud with her if she wanted to be my favorite patient, she exploded with rage. She then became internally preoccupied and "switched" to a younger child personification. As if verifying the interpretation in a manner typical for such patients, she was then consumed by inner terror—auditory hallucinations of "the Admiral" 's menacing voice threatening to come after her because she was "his" favorite. Having an alliance with her in this altered state, I maintained contact with her and she eventually "switched" back to her usual self and sobbed violently. But she had amnesia for what had just transpired and did not know why there were tears all over her face when she "came back." I cautiously reintroduced the word *favorite*, and she had a glimpse of recognition, ever so briefly recalling her own desperate wish to be her father's favorite. She longed for the love of a father in spite of, and at times because of, the things he made her do and how it made her body feel. She initially could not tolerate the awareness of the profound shame, guilt, and pleasure associated with him and was prone to fluctuations of consciousness. She was appalled to eventually discover a peculiar sense of empathy for him, as she somehow just "knew" that she should make up for his past pain. She found herself automatically writing the verses of a famous poem about war, which was "the Admiral" 's way of expressing a totally new affect—sadness and grief. Through analysis of the transference, she eventually became able to differentiate the dissociated inner representation of her father from her external father. Eventually, she was able to reconstruct how desperately she longed for his love and how she used to feel as though she were living in a version of his own past trauma. She learned to recognize how her feelings in the here-and-now were defended against by the activation of such personifications. Through profound abreactive experiences, a greatly increased observing ego, and a tremendous desire to get better because of her family, she eventually became able to own these parts of her mind as she integrated (see chapter 8). These personifications, resembling psychological teratomas (Ferenczi, 1929a) were apparently linked to a traumatic past in such a way that "they" lived out scenarios more vividly than her current reality and seemed to have lives of their own.

CONCLUSION

The seemingly delusional preoccupations and quasipsychotic symptoms of even the most severe type of dissociative pathology may become comprehensible through an appreciation of the vicissitudes of trauma. The phenomenon of transposition, although originally described in children of Holocaust survivors, is not unique to this population, and may be a factor in the confusion between the past and present seen in more regressed patients. It appears that such individuals may have been severely traumatized in childhood by parents who had been traumatized themselves. Parental trauma, childhood trauma, and developmental processes apparently condensed into complex autohypnotic, defensive altered states of consciousness. Depending on the level of integration of self and object representations at the time of trauma, the internalization of the traumatizing parent could be experienced as a separate, dissociated, inner persecutor. Under those circumstances, the transmitted trauma of the parent seemed to become incorporated into the life history of the personification, instead of a more diffuse, global sense of living in two worlds simultaneously. Recognition of this possible contribution to the development of dissociative pathology may be helpful in translating seemingly bizarre symptoms into potentially treatable complications of trauma.

Chapter 7

REVISITING THE DEATH INSTINCT

> Self preservation may then be considered due to the pre-established order of the contest between the sexual and the death instinct in every organism [Federn, 1952, p. 272].

The death instinct, also known as thanatos, and its putative energy, mortido (Federn, 1932), or destrudo (Weiss, 1935), is one of Freud's most disputed and refuted theories (Jones, 1957). It has not been able to rest in peace after seventy-five years of heated debate (Akhtar, 1995). One can still read that failure to acknowledge the power of thanatos may lead to a destructive repetition in someone not conscious of its influence (Steiner, 1995). Such themes are pervasive in popular culture, also. For example, some of the most enduring creatures in horror movies are vampires and werewolves, who live in the world of the undead and repeatedly wreak havoc on the unsuspecting townspeople, who either don't believe in them or think them long dead.

In his theory, Freud tried to explain why people repeat painful or traumatic experiences, an apparent contradiction to the pleasure principle. He sought a universal law governing organisms which he based on contemporary scientific knowledge, his own observations, and philosophical reflection. Concluding that "the aim of all life is death" (1920a, p. 28), he conceptualized an instinct that operated silently and unobtrusively "to return to the quiescence of the inorganic world" (1920a, p. 62). The aim of reducing unpleasurable levels of excitation operated under the Nirvana principle, and its logical conclusion was the peacefulness of the lifeless state. To counterbalance this

---

An earlier version of this chapter was presented at the Annual Conference of the International Society of Traumatic Stress Studies, November 4, 1995, Boston.

force, he invoked " 'Eros' (which) operates from the beginning of life and appears as a 'life instinct' in opposition to the death instinct, which was brought into being by the coming to life of inorganic substances'' (1920a, p. 61).

A major reason that many analysts disagreed with the concept of a death instinct, per se, was that it met only one of three criteria—it had an aim, but not a focal bodily source, nor was it directed toward an object (Simmel, 1944).

Its value was also questioned because clinical manifestations of the death instinct could not be proven or convincingly demonstrated by psychoanalysis (Bibring, 1941; Fenichel, 1945; Waelder, 1956). Although it was ascribed to aggression, sadism, masochism (Freud, 1924), and massive resistance in analysis (Freud, 1937), there was much controversy. Considered by some to be more autobiographical than universal, Freud's own health, mental state, and unresolved grief were seen as factors in his development of this theory (Hamilton, 1976). Indeed, Chasseguet-Smirgel has noted that Freud's major contributions on femininity also coincide with his cancer (1976). His associations between the threat of death (1925b) and the female genital, the entrance to the former home of all human beings (1919a, p. 245), brought him back to the site of the origin of life. Others simply relegated thanatos to the numinous or spiritual world, an area beyond analysis, so it was banished to the Jungian land of archetypes and the collective unconscious (Loewald, 1977). Melanie Klein (1933, 1952), a notable exception, embraced the notion of a death instinct, because it helped her explain the presence of annihilation anxiety in preoedipal children.

As a result, many writers have sought alternative explanations for the repetitive nature of such mental phenomena as traumatic dreams, children's play, and the transference. Regulatory principles of the id such as the unpleasure principle (Schur, 1966), or the pleasure principle itself (C. Brenner, 1982), did not invoke the death instinct or its agent, the repetition compulsion, so these revisions brought analysts back to more comfortable territory. Consequently, the evolution of mainstream American psychoanalytic theory has left the concept of the death instinct in a bit of a lifeless state, but not completely.

Although a link between trauma and the death instinct was described early on by Ferenczi (1929b), such ideas are only recently being rediscovered, as the recognition of the importance of psychic trauma and its sequelae has sparked renewed interest in such early theories. It has been suggested that the study of severely traumatized patients, such as those with dissociative disorders, could provide the opportunity to advance our knowledge in this area (Marmer, 1991). The great tendency toward retraumatization in this population, for example, supports the notion that some principles regarding repetition may be operative (Kluft, 1990). The destructive quality of this repetition does not always seem in the service of mastery or adaptation, but rather like a broken record stuck in a groove. Cognitive and neurobiological theories have also been put forth to explain this phenomenon (Terr, 1983; van Der Kolk and Kadish, 1987). Nevertheless, some analysts (Alexander, 1929; Weiss, 1935; Menninger, 1938; Federn, 1932; Nunberg, 1955; Eissler, 1971; Garma, 1971; Fayek, 1981) continued to find the notion of a death instinct a compelling way to understand the vicissitudes of aggression. Rosenfeld (1971), for example, in his description of certain refractory, self-destructive, narcissistic states, is of particular interest here.

In my own work with the dissociative disorders, like a number of other clinicians, I am struck by the profound amount of internalized aggression, self-destructive behavior, repetitive trauma, and preoccupation with death in this group. Conceptually, I have found it clinically useful to think of a continuum of dissociative character pathology in which Dissociative Identity Disorder (DIS) is at one end, while a more integrated psyche that also employs defensive altered states, is at the other end (chapters 2 and 3). I have also demonstrated how the containment, encapsulation, and disowning of aggression may be one of the central tasks of the developing psyche in such cases (chapter 4). In addition, it seems that perverse sexuality is one of the organizing influences in this encapsulation because different identities may coalesce around the various sexual pathways in the formation of alters.

It then occurred to me that if the death instinct or its derivatives could truly be manifested clinically, it might be in such a severely traumatized, suicidal individual who was also terminally ill. A patient suffering with DID and AIDS brought just these issues sharply into focus, and I will present elements of this case. I will try to illustrate how an awareness of the struggle between life and death forces was useful in her treatment. I will also describe her repetitive, self-destructive scenarios, and focus on a unique feature of multiple personality, the dissociated disowning of one's body. This is a phenomenon I have encountered extensively, and it can have fatal implications. The challenge of working with such a patient in today's climate will be addressed, too.

Case Report

Tracey, a 27-year-old mother of two who was of Caribbean descent, was transferred to a dissociative disorders treatment unit after an extended psychiatric hospitalization failed to resolve her suicidal crisis. She had had no prior psychiatric history and was successful in her career. The patient, upon learning that she had contracted the AIDS virus, possibly after a blood transfusion for obstetrical complications, had taken a lethal amount of drugs. She was discovered just in time to be resuscitated by heroic medical treatment. Following her stabilization, she was admitted to a psychiatric unit whereupon her behavior and mental status deteriorated. She became progressively disoriented, hallucinating, and labile but was unresponsive to antidepressants and antipsychotics. After she started headbanging, trying to cut herself, going AWOL, and assaulting staff, she spent much time in restraints or in the seclusion room.

Careful observation, however, revealed distinct changes in her speech, body language, and attitude. Generally, she was pleasant and cooperative, but at times would become provocative, vulgar, agitated, and challenged all authority. At such times, the patient eventually told her doctor her deeply concealed secret—she was really not Tracey, she was "Lacey," someone who did things that Tracey would never dream of. A diagnosis of DID was considered. "Lacey" soon acquired the title of being "a sociopathic alter" and did everything she could to live up to her reputation. "Lacey" insisted that she was needed to protect Tracey from dangerous or abusive situations and was completely aware of everything going on. Tracey, however, was amnestic when "Lacey" was "out," which helped explain her episodic disorientation. The patient eventually disclosed that during latency to adolescence, she was sent to live with relatives, and she thought she was subjected to physical and sexual abuse. Her incarceration at the hospital seemed to be triggering disjointed memories and flashbacks of being in that helpless situation as a child, which resulted in her regression. Although open to the diagnosis of a dissociative disorder, the unit was not prepared to treat her any differently from an agitated schizophrenic, so her condition worsened. Arrangements were subsequently made for her transfer and she was in the above state of mind when I first met her.

Her absolute terror, disorientation, and fragmentation, coupled with her life-threatening medical condition, clearly could not be treated in a time frame consistent with the tenets of managed care. Indeed, she had already languished for a half year elsewhere. Consequently, an essential ingredient to establishing her holding environment was the addressing of this reality with her, her family, the insurance company, and the hospital. Much time was spent trying to allay the patient's fear of being discharged before she was ready. In order to do this, it was necessary to confirm her generous benefits from an indemnity insurance policy, to have a hospital Utilization Review staff member work closely with us, and to develop a cooperative alliance with a reviewing physician to get weekly approval for continued inpatient care. Ten months of five times per week intensive psychotherapy will be summarized here.

Despite her HIV status, Tracey initially looked very healthy and her white cell counts were in the low normal range. This presentation, coupled with a certain disingenuous quality that she exuded, made one of her medical consultants doubt the HIV diagnosis. This uncertainty quickly introduced the issue of trust and credibility, so, when the diagnostic tests were reordered, she became outraged and very hurt that she might not be believed. Interestingly, this doubt resurfaced from time to time despite the clearly positive lab data! Being believed by others and believing herself was a major theme in that several key "alters" refused to believe either of her diagnoses, also. For example, the "sociopathic alter," who came to be seen as more streetwise and vulgar than lacking a conscience, viewed her DID as "a housing problem," i.e., too many people sharing a cramped space. She and other parts of the mind saw the HIV as simply Tracey's problem. Then, as her medical condition deteriorated, following a respiratory arrest, multiple seizures, neurogenic urinary retention, intolerable joint pain, and inability to walk, the patient's unconscious undermining of her treatment came to be one of the major therapeutic challenges in our work. As a result, building a therapeutic alliance with the patient while she was in her numerous dissociative states became a central task for us.

Because of the possibility of AIDS dementia, it was not clear if or when this problem might arise and how drastically it might affect our therapeutic work. Periodic MRIs and EEGs were negative, however, despite evidence on psychological testing of memory and slight cognitive impairments. Interestingly, certain alters, especially the most negativistic and destructive ones, showed excellent recall, extremely quick thinking, constant alertness, and a great capacity for abstract, metaphorical thinking. Coordinating this and other medical issues related to her HIV disease required ongoing consultation and communication with her neurologist, infectious disease specialist, rheumatologist, gynecologist, and two pain specialists. Her internist shared this responsibility with me, as we constructed an elaborate therapeutic holding environment.

A team approach was essential in such a complex patient, whose problems increased over time. The primary nurse helped monitor all the medication and observation of her behavior throughout the day while the social worker was the key liaison to her family. A "therapist–administrator split" was also put into place to allow the unit psychiatrist to oversee her privileges and adherence to the basic rules and regulations, so I could focus on the psychodynamic issues. It took a number of weeks for this structure to develop, but needless to say, the patient's suffering could not wait until we were fully ready.

When the patient arrived, she appeared terrified, disoriented, and very childlike, as she was in altered states during most of her transition. Several "child alters" predominated: "Barbie," who was doubled over due to groin pain; "Daisey," who was convinced that she was bleeding from her vagina; and "Rosie," who was mute but prone to head banging and punching herself. Considering the dual nature of dissociation which defends against anxiety in the here-and-now through the reactivation of altered states from past trauma

(Brenner, 1995; chapter 2), it was eventually understood that she was expressing her feelings about being transferred to a new hospital. Having to leave a familiar place for the uncertainty of a new place with strangers, she seemed to be reliving the time she was sent away from home. Her father died when she was 4 and her alcoholic mother could not care for all the children, so she was sent to live with relatives, one of whom was a preacher. While there, she reported physical and sexual abuse but had few memories of it in her usual state of consciousness. I told the patient that I thought she was scared here, because she feared that bad things would happen again. She agreed and initially seemed relieved, as the "young ones" receded for several days.

During this time, the patient revealed more history of her troubled childhood and how her mind seemed to be populated by many others who remembered her private horrors. She was especially plagued by the smell of blood which terrified her, made her nauseated, and filled her with suicidal urges. She warned that her menses, which were rapidly approaching, were a dangerous time for her, requiring restraints during her recent periods. She begged for help so as not to harm herself, and as we explored the meaning of blood, she said that she could not tolerate the smell of urine or feces either. Recurrent flashbacks and nightmares incorporating the smell of these body products were overwhelming. Over time, when she spontaneously lapsed into altered states, her "child alters" cautiously revealed, under threat of internal punishment, that her uncle performed unusual rituals to cleanse her of sin. She said that he would insert sharp implements in her vagina to make her bleed while quoting scriptures, warning her, and then demonstrating the evil desires of men. To complete his purification rituals, he would then urinate and defecate on her, incorporating this degradation into what sounded like a perverse interpretation of his fundamentalism. He reportedly conducted a weekly bible study group in which several others also participated in the sexual abuse and toileting on the young girl. She became nauseated during the sessions when she would seemingly relive these experiences, as the olfactory memories filled her with intolerable revulsion.

In the meantime, with the patient's menses rapidly approaching, her terror escalated. She embarrassingly and helplessly revealed that only "Lacey," her tough alter ego, could use tampons and handle the body during menstruation without being self-destructive. Her counterphobic defense had broken down. Tracey was now worried about "letting" "Lacey" come out, fearing her behavior would get the patient in trouble, but she felt she had no choice or she would find herself seriously hurt. "Lacey" did emerge, in a most provocative way. In stark contrast to Tracey's tearful, sad, and matronly appearance, "Lacey" preferred thick makeup, gaudy jewelry, and revealing clothing. She informed me that she had a "night job" that Tracey knew little about and would be opposed to. In other words, Tracey was generally amnestic when in her "Lacey" altered state but not vice versa. As she strutted up and down the room with a lascivious grin, she laughed mockingly at her counterpart's circumstances, insisting that it had nothing to do with her— "just a housing problem," she repeated. "Lacey" handled all the interpersonal problems but for a price. She was a type of protector, as it were, and felt contempt for Tracey's weakness and vulnerability. She raged at the uncle, declaring that she could cut off his genitals in a minute if she ever had the chance. She trusted no one and had to be in control of all relationships. She then bragged that her "night job" was as a topless dancer, where she could get pathetic men to lust after her and then triumphantly crush them like bugs. Since "Lacey" did have "coconsciousness" when Tracey was out, she knew why she was being summoned and ridiculed the patient for being so inept with tampons. During "Lacey" 's intermittent appearances, she could better tolerate the screaming in pain of the "little ones" inside, where it seemed that the menstrual blood was equated with the bloody vagina from childhood. The patient hallucinated the genital pain of rape and the insertion of sharp implements, as she would hold her groin and see blood dripping down her leg. "Barbie" cried helplessly until "Lacey" would take over and push the screams back inside her head, where utter chaos seemed to reign each month.

A hard fought alliance with "Lacey" was eventually forged, and I learned more about this dissociated self. She came into existence during menarche, just as the patient was about to return home. The patient apparently lived a secret life of delinquency, alcohol, promiscuity, and an aggressive aloofness, existing side by side with a traditional developmental path. She denied being a prostitute or a lesbian but did admit that her preferred sexuality was a sadomasochistic menage-à-trois, an arrangement she regularly engineered by picking up couples who would come to watch her dance. Everything seemed to be working out, until the birth of her children upset this precarious psychic equilibrium. Eventually, Tracey started to suspect that "Lacey" was engaging in unacceptable sexual behavior at night but was unable to control it, so she started to take drugs to put "Lacey" to sleep. When the HIV disease was discovered, she then took the massive overdose to try to end everyone's misery, resulting in her extended hospitalizations.

"Lacey" begrudgingly agreed to participate in treatment after much testing of limits. She had wanted to demonstrate her hypnotic power over men, knowing that Tracey would be humiliated beyond recovery were she to disrobe during a session. One day, as she stood up to perform, she pranced around and very slowly started to unbutton her blouse looking very intently for a reaction. It became clear how desperate she was for some affirmation of her desirability because by this time, her health was a daily issue, marked by blood work, frequent consultation, and progressive joint pain. Confronting her behavior required considerable delicacy, as her underlying narcissistic vulnerability was directly proportional to her sexual provocativeness. I tried to explain to her as empathetically as I could under the circumstances, that exposing her body was a violation of boundaries which was intended to test me, seduce me, excite me, control me, and greatly distract us from dealing with her problems. I also told her that since she was so used to being admired for her beauty and sexual charms it may have been the only way to get someone to care for her. The patient stopped in her tracks, glared at me, and "switched" back to Tracey, who seemed to have had a glimmer of what had transpired. She sobbed uncontrollably, begging for forgiveness, and cowering in shame for several days afterward. From then on, "Lacey" 's collaboration increased slowly and steadily, as more observing ego or "coconsciousness" developed between these two parts of the mind.

Nevertheless, the patient continued to be plagued by flashbacks, night-mares, hallucinations, and amnestic periods. Tactile and olfactory sensations which were linked to fragmented memories of early trauma tortured her. These memories of sensory experiences were crucial links to her past (Brenner, 1988). Reliving these scenarios resulted in uncontrollable nausea, vomiting, and days of anorexia which were extremely dangerous to her health. Her white count was erratic, at times dropping below the 2000 range as her T4 cell count fell proportionately. In addition, as she experienced genital pain and tried to reconstruct her trauma, she often had surges of vaginal bleeding, which upon gynecologic examination failed to reveal underlying pathology. With these apparent psychosomatic reactions, the prospect of increased anemia, dehydration, electrolyte imbalance, and weight loss could have been life threatening for her.

The patient appeared to be in the throes of a negative therapeutic reaction, as her body seemed to be rebelling. Various fluids would come out of her orifices with such intensity and regularity during sessions, it seemed very risky to continue, but it was not possible for her to just shut her mind off. Indeed, that was why she was there. She was medicated with tranquilizers, antiemetics, and antidiarrheals before each session, while suggestions were made to let the process slow down. The revulsion and horror of her memories increased, however, as she began to assemble the jigsaw puzzle of her childhood. She recalled her mother's drunken rages, where she, as a terrified preschooler, would cower in a corner to avoid getting hit by wild hands or flying kitchenware. Her siblings would run away, but she would stay. When her mother finally slumped into an exhausted stupor, covered in vomit, the patient would cautiously clean her and hold her head until she awoke, extracting whatever sense of love she could get from her. The poignancy of this memory was felt by both of us, as she would punctuate our sessions by filling a trash can with her own vomit, feeling utterly humiliated, ashamed, and disgusted with herself. She longed to be comforted in the transference the same way she had tended to her mother. Any treatment short of unconditional idealized love confirmed her sense of unworthiness and total inner badness. I pointed out her wish to be taken care of by me forever, and she cried knowingly, feeling relieved to finally be able to talk about it. Realizing her exquisite sensitivity to rejection, it was crucial to work through my own feelings so I could maintain empathy as I watched, smelled, and listened to her projectile vomiting, punctuated by her uncontrolled sobbing. In the midst of this intensity, she was reminded of how proud she had felt when she kept a vigil for a fatally ill friend because she was there at the moment when he had died. Her symptoms then lessened for several days, as she felt close, protected, and cared for.

As though the closeness and relief were unacceptable, her respite ended abruptly with the emergence of a strangely terrifying symptom—auditory hallucinations of her uncle. She seemed to be convinced that he had found her again after all these years, and she helplessly awaited his next assault. She feared for her life, experiencing a paranoia from deep within, as flashbacks, nightmares, and psychosomatic symptoms escalated. She was sure she would die if he were to "come out and take over the body," sensing that it was inevitable. I reminded her that the therapeutic process required getting to know her in all states of mind, which included, as repugnant as it seemed to her, this representation of the uncle. She berated herself for wanting a father's love from him, feeling that she must be quite depraved. She warned me that he was intelligent, manipulative, and had converted many people to his church, so she worried that I, too, might be taken in by "his" charisma. I assured her that I was *her* doctor and was treating the whole person, yet I recognized her fears of being betrayed. Several days later, the patient switched during a session, and I came face to face, as it were, with "the reverend."

The patient, in her "reverend" dissociative state, was dramatically different and quite imposing. "He" fashioned a pulpit out of the furniture and delivered a fire and brimstone sermon, quoting scripture with a piercing, menacing look in "his" eyes. "He" insisted on knowing my religion, making grandiose claims about the thousands of people "he" converted. Obsessed with sin and purification, the patient preached with a violent and chilling fervor. As the hour was ending, it was clear that this alter, too, was trying to intimidate and test me, as the "reverend" refused to let Tracey return. The patient, in this state of mind, felt omnipotent and claimed to be able to inflict limitless torture upon the body. Having convinced me of "his" great importance, I expressed a wish to get to know "him" better and discussed the ground rules of therapy, which the patient laughingly scoffed at. We eventually agreed to meet at some point during the next session, and the patient soon returned to her former state of mind. She was amnestic, disoriented, and sobbed pathetically to learn not only that "he" was indeed inside but that "he" also had emerged.

The "reverend" "returned," and efforts to develop a therapeutic alliance followed a stormy course. "He" insisted that "he" always sit higher than me as "he" preached "his" sermon for the day. Determined to test my vulnerability and susceptibility to "his" way of thinking, the patient barraged me with personal questions about my religion and sex life. Any attempt at discussing the patient's problems of emerging memories were met with provocative innuendos about my being a voyeur or having a secret interest in doing the same thing to little girls that "he" did. This resistance was compounded by the patient's exhaustion and array of psychosomatic symptoms which were sadomasochistically inflicted upon herself by the "reverend" alter, as punishment for a variety of sins. One day, in a display of "his" power," at my request, "he" "brought" the patient back in such a way that she was asymptomatic for days. This demonstration of "his" ability to induce or take away her nightmares, headaches, vomiting, and even her vaginal bleeding became a central aspect of "negotiations" as "he" was determined to torture her for revealing the secrets of her sexual abuse.

Most significantly, the "reverend" state of consciousness was, at the very least, indifferent to the possibility of death, for "he" believed that the fate of the others and of the body did not affect "him." "He" was convinced that "he" would live on and had complete faith in the Lord. He was not concerned about the lethality of the AIDS virus for the same reasons, insisting that God would cure "him." The "reverend" 's omnipotence extended to the belief that "he" could do away with the others and either take over the body or find another more suitable one. "He" was very unhappy about being stuck in the body of a woman and wanted to change it. Later on, when the patient's urinary retention required regular catherizations, she expressed her transsexual wish (Brenner, 1996) in the "reverend" ego state by imagining that it was a penis, which made "him" feel more powerful and complete. Unfortunately, during these dissociative reveries, the patient was unable to empty her bladder properly which humiliated and embarrassed her as she required assistance to keep her atonic bladder from getting further weakened.

As I got to know the parts of her mind better, the patient revealed more and more about the bizarre practices that she was subjected to. Not only did she report being urinated and defecated upon, she also reported animal sacrifices and smearing of blood on her body in ritual practices. As the material became progressively more depraved and hints of involvement in atrocities came to the fore, the patient took a turn for the worse. Vomiting, headaches, vaginal bleeding, and internal threats of imminent death plagued her day and night. The "reverend" alter assumed a more demonic quality as "he" mockingly revealed that "he" used "his" church as a cover for "his" true religion, an ancient secret sect whose members swore an oath of silence under the threat of death to anyone who told or was told about their practices.

The patient was violating the oath and had to be silenced permanently. The "reverend" again insisted that "he" could kill off the others and survive. The patient experienced a grand mal seizure several days later, despite therapeutic blood levels of anticonvulsants, and required respiratory support until she recovered. Several days after that, she reported a rare, vivid nightmare which awakened her with grief and terror: she went to see me for a therapy hour in a strange house that was full of strange looking people and found me in a back room. As she approached, she gasped in horror seeing that I was dead, slit open from the neck down, lying on my back in a pool of blood. Strange inscriptions were carved into my body. She apologized profusely for having such a dream, linking it to "the reverend" 's death threats for revealing secrets to others. She feared for my life in a genuine way, wondering if "his" agents had us under surveillance and were ready to strike. She then suddenly switched and the "reverend" emerged, as menacing and threatening as ever. I was momentarily on edge and very wary, as her inner persecutory world drew me well into her paranoia. Sensing my uneasiness, the "reverend" warned me to be careful because "accidents can happen." I specifically asked if "he" were threatening me, feeling the kind of uncertainty the patient constantly lived with, allowing myself, for the moment, to imagine that this crippled woman might find a way to attack me when I least expected it. I then said that I sensed how powerful "his" influence must be on the rest of the patient's mind, as she was living in constant terror. "He" laughed triumphantly, bragging that "he" had convinced the patient that I was poisoning her with the medication, that the pain consultant was driving her crazy with the relaxation/self-hypnosis exercises, and that a certain staff member was really one of "his" henchmen.

It became clear at this time that the patient was not able to tolerate knowing (Laub and Auerhahn, 1993), imagining, or remembering any more about her past. She kept remembering and forgetting, daring not to ask what I might have learned from the "reverend," thereby discontinuing her attempts "to learn what the others knew." She had an eerie sense of having participated in criminal behavior and wanted to turn herself in to the authorities, to spend the rest of her life in jail. The "reverend" part of her violently opposed further disclosure and it appeared that "he" was trying to speed up the patient's death. It seemed that on one level the patient was experiencing massive guilt and a need for tremendous punishment, both internally through her "reverend" alter and externally through wanting to "confess" to the authorities. The process of becoming conscious or knowing more about her past seemed to result in a negative therapeutic reaction with an accelerated deterioration of her fragile health. A major contributing factor which I had only recently discovered was that a relative had contacted an attorney who was aggressively trying to "pursue justice" for the patient and who had been making numerous calls to her.

This downward spiral needed to be interrupted, which I expressed to her as making a truce with the "reverend." Tracey and "Lacey," however, were opposed to acknowledging or living in peace with their perpetrator, still having a difficult time differentiating this internal representation from the real "reverend" of her earlier life. "Lacey" 's plan was to wait until "he" "came out" again and slit "his" throat, as she too had trouble conceptualizing that killing off any other part was tantamount to suicide. Over the next several weeks I pointed out to the patient, in piecemeal fashion, that there seemed to be a very powerful force operating in her mind and body that was drawing her closer to death more quickly than necessary. This force seemed to be partly related to her AIDS virus which was a mortal illness, but psychological factors were accelerating her demise. These factors were related to her early trauma, which resulted in murderous rage, irrational guilt, and a self-destructive tendency to repeat elements of her past. As a way of both trying to master her trauma and to reinflict herself, her mind created a replica of her uncle who could "get her" any time he wanted. Through the development of alters, she could endlessly relive her earlier life, as she experienced her intrapsychic conflicts as internalized interpersonal conflicts. Her mind had tricked itself into a suicidal tailspin by thinking that killing off one part would not affect the others. I then added that while we could not prevent her inevitable demise, which could occur any day by her own hand or by a major medical event, it was also possible that she could live for many, many months. Perhaps, I wondered, there were ways we could bolster those forces within her which supported survival.

The patient's reactions to this extended series of interpretations, supportive exhortations, and clarifications of reality was significant. She recalled that her massive overdose prior to her hospitalization was in an effort to quiet down her voices and to put the others to sleep. She had become aware of her decline in function, her progressive amnesia, and a sense of being "possessed," but was helpless against the onslaught. Feeling overwhelmed, she gave little thought to her own fate as she tried to get rid of the others. It remained a puzzle to her that all of these seemingly disconnected parts were really aberrations of her own mind. She did, however, observe that of late she and her tough alter ego, "Lacey," were closer than ever, as they were sharing thoughts, memories, and their views of the world. As the patient's observing ego increased, she apparently was on the road to a fusion, as it were, between these two personifications.

The patient then recalled that she first became aware that something was wrong with her mind immediately after the birth of her first child. At that time, when her newborn was placed in her arms, helpless, vulnerable, and covered in blood, she panicked and did not know what to do. She was over-come by fears of harming her baby and immediately gave him back to the nurse. As she described this incident, she was overcome with dread that she might have been forced to do bad things to a newborn and if she had she would have to be punished. Sensing the growing panic in the patient at this time and her conflict over knowing, I opted for more reality testing to try to soften her vicious superego. I told her that even if she had turned herself in and even if her claims were taken seriously, it would probably take months for any investigation to take place. And, even if there were any evidence found on which charges could be made against anyone, how could she be held responsible, since she was a minor and was a victim, too? Hypothetically, were there ever to be a trial, she sadly would have probably died of AIDS before then anyway. Apparently, she felt she had not suffered enough, even though her life was ending prematurely and she already was in constant pain. The patient then switched and the "reverend" emerged, rebuking me for not trying hard enough to keep her from remembering. "He" was very angry that a lawyer had been consulted and feared that if Tracey remembered any more details, she indeed might decide to proceed with legal action. I pointed out the obvious conflict over "confessing," and the confusion between past and present, reality and fantasy, inner and outer, and victim and perpetrator. I then told the patient that I would use my influence to postpone any meeting with lawyers. Therapy needed to precede "justice," whatever that might or might not entail. In exchange for my intervention would be a truce, which would consist of refraining from all self-destructive behavior and from in-terfering with any medical or psychiatric treatment. The "reverend" then gloated over the time he forced the patient to throw out a prescription for a new AIDS medication after seeing a consultant several weeks before. He was not yet ready to give in.

Over the next several weeks, the patient's struggle over whether she deserved to die for her sins, real or imagined, manifested itself in the negotia-tions over the truce with the "reverend." Interestingly, the patient expressed a renewed interest in seeing her children and they felt like her only reason to live. She became very concerned about her daughter's tendencies to "lock up her worries and throw away the key," fearing that she, too, was developing dissociative tendencies.

The daughter had entered therapy and arrangements were made for more regular family visits. The patient began to envision life outside the institution, daring to hope that she would be strong enough to survive on her own and take care of her children again. The "reverend," however, refused to ratify our safety contract. Although there was much less interference with treatment, "he" would not promise not to suicide postdischarge. Knowing that she could not go home unless this were so, I interpreted to the patient that the "reverend" seemed to be expressing one side of her ambivalence over leaving the hospital. The patient's attachment in the transference and her dependence due to the reality of her circumstances, made the prospect of discharge a potential life and death situation, which was the "reverend" 's domain. "He" apparently did not feel ready. It appeared that even in this state, the patient was beginning to take an interest in her health, although it was denied when brought to her attention.

A turning point then occurred during my summer break when she suffered a life-threatening electrolyte imbalance which required ICU management. The patient experienced a frightening delirium from which she thought she would not recover. Her condition stabilized, her sensorium cleared, and further tests showed that her body had not significantly deteriorated. She was very shaken by this close call, reinforcing her belief that she indeed could die suddenly. While she was outwardly expressing her gratitude to the doctors for saving her life, inwardly the battle was rekindled one more time. She revealed that several of her toenails had been pulled off at night, just as she was starting to feel better. This self-mutilation seemed to be a statement from the "reverend" that "he" was still in control. When "he" emerged in the next session, "he" wearily admitted "his" involvement and threatened to tear off another one in front of me. I expressed puzzlement over this choice of mutilation which was quite painful but relatively benign for one with so much power. Sensing at this point more of a wish to create a nuisance than to actually self-destruct, I confronted the patient with the gravity of her recent medical emergency and the need for "everyone" to work together if she wanted to survive. Surprisingly, I received a written safety contract the next day from the "reverend," who rather quietly acknowledged that "he" was beginning to feel the joint pain also. The awareness of this pain helped "him" believe that maybe "he" too was actually connected to the body and should take care of it. In fact, the patient rather offhandedly mentioned that Tracey was gradually becoming able to listen in on the "reverend." This dramatic development reflected increased ego strength which enabled her to observe herself in this altered state and to have more control over her self-destruction.

With the acquisition of a coconsciousness with the "reverend," Tracey was able to enlist "Lacey" 's help and reassure the little ones that things were changing inside. It would not be so dangerous anymore and all parts could begin to work together to take care of "their" body. Their true enemy was the virus, which affected everyone. Discharge plans then proceeded in earnest when all were assured as much as possible that the psychological forces for self-preservation were stronger than those of destruction. A follow-up visit two years postdischarge revealed several important things, most notably that she was still alive. No doubt in large part due to advances in the drug treatment for AIDS, the patient also reported advances in treatment with her outpatient doctor and validation of her memories through an admission of guilt by her uncle.

DISCUSSION

The quasidelusional disowning of one's body has been a ubiquitous finding in the several hundred patients with "multiple personality" with whom I have had clinical contact. Suicidality, when present, almost always manifested itself through a conflict between dissociated ego states such as a personification expressing a wish to get rid of or kill another personification, in order to possess the body. A variation of this theme is one personification expressing a persecutory fear of being attacked or killed by another "inside person." In such cases, the self-destructive impulses which may get expressed by mutilating or harming the body are perceived as an effort to "get at" another inhabitant. Being in an autohypnotic state, the alter personality committing the act often feels numb and disconnected, which falsely confirms the narcissistically invested illusion of separateness. As was almost the case with Tracey, this type of psychic organization may have lethal consequences. In her effort to stop "Lacey" 's sexual enactments, Tracey tried to kill herself, being somewhat convinced that she would only hurt "Lacey." Similarly, the "reverend" 's repeated inducing of psychosomatic symptoms was perceived as hurting everyone else but "him." "He" was indifferent to AIDS, undermined the treatment, and envisioned jumping to another body after it died. And, finally, "Lacey" 's urges to slit the "reverend" 's throat just as "he" was about to take over the body reflected the same omnipotent belief. For her, it was a "housing problem." Freud's (1920b) observation that in order to have the energy to commit suicide one needs to be "killing an object with whom he has identified" (p. 162), seems to be especially salient in such cases of "multiple personality."

The therapeutic challenge of helping the personifications realize that they share the same body and therefore the same fate seems to be necessary for the preservation of life in these cases. The uniting, object-seeking quality of libido needs to outweigh the divisive, destructive quality of the aggressive drive. It usually requires the working through of traumatic scenarios which are perceived to have been experienced by the various alters who share the body. What may have been an adaptive defense as a child may predispose one to suicidal errors in self-perception in later life. Quite often, there is a repetitive quality to these dissociated, dreamlike stories from childhood, variations of which may persist into adulthood as reports of continued victimization. In addition to recurrent dreams, flashbacks, and hallucinations, Tracey's repetition compulsion seemed to involve contact and a highly charged relationship with body fluids—her mother's vomitus, urine and feces from her perpetrators, her own vaginal bleeding, AIDS contaminated blood in her work, and, finally, her own AIDS infected body fluids. She had even begun to explore a possible unconscious wish to contract AIDS (Brenner, 1991), and that work continued. Another aspect of her repetition compulsion seemed to be in her sexuality, the menage-à-trois. She turned passive victimization from the "reverend" and his bible group into active orchestration of the sexual activity of the couples she would pick up. She was always in control and the participants were at her mercy as she lived out this reparative fantasy.

The task of moving toward a continuous consciousness and an increased observing ego required an extension of the therapeutic alliance to her aggressively derived internalized objects. In so doing, that part of the psyche which felt most disconnected, frightening, and reprehensible to her needed to be accepted in treatment by her doctor. Over time, the internalization of an accepting helper initiated an inner process of assimilation and neutralization. With a resulting softening of her superego which had already sentenced her to death row, as it were, her efforts at self-preservation were strengthened. A healthy secondary narcissism may have developed (Kestenberg and Brenner, 1995). Schwartz's (1994) synopsis of this process from a relational viewpoint elaborates on the importance of increased internal communication in the patient's compartmentalized mental world. He described this situation as originally mirroring one's external object world of silence, deception, apathy, and exploitation.

Interestingly, Rosenfeld's (1971) description of the therapeutic process in narcissistic states which involves a freeing up of the psyche from the clutches of the death instinct is strikingly similar:

> [T]o help the patient to find and rescue the dependent sane part of the self from its trapped position inside the psychotic narcissistic structure as it is this part which is the essential link with the positive object relationship to the analyst and the world. Secondly, . . . gradually to assist the patient to become fully conscious of the split-off destructive omnipotent parts of the self . . . because this can only remain all-powerful in isolation . . . and then the omnipotence which has such a hypnotic effect on the whole of the self gets deflated and the infantile nature of the omnipotence can be explored. (This) infantile part . . . not only pulls him away toward death but infantilizes him and prevents him from growing up, by keeping him away from objects who could help to achieve growth and development [pp. 175–176].

Rosenfeld, in the Kleinian tradition, points to a pathologic imbalance in the fusion between the death instinct and libido, as seen in perversions, which needs to be reworked so that a healthy refusion can take place.

In Tracey's case, her AIDS not only increased her underlying sense of helplessness and narcissistic vulnerability, it may have also contributed to her somatic reactivity due to her weakened state. Having apparently warded off the overstimulation and rage due to repetitive childhood trauma with defensive altered states of consciousness, the patient grew up believing that what was happening to the body was occurring to someone else, e.g. "Barbie," "Rosie," or "Daisy." In the same vein, sexual development seemed to follow two perverse pathways, transsexualism and a sadomasochistic menage-à-trois, in an effort to encapsulate her aggression and allow some healthy ego development to occur (chapter 4). This containment of aggression and its repercussions was a major function of her unintegrated psyche, in which she was prone to repetitive enactment of her early trauma. Her profound underlying abandonment anxiety and helplessness seemed to intensify and solidify her infantile omnipotence into a needed characterological defense. During her decompensation, it appeared that she was being drawn inexorably closer to death, and one might consider that AIDS merely potentiated her "death instinct." In order to stave off the inevitable, one could hypothesize that her internalized aggression needed to be fused and neutralized.

But, despite the clinical evidence, such a formulation in and of itself cannot prove the existence of a death instinct. Ironically, what seems like an archaic notion may actually be very far ahead of its time. Hartmann, Kris, and Lowenstein (1949) criticized the speculative nature of this theory, so it is not surprising that biological disciplines outside of psychoanalysis are needed to provide scientific proof. For example, there is growing evidence for "mortality genes" which affect the rate of aging and may be switched on and off by chemical influences (West, Pereira-Smith, and Smith, 1989). Furthermore, such a process may shorten the DNA strands during cell replication which increases the chances of mutations, resulting in diseases (Hastie, 1990). These genes of planned obsolescence are being mapped out by researchers in the Human Genome Project (Kevles and Hood, 1992). As a result, the death instinct at its most basic level may come to be thought of as a sequence of nucleic acids. If this were so, what would then need to be explored is the mutual influence of early, prolonged unpleasure leading to hostile, destructive aggression (Parens, 1979, 1993) and this death instinct. For example, how does the environment stimulate inherited tendencies to aggression (Hamburg, 1973)? What are the psychophysiologic mechanisms that contribute to the compulsion to repeat, the premature expression of the stigmata of aging (Kestenberg and Brenner, 1996), and vulnerability to disease (Gaddini, 1972)?[1] Does prolonged hyperarousal due to rage activate

---

[1]Regarding the disease in this case, the AIDS virus is an RNA retrovirus, which is thought to be related to some of the most ancient quasilife forms on earth. They may lie dormant for eons, waiting for a suitable host, at which time they hijack the cells' reproductive machinery and seem to come to life, replicating themselves ad infinitum until the host dies or until they

the hormones in the hypothalamic pituitary adrenal axis which mediate the expression of such genes?

If an individual has been severely traumatized and is struggling with profound amounts of internalized aggression, a lethal partnership could then develop between such psychological and biological factors. Whether a chromosomal death instinct is truly an instinct, has mental correlates, and is the origin of aggression, or whether it just gets activated by acquired aggression, the modulation of these powerful destructive forces is an essential goal of treatment. Developing a therapeutic alliance with the psychic derivatives of these forces may promote a relationship with the external object world for the first time and provide a life-extending experience.

CONCLUSION

The death instinct as a basic fact of mental life, which is the origin of aggression, continues to be a difficult concept to prove and may have been held to a higher standard than other cherished psychoanalytic concepts. However, I feel it has considerable empirical value in working with traumatized patients who are prone to repetitive self-destructive symptoms and behavior. With regard to those with severe dissociative pathology, this notion is especially useful. It can be demonstrated through psychoanalytically oriented therapy that the unique feature of disowning one's body through altered states of consciousness is a complex defense against internalized destructive rage. As such, it can be seen as a compromise formation which results in partial gratification through self-mutilation and revictimization, while it is experienced as happening to someone else. It may have been an adaptive elaboration of infantile omnipotence under potentially life-threatening conditions in childhood but can predispose to suicidality later on. Such an individual may be prone to recurrent traumatic symptoms, self-destructive relationships, unconscious exposure to life-threatening illnesses, psychosomatic illness, and other situations which pull him or her toward the inevitable. If one is aware of these issues, intensive therapy may help free the patient from what feels like a personification of the death instinct.

---

can find another suitable host (Preston, 1994). As a result, the process of returning to our own lifeless state would obviously be accelerated by the invasion of such a virus which, according to Freud's theory of the immortality of unicellular organisms (1920a), has its own primitive life instinct.

PART III

TECHNICAL CONSIDERATIONS

Chapter 8

THE UNIQUENESS OF INTEGRATION

> [S]oon it becomes extremely difficult to maintain contact
> without confusion with all the fragments, each of which
> behaves as a separate personality yet does not know of even
> the existence of the others. . . . I hope even here to be able
> to find threads that can link up the various parts [Ferenczi,
> 1933, p. 165].

The textbook goal of treatment for patients with "multiple personality" is
the integration of their personalities, which is considered the hallmark of a
"cure." Wholeness for a severely traumatized patient is a seemingly impossible and mythical state. Even the most motivated, intellectually gifted, and
creative (of which there are many), has trouble imagining a time when they
could truly own all of their memories and pain. But, as succinctly summarized
by Furst, "no truly traumatic event is ever wholly assimilated . . ." (1967, p.
41). Nevertheless, successful treatment may indeed result in profound integrative experiences in which the dissociative or "it's not me!" self is dis-
solved, allowing the patient to ultimately know that indeed, "it was me,
after all!"

I both regret and welcome whatever ambiguity may be inherent in the
name I have chosen for this "self." Its allusion to Winnicott's (1953) description of the transitional object's importance as the first "not me" possession
acknowledges Marmer's (1980) recognition of the transitional function that
alter personalities may serve. However, the more disturbed patients may initially experience their alters as a totally disconnected, separate presence who

---

An earlier version of this chapter was presented to the Northwest Alliance for Psychoanalytic Study on April 12, 1997, in Seattle, Washington.

is "not me!" (Sullivan, 1953). For them to reach a point in treatment to even consider these creations as "a part of me, but not me," considerable work needs to take place. While on the road to integration, the patient might be seen as traversing three phases characterized by feeling that her alters are a (1) "not me!"; (2) "a part of me, but really not me"; and finally (3) "really me, after all. . . ."

While I was initially hesitant to coin yet another metapsychological self in the already overpopulated human psyche, which already includes, for example, the false self/true self (Winnicott, 1960), the grandiose self (Kohut, 1971; Kernberg, 1975), the infantile psychotic self (Volkan, 1997), and the traumatized self (Volkan, 1996), the "it's not me!" self offers a perspective that also has some therapeutic value. I have already ventured into the arcane world of metapsychology further than I have expected, building upon empirical, clinical observation as my foundation. The "it's not me!" self is conceptualized as housing those ego functions necessary for the creation and maintenance of personifications. This unconscious construct essentially tricks the patient into believing that they are not part of her, like an operator behind a curtain who wants to be ignored while he creates a Wizard of Oz type of illusion. Through the work of analysis of resistance, analysis of defense, and the analysis of a particular type of transference, when the patient becomes ready and able to give up this form of maladaption, integration may then proceed naturally. In contrast, most of what is written about integration in multiple personality involves hypnotherapeutic techniques where direct suggestion, and even integration "ceremonies" have been described (Kluft, 1982, 1984, 1986a, 1993; Ross, 1989; Putnam, 1989; Greaves, 1989; Fine, 1991, 1993; Watkins, 1992; Watkins and Watkins, 1993). Although the hypnotherapist's timetable and agenda may leave an artifactual imprint, patients have reported profound emotional enlightenment, a blending of personalities, certain changes in perceptual acuity (Braun, 1983), and long-term benefits (Kluft, 1993). Others, however, including the scores of patients I have seen in consultation who have claimed to have "been integrated" (a passive experience for many), reported disappointments in their results. One common lament, for example, is there was "an unknown alter, worse than all the others that was missed." Another complaint is that integration "did not hold" under the pressure of a new life stress. These puzzling complaints made me wonder about the extent of the underlying resistances (Waugaman, 2000) and the overall lack of understanding of the mind that many of these patients possessed. It was as though a basic tendency to disown mental contents still existed which had not been analyzed or worked through. It is this organizing influence that I consider the "it's not me!" self, which not only could remain intact despite hypnotic attempts at integration, but could persist indefinitely unless specifically addressed in treatment.

I will describe such an effort as it unfolded over a three-year period in which dissolution of the "it's not me" self and integration followed spontaneously. I have organized the treatment into five phases in order to more easily simplify the description of the treatment process.

CASE REPORT

Initial Presentation and History

Barbara, a Hispanic woman in her mid-thirties, was referred to me in a most desperate situation. She had been deteriorating for several years since a marital separation when she became suicidally depressed. She was also observed to be experiencing amnestic states, fugues, and unusual behavior. She would lapse into altered states and sometimes behave in an infantile manner, whereas at other times she was prone to violent explosions toward herself or others. Although she had been in treatment intermittently since her early twenties for depression and borderline personality disorder, her deterioration was unprecedented. A successful, hardworking career woman with a graduate degree, three children, and a supportive husband, she epitomized the self-made woman who came from an impoverished background and tried to forget about her past. Several episodes of wandering, muggings, rapes, and self-inflicted stab wounds to the abdomen requiring emergency surgery, culminated in a series of progressively longer hospitalizations with a dismal prognosis. Although she had not been thought to be schizophrenic, her reported auditory hallucinations and conviction that other people inhabited her body nevertheless raised the diagnostic question of a later onset schizophrenia. However, antipsychotic medication did little more than obtund her; and her remarkable capacity to reconstitute to a level of adequate functioning defied explanation. It was not a cyclic mood disorder and could not be explained on the basis of any therapeutic regimens that had been implemented.

In the midst of her regression, recently revealed information regarding physical mistreatment of an older sister increased Barbara's own long standing suspicions that she, too, may have been very poorly treated as a child. Until then, she was remarkably disinterested in and unable to remember much before she ran away at age 17. She was then asked to participate in legal proceedings against her stepfather as the sister's attorney had accumulated sufficient evidence from old police and hospital records. When asked to remember, Barbara began to have momentary flashbacks and nightmares of such intensity that she could not always distinguish between the end of the dream and the waking state. Her therapists were quite impressed with the severity of her distress and the emerging consistency of her aberrant childhood history, but could do little more than watch this once functional woman regress into a chronic mental patient, waiting for the right moment to end her life. Barbara, however, despite her despair, in her moments of lucidity, showed a remarkable instinct for survival and searched for help. After consulting a number of specialists in different cities, the diagnosis of "multiple personality" was entertained as a possibility, but little was offered in the way of treatment. To Barbara's credit, and a sign of her great determination to get help, which undoubtedly contributed to her success in therapy, she sought out treatment centers on her own, and eventually ended up under my care for an extended hospitalization. She was convinced that she could not have lasted much longer without being in a safe place where people understood her condition. Judging by the scars on the visible parts of her body and those discovered through physical exams on her abdomen, breasts, and inner thighs, she was probably correct.

I initially was impressed by Barbara's straightforward, sincere manner, which may sound ironic given all the secrets and altered states of which I knew nothing when we first met. Her personal struggle to find help and her desire to get better for the sake of her children reflected a certain maturity and perspective on life that was not always present in younger, childless patients which the same affliction. She expressed a desire to work hard and do whatever was asked of her, again expressing an appreciation of her one last opportunity in life. But, with an apologetic, almost mischievous smile, she warned me that at times she could be a most challenging patient and would not always be able to follow the rules. With this understanding in mind, our work proceeded on a specialized inpatient unit for the treatment of dissociative disorders, with the administrative staff handling the day-to-day rules and regulations, thus freeing me up for five times per week psychotherapy. Barbara's medical management was handled by an internist who, for example, attended to her collagen autoimmune type illness which waxed and waned. This type of problem was quite prevalent on the unit and could be seen as a major resistance at times. I was then able to focus on our primary and major ongoing task, which was the development and maintenance of a therapeutic alliance.

Therapeutic Alliance

I explained to Barbara that I wanted to get to know her as well as possible and that could be achieved by learning as much as I could about her past, her current functioning, and how her mind worked. I gave her the standard instructions for free association and included her reporting on what she heard inside, also (see chapter 4). She had doubts about the certainty of the diagnosis but since epilepsy and other organic illnesses had been ruled out, she had no better explanation for finding herself so out of control in so many dangerous situations. And so, she was terrified about discovering "who else" might be inside but already had collected much data. Cautiously, she showed me voluminous notes and journal entries, many with different handwriting styles, along with artwork which she did not remember producing over the years. At this point, early in therapy, I began to speak to the "whole person," not just to Barbara, because she appeared to be more of a socially compliant shell and professed to have little or no knowledge of her inner life. Her function seemed to be limited to adapting to the expectations of the outside world as a so-called "host personality." It seemed necessary to address "everyone" because throughout our conversations, she would have memory lapses and her "parts" would emerge, telling me things about the patient and then disappearing "inside," leaving Barbara dazed and confused. In so doing, I appealed to the kernels of observing ego in what I considered her "it's not-me!" self. By not directly confronting her defensive belief in separateness, but cautiously and intermittently pointing out the medical reality of there being only one brain and one body, I gently acknowledged the contradiction without challenging it. In so doing, I permitted myself to address her in totality or in part, depending on the circumstances.

I was mindful of the dilemma of reifying and unwittingly reinforcing her belief about other inside people, but failure to acknowledge her subjective experience would not have been empathic. Therefore, I waited until there was substantial clinical evidence before addressing any of her altered ego states by name, and when I did, I tried to extend the therapeutic alliance by asking a number of questions each time I "met" one of her personifications. For example, I would inquire about the timing of each one's appearance, asking why and how it was decided that they come out at any given time. In this way I began to inform the patient that these were not random appearances and, therefore, had dynamic significance. I was also able to learn about the perceived relationship between alters, if I were told, for instance, that one alter had been instructed, pushed out, or otherwise influenced by another to appear. In addition, I tried to learn what the extent of insight, observing ego, and belief in separateness was at any given time, as it often varied from one personification to the other. Learning about these basic issues took several months since I did not want to hypnotically access her altered states. I wanted them to appear spontaneously, in vivo, as a defensive response to anxiety in the therapeutic situation. Consequently, I was able to make observations about their function and relatedness, when, for example, a child alter might emerge and enact a scenario in the first person, in the course of eliciting an aspect of history about which Barbara knew nothing. Another regular occurrence was the spontaneous switching to a hostile, threatening ego state, in which the patient cursed me out in graphic four letter words, trying to scare me into stopping my questioning or risk being threatened with a bodily assault.

Initially, it appeared almost as a caricature of Tourette's syndrome, as Barbara would be in the middle of talking to me when her eyes would suddenly go out of focus, and then she would blurt out her expletives only to "come back" moments or minutes later, having blocked out what we were previously discussing. In these bewildered states, she felt helpless, embarrassed, and very mentally ill. If she were curious about what had transpired, I might help her fill in the blanks, but more often than not at first, she either did not want to know or did not even realize the extent of the lost time. Significantly, the extent of amnesia and lack of curiosity were generally directly proportional to the intensity of negative, painful affect associated with either the history or the wishes being expressed at the time.

Because much of the earlier treatment was conducted in a secure inpatient setting, I could tolerate the patient leaving an hour in a more agitated, disoriented state, knowing that I could ask the nursing staff to observe her until she regained her usual composure and became safe from self-harm. Were this not the case, the extent of regression within the sessions would have left her in a dangerous state if she had to leave the office and travel a distance to get back home. If that were the case, it probably would have been necessary to allot more than a two-minute warning at the end of each session (see chapter 4) to help her get reoriented and reaffirm her safety contract. Assuming this could have even been possible (and I do not think it was at this early point in treatment), given her penchant for self-harm, her therapy would have been greatly slowed down by these time-consuming measures. Ironically, therefore, I felt much more comfortable encouraging the patient to say whatever came to mind, i.e., free associating, in the secure environment of a closed, inpatient unit than as an outpatient, and was able to approximate an analytic process, albeit with many parameters. In times of my own doubt about the wisdom of this approach, Ferenczi's thoughts about the necessity of hospitalization in order for analytic work to proceed in certain traumatized patients (Ferenczi, 1929a) sounded very refreshing and encouraging to me.

During this initial phase of treatment, we began to piece together more early history, as I was pursuing the therapeutic alliance with the major inhabitants of her inner world. The developing picture in the early months of therapy was as follows:

Barbara was the youngest of three siblings, born almost ten years after her sister and almost fifteen years after her brother. Her mother, a downtrodden, chronically depressed, ineffectual, and emotionally unavailable woman, mercilessly referred to the patient as the product of a drunken rape by her rather brutal father. Following her birth, her mother then got divorced, but married an equally violent man shortly thereafter. Her stepfather was the undisputed master of the house whose will was obeyed or else there were consequences in the form of food deprivation, being locked up in closets, and being beaten. He drank very heavily, and before he fell into his nightly stupor, would erupt into a rage with little provocation. Barbara felt little love from her stepfather and no protection from her mother, whose best intentions were never followed through. Barbara lived in fear and found solace in school where she did well in academics and athletics. She developed a tomboyish nature, playing male-dominated sports and exuding a tough exterior as a counterphobic character armour. Barbara met her husband-to-be while still in high school and moved in with him before graduation, after running away from home. At this point, she could not remember any precipitants, attributing only general unhappiness to her flight. Barbara was a hard worker, throwing herself into college and graduate school work while never looking back. As if her life at home never existed, she sought a career in a helping profession wanting to care for others in a way that she would have wanted for herself. An accident on the job jeopardized her pregnancy and she began spotting. She developed a severe panic disorder which lasted for weeks, and became temporarily unable to function, with persistent, unnameable fears. She eventually recovered, but upon the birth of her first child, she decompensated when the helpless newborn was entrusted to her care. Barbara became overwhelmed with fear that she would injure or kill her baby and became profoundly depressed. Medication and supportive therapy helped her reconstitute, and she had a period of adequate functioning until her daughter turned 5. For reasons unknown to her at the time, she became morbidly preoccupied with the child's safety, fearing she would be kidnapped, mistreated in a most vicious, unspeakable way, and lost to her mother forever. Barbara became paralyzed by her inability to let the little girl out of her sight and became unable to work. The sight of blood sent her into a panic again, followed by a dazed stupor. She began to experience disturbing nightmares, flashbacks too fleeting to remember, and periods of amnesia once again. After several fugue states and suicidal regressions, she had a series of hospitalizations, as her life seemed to unravel. This time, she was not able to recover, and she was deteriorating steadily into a treatment refractory patient with symptoms of hallucination, amnesia, depression, and suicidality.

Delineation of the Mosaic Transference

Barbara's inner world essentially consisted of victims, perpetrators, protectors, bystanders, and those with specialized functions for dealing with the outside world. For the sake of simplicity, I will mention only the key personifications who played a central role in therapy and those who were representative of other less fully formed or less prevalent but seemingly related states of consciousness. All told, these alters numbered more than forty but appeared to have been organized into the five groupings mentioned above. The states of victimization were personified by "Baby," age 5, and "Susie," age 8. "Baby" lived in perpetual fear of being attacked for revealing the secrets of her abuse. The patient's internal persecutor was "the Admiral," an adult male alter whose lurking presence required constant vigilance because "he" would hurt the body by cutting or burning her breasts and vagina. "He" apparently took his orders from a military hierarchy, which included an enigmatic "Chief of Staff." "Baby" 's protection was afforded by "the Woman" and "Sandy." "The Woman" was a prim and proper maternal presence who was always polite, well-behaved, and more like a guardian. "Sandy," on the other hand, was a rebellious teenager who challenged authority, broke rules, and could get violent in self-defense. In the outside world, "Sandy" got raped repeatedly by men and preferred gentle, older women as sexual partners. For short periods of time, "Sandy" could stave off "the Admiral" all on her own but would weaken over time unless a concerted inner effort or external controls such as medications, physical restraints, or self-administered alcohol would quell "his" inner directed rage.

"Susie," the other child victim, age 8, also lived in terror and was easily activated by stimulation in the outside world. She was preoccupied with an event or series of events that occurred at a secluded cabin. She was extremely fearful of men whom she saw as potential rapists and would try to hide inside behind a large immoveable, mute object known as "the Rock." "The Rock" could not take sides but seemed to be willing to provide a wall-like shield from perceived would-be attackers. When all protective measures failed, another mysterious presence, known as "P," would then instruct "Susie" to open up her stomach in order to remove or undo something that occurred during that time of helplessness, degradation, and pain while at someone else's mercy. At such times, "Susie" stabbed herself in the abdomen so deeply and with such intensity as to require emergency surgery to save her life. For reasons that did not become known until much later, "her" choice of destructive action had great significance.

Other major altered ego states, who later became known and whose significance in the external object world were enormous but kept hidden, were "Bessie" and "Tessie." "Bessie" had a secret life as a lesbian and tried to convince "the Woman" to join her in this way of life. "Tessie," on the other hand, would pick up and seduce men, initially being in complete control of the situation but inevitably finding herself in high risk, dangerous, and even life-threatening situations, not unlike "Sandy." At the outset of treatment, each of the alters knew very little or nothing about the others, i.e., there was little coconsciousness or observing ego. Furthermore, when awareness of the others did occur, there was a conviction of separateness, an ongoing fight over the exclusive possession of the body, and the quasidelusional belief that if one part killed off the other, "he" or "she" could survive as the winner. This belief seemed to encapsulate a dissociated, suicidal wish which was not conscious when the patient engaged in life-threatening activities for "other" reasons.

The therapeutic alliance was extended to as many of these altered states as possible. In so doing, the patient expressed herself to me in quite different ways through her personifications. As described earlier, the timing of her switching had dynamic defensive significance, and the tension between two or more of the alters was a reflection of intrapsychic conflict experienced as an internalized interpersonal struggle. And, as time went on, when these states emerged, I began to explore another aspect of "their" way of seeing the world, i.e., how "they" felt about me. It had been my experience that when other modalities failed, analysis of the transference could be a unifying, albeit potentially volatile, experience, and I was quite aware of the extremely impulsive behavior that could erupt also at any time with Barbara. Consequently, I permitted each alter's feelings about me to develop at its own pace. Given her easily agitated condition, as might be expected and as is seen in this primitive characterological condition, some of the transference reactions were almost immediate and very intense. In contrast to Barbara and "the Woman" 's polite, obsequious, and beseeching attitude, "Sandy" was obnoxious, provocative, and full of four letter words for me. "Baby" and "Susie" were terrified of being hurt by me, hiding in a corner, and often cried incessantly until the patient switched back to "Sandy" or "the Woman."

"P," on the other hand, was enigmatic and did not speak directly to me but eventually started leaving written messages in a secret code for Barbara to discover. The code was a mystery to Barbara, herself, who only knew there was great danger lying in the recesses of her mind. She found written scraps of paper all around her room written by "P" which she thought might lend a clue. She somehow "knew" that she should give these notes to me, even though she could not understand them, hoping that I would know what to do. Therefore, I sensed that she had thus invited me in to help her decipher the meaning of her overpopulated mind, through the gesture of turning over these messages written in her idiosyncratic foreign language.

After studying several dozen messages, I was able to break the code, which substituted numbers for letters. However, I decided not to inform the patient of my success in interpreting these messages as yet, because to do so would have been equivalent to making a premature interpretation. Instead, I quietly read whatever notes were shown to me, which usually telegraphed the patient's unconscious, dissociated, suicidal impulses, expressed in statements like "Barbara must die" or "Kill the bitch." "P," therefore, became my unwitting informer as I was able to monitor the crescendo of her internalized rage with the help of these cryptic messages.

"The Admiral," however, became my nemesis, as "his" presence posed a genuine threat to my physical safety. In order to try to scare me away from trying to help the others, which required their telling of "secrets," the patient screamed, yelled, threw things, and attacked the staff. On several occasions, the patient went berserk in a destructive rampage, requiring several staff to subdue her by using physical restraints. The risk of sadomasochistic enactment was an unavoidable possibility at such times, as she induced others to physically contain her, thereby easily misinterpreting the staff's action as an assault upon her. Every effort was made to avoid such confrontation, but the depth of her fury posed a danger to others despite high doses of sedatives and neuroleptics at such times. "The Admiral" saw me, naturally, as the biggest threat of all, not only because of my "interference" with the inner children, but because I had a male body which "he" desperately wanted to have. The envy, feelings of inferiority, fears of "homosexual" rape, and subsequent rage (see chapter 4) created such a volatile situation that "Sandy" and the others warned me if his emergence was imminent. At such times, the patient would hallucinate the roar of "his" engines increasing in volume as "he" got closer to coming out and taking over consciousness. "Sandy" would always try to fight him off, i.e., prevent a switch, but several months into treatment I said that one day I would have to take a chance and meet "the Admiral" face to face, as it were. I had a thorough discussion with the patient about the risks of my being assaulted versus the risks to therapy if I were to only meet "the Admiral" in restraints. Until that time, my only direct contact with the patient during her "Admiral" state of consciousness was when I was called by the staff after an emergency requiring her to be subdued. At those times, she was already in restraints, and I would try to talk to her, only to be verbally barraged as she violently thrashed about trying to break her shackles. After several hours she would become exhausted, fall asleep, and awake as someone else who could maintain control but was generally amnestic for the violent episode.

A plan was devised with the patient on how I might be able to engage "the Admiral," but I was advised against it. My thought was to wait until the next time I heard from her that "he" was nearby and ready to burst forth. But, instead of preparing for violence which had always occurred, I suggested meeting "him" outside, on the fenced-in hospital grounds, where I knew the patient had enjoyed going in order to smoke a cigarette. I assumed that if Barbara, "Sandy," or "the Woman" had started such a session, under these conditions, it would take very little on my part to summon "the Admiral," since I was told that "he," too, liked to smoke cigarettes but had not been outside in many, many months.

Negotiations with "the Admiral" were made through "Tessie," whose function as an intermediary was made known to me at this time. (I did not discover her other function as a sexual seductress until much later.) So, when a suitable time arose several weeks later, I reminded the patient of our strategy. Once again, I was warned not be caught alone with "the Admiral," let alone be outside without staff support. This time, however, "Sandy" had volunteered to be nearby inside, using all her strength to keep "the Admiral" from attacking me. I took this offer as a sign of my overall increasing alliance with the patient and intuitively sensed that the risk of harm would be less now than ever before, as long as the patient did not feel cornered or threatened by me. We also agreed that if we got separated for any reason, then "Sandy" would eventually find her way back to the unit.

So, with this plan in mind, we had a session outside, and I procured a lit cigarette for the occasion, a rather crude alliance-building technique I acquired while working with very regressed patients at the V.A. years ago. Holding the lit cigarette in my hand as a gesture of friendship and sharing, I then simply asked to speak to "the Admiral." After a few seconds of unfocused gaze and fluttering of eyelids, the patient suddenly stiffened and stared clearly into my face with a menacing body posture that initially startled me. The patient growled at me, asking me what I wanted. I regained my composure and quietly offered the cigarette to the patient, whose voice had become much lower, more gruff, and whose overall demeanor had assumed a decidedly male, swaggering quality. Peering at me suspiciously through hostile, squinting eyes, "he" cautiously stole the cigarette from my hand and inhaled deeply, trying to hide "his" pleasure at being let outside to enjoy such a treat. Then, as quickly as "he" had snatched the cigarette, the patient abruptly lurched toward me with a sneer, suddenly stopped her forward motion, stood up, and ran away from me. I called in vain, but the patient quickly disappeared around a building, and I decided not to give chase.

The sequence of events happened with such rapidity that I was stunned and just stood there dumbfounded, trying to collect my thoughts. I then remembered the agreement that was made with "Sandy," promising to return to the unit if we got separated, and felt vaguely reassured. Nevertheless, I felt a bit dubious about the success of this encounter with "the Admiral" and informed the unit of the patient's flight. By the time I reached a phone, I was told that the patient had already returned to the unit in a dazed, but unharmed state, and then I smiled to myself. Although I could not have known all that had transpired in her mind, I felt that enough inner cooperation had developed which ensured both of our safety, and that was further evidence of our strengthening alliance. I learned in our next session (held inside!) how the patient experienced what had transpired outside the day before. "The Admiral" had planned to lay a trap for me, promising through "Tessie" that "he" would not misbehave if taken outside. "He," however, had lied and was about to punch me in the face when "he" lurched forward. "Sandy" became aware of "his" intentions and could not stop "him" completely. Instead, "she" somehow got control of the legs autohypnotically and pulled the body back. But, in order to protect me completely from assault, she ran away in the opposite direction. "The Admiral" 's treachery having been foiled, "he" then retreated back inside, and "Sandy" dutifully returned to the unit. Through this incident, and many more similar ones, it then became clearer to me how each of the personifications had their own transferences but could also be understood in light of a larger conflictual transference developing in the "whole person."

Like separate tiles fitted into a large and complex mosaic, Barbara's personifications needed to be viewed from a certain distance in order to see the big picture. And, the bigger clinical picture that was emerging centered around danger at all levels of development. Tortured and persecuted by a savage, archaic superego, she lived in constant dread of punishment from her internal attacker. The preoccupation with and extent of bodily damage and injury, i.e., castration, suggested hidden oedipal dangers lurking beneath the surface, but what was more evident were dangers associated with abandon- ment and annihilation. Weekends and vacations precipitated suicidal crises where she feared never seeing me again. But, overall in the transference, I was seen as a dangerous object, but one whom the patient needed to trust in and depend upon, as though her life depended on it. A melding of an unavail- able, ineffectual mother and a brutal, sadistic exploitative stepfather made it almost impossible, at times, for her to believe anyone really cared and would want, let alone be able to, help her. A combination of fantasies, memories, traumatic reliving, projections, and enactments colored this often confusing jig-saw puzzle as Barbara incorporated me into her mental life.

Challenging the "It's Not Me!" Self

As the various personifications and their "mosaic transference" began to flesh out a multilayered picture in our sessions, I was able to anticipate her reactions to events on the unit, to relationships with other staff, to family contact, and to me. Her hypersensitivity to perceived criticism, her constantly feeling misunderstood, and her wish to be seen in the best possible light were prevalent themes. Her deeply ingrained tendency to feel blamed and scapegoated for trivial things belied a deeper sense of being a criminal out of a sense of guilt (Freud, 1916) as she would get reprimanded on the unit for things she did not do, but would get away with minor transgressions that she did do. Her daily confusion over what indeed she actually was responsible for seemed to replicate her lifelong doubt over who actually did what to whom and why. Her amnesia when certain personifications were out made it impossible for her at times to accept some of the reports of her behavior, and the possibility of secondary gain by exaggerating her memory problems as an alibi, further complicated efforts to help her with her dissociative problem. This symptom–defense constellation seemed to be kept in place by an almost impenetrable set of resistances, as forgetfulness, negation, denial, shirking responsibility, blaming, and irritable hyperactivity made it quite difficult, at times, to discuss here-and-now issues, not to mention the deeper secrets of her past. But, because her anguish was so ego dystonic, she persisted in treatment and a so-called "internal communication" started to develop. Essentially, her observing ego, a growing awareness of what was said, done, or remembered in the various altered states, enabled the patient to "listen in" more when others were out. What was heard was not always remembered afterward, but little islets of preconscious recognition seemed to be formed, so when a topic would arise again in sessions, there were vague acknowledgments of having heard it before. For example, "Susie" 's ordeal at the secluded cabin started to get elaborated upon as a story unfolded of being seduced by a girl friend's father into taking a ride with him and reportedly being held down by others while gang raped. Gruesome, bloody details emerged many months later, but in the meantime, there was no doubt in "Susie" 's mind that something very, very horrible had happened to her, so "Sandy" and "the Woman" were not about to let anything ever happen to her again, if they had any say in the matter. That "Susie" had been severely traumatized came to be a given and was not questioned by the patient, but it was experienced as happening to a separate 8-year-old girl, not to Barbara, herself, or the others. The clinical challenge, therefore, was how to help the patient learn, believe, know, feel, and accept that whatever it was that may have happened to "Susie," actually happened to her, i.e., all of her.

I would take every reasonable opportunity that arose to gently wonder aloud with the patient that if indeed "Susie" were a totally separate girl, how was it that the others inside were becoming able to listen in on her conversations. Barbara and her alters had no answer at first, preferring to sidestep the questions or give a flippant response to avoid the consequent anxiety associated with the issue. Furthermore, when the issue of separateness was extended to everyone inside, her rebuttals were strengthened by the growing knowledge of how different the people were. How could it be, she countered, that a poor little traumatized girl could be the same person as a tomboyish, lesbian teenager, or maternal caretaker, or a violent man stuck in a female body, desperately wanting a sex change operation? The fact that it apparently and genuinely felt to the patient as though these parts were truly different people needed to be kept in mind, because as she began to read about the condition and acquire considerable knowledge about it, it did not really help her feel any better. Barbara's "it's not me!" self was being challenged on a daily basis in treatment and the threat of outer or inner directed violence was a sobering reminder of the paradoxical fragility of this defensive organization which would collapse if she were overwhelmed too quickly with the reality of her plight.

The central therapeutic approach, therefore, consisted of a cautious traditional analysis of resistance, defense, and transference, but it was augmented by several other modalities. Barbara found it much easier at times to express herself artistically, so she often wanted to bring in drawings, paintings, collages, and elaborate symbolic renditions of her internal world. I accepted them without hesitation and would try to incorporate them into our sessions as associations. What she created in her childlike altered states often portrayed scenarios of sexual abuse, violence, blood, and pain in which a young girl was being assaulted by one or more adults. At first, she would not even be able to look at the artwork with me, as she functioned like a courier from her inner world, delivering a package that belonged to somebody else.

In addition to artwork, Barbara continued to keep a journal intermittently, and would show me selected entries from time to time. Here, too, I would read whatever she allowed me to, as I found that at this point in treatment she was simply unable to directly express in words what was known by others inside. Indeed, there were times when she could not even allow herself to read what was written before her session, and if she had, she just as often forgot it by the time she arrived. While I certainly realized that patients can use the written word to hide behind or avoid an affective connection with painful material, I was more impressed with it being an enormous leap of trust for Barbara to reveal her very private dissociated written thoughts at this point. As such, I felt that to refuse to read her journal or to redirect her to express herself only in a verbal mode would have been not only misunderstood and hurtful, but also a missed opportunity to learn more about her in the only way she could tell me.

Barbara's symptoms did not abate at night, and she reported chronic exhaustion, often feeling as if she had been worked over all night long. Nursing observation confirmed the patient's complaints, as severe insomnia, nightmares, and somnambulism kept her quite busy. She would throw furniture, wander around aimlessly, and tear the sheets off her bed. In addition, she would hide in a corner of her closet and often found herself curled in a fetal position when she awoke. Her terror and nightmares blended into the morning, as she could not clearly differentiate between the waking and dreaming state. In a last ditch effort to manage this refractory "sleep disturbance," it occurred to me to ask her to keep a nighttime log of her activities (see chapter 5). I simply asked whoever was out to "sign in" before going to bed and whenever someone awoke throughout the night. The patient was to record any dreams, feelings, or impressions also, and a review of this data revealed an important pattern which furthered the therapeutic process. A typical night consisted of Barbara going to bed and sleeping for one to two hours. She would then awake from a nightmare in which a little girl was being hurt and sodomized while sitting on a man's lap. Sensations such as the smell of alcohol, the sound of an old radio or TV, and a disgusting, sticky, tactile feeling often were reported in the dream. Not long after Barbara's dream entry, "Baby," the 5-year-old would then sign in and wander around the unit looking for possible attackers. Once reassured, she would comfort herself with ice cream and then go back to sleep. The patient would awaken once or twice again and "Baby" would fear her stepfather's entry into her bedroom and hide in the closet. "Sandy," however, would briefly emerge and have violent tantrums, tearing off the bed covers and throwing the furniture around. Barbara would then awaken in the closet in a fetal position sucking her thumb, disoriented, terrified, exhausted, and quite ashamed.

Over time, it became possible to bring this clinical evidence into the treatment situation by pointing out the striking similarities between the nightmares and "Baby" 's first-hand accounts of her father's rapes. "Baby" painfully relived accounts of being forced to sit on her drunken stepfather's lap in a dark room watching TV late at night. During these ordeals, she, under the threat of a vicious beating, had to be absolutely quiet when he penetrated her so as not to alert her mother. As Barbara gradually began to listen in on these harrowing accounts, I empathically confronted her on how it was that she would have and *could own* recurrent dreams of an unknown girl being violated in the identical way that her dissociated alter, "Baby," reported. Barbara ruefully acknowledged that it might be more than coincidence, but she at first could not elaborate any further. Eventually, she could consider and began to feel that indeed "Baby" was a part of *her*, but not *really* her. With Barbara's growing affective connection to "Baby," she then had to consider that perhaps all of her personifications might be part of her, also. Affectively reliving scenarios of abuse and trauma with progressively increasing observing ego resulted in more continuity of consciousness for the patient which resulted in a mutually reinforcing cycle with these reconstructions.

Barbara, interestingly, had allowed her former therapist to videotape her during a prior hospitalization where she had been quite out of control and had been switching quite frequently. She was absolutely unable to view these tapes without violent, dissociative regression, foiling her therapist's attempts to try to help her see with her own eyes how others had seen her. He had hoped that the tapes would help her see herself better, a technique that has been described with some success in "multiple personality" (Caul, 1984). But, Barbara simply could not tolerate this direct assault on her "it's not me!'' self at the time. She had, however, reached a point in therapy with me about a year later when she mustered up the courage to try it again, intuitively sensing that if she could look at herself in the various altered states then it could help her heal. I was a bit dubious about this modality when she first proposed looking at the tapes again, and did not quite know how it might be incorporated into our ongoing work, but I listened to her. Arrangements were then made for us to view the videotapes, and the patient's anxiety escalated into panic as the appointed day arrived. She was not able to see more than two minutes of the tape before she felt herself slipping into an altered state with very strong urges to either run or stab herself, so this exercise was immediately stopped. Lest she feel like a failure, Barbara insisted that if she somehow could be assured of her safety, she would somehow find the strength to look at the tapes. It was clear that she was nowhere ready to do this on her own, and the idea of heavy sedation in order to blunt her panic seemed a bit counterproductive, for it would also blunt her perception and memory. Barbara concluded that the only way would be if she were externally prevented from running or harming herself and suggested she be placed in physical restraints for her protection.

Once again, I was concerned about her unconsciously inducing a sado-masochistic enactment and becoming retraumatized if she were held down and made to look at something very painful. I tried to analyze these aspects with her as best as possible over the next several weeks as transferential issues assumed more importance in the treatment. For example, I reminded her of the story of ''Susie'' 's trauma, of being held down and raped in the cabin, and as the patient listened inside to her screams, she learned that ''Susie'' was very opposed to the restraint idea. Over time, the others reassured her that I was different and would not harm her. But, when elements of a sadistic paternal transference became too intense for her, I would remind her that I was not her stepfather, an interpretation that I made with increasing frequency to her various child alters who relived their versions of the past with such vividness that I often felt as though I were waking her up from a nightmare with my recurrent refrain.

After much discussion, I eventually relented and assented to Barbara's insistent counterphobic wish to master the dreaded tapes. We discovered by trial and error that one video viewing session every week or two in which she was voluntarily restrained in a straitjacket by the nursing staff who stayed in or around the room was a very powerful but manageable experience. During these highly unusual sessions, we would watch several minutes and process what was viewed. Barbara herself insisted that she be the one to watch, and when I sensed her retreat into an autohypnotic state or when she began to violently thrash about in protest, I encouraged her to ''stay'' until I stopped the machine. In this way, we slowly viewed the three hours of tape over several months in which she had the chance to observe herself switch into "Baby," "Susie," "Sandy," "the Woman," and "the Admiral." The patient was devastated to watch the emotional and physical changes she underwent during her switches as she shifted from a crying, rocking little girl to a truly frightening and dangerous male personification who more than once had broken the shackles in an all out attempt to attack "his" jailers.

As Barbara got more familiar with this most menacing part of her mind, we were then able to have regular sessions even when the likelihood of "his" emergence was quite high. I learned that while in this altered state she felt no pain, and this hysterical anesthesia, as it were, reinforced the patient's conviction of "his" separateness. Any self-inflicted injury caused by "him" would suddenly become very painful when she returned to her usual self, and this perceptual change would support her psychic reality that someone else had harmed her. Even more disturbing to her, however, was her deeply humiliating and embarrassing secret about her sexual feelings after "the Admiral" inhabited the body. She reported uncontrollable orgasmic sensations which were triggered off and subsequently concealed by the defensive rage. Needless to say, the great vulnerability she felt in the transference while expressing these waves of pleasure added an extremely important dimension to understanding the role of "the Admiral"'s aggression. The patient's primitive attempts to punish herself and stop these feelings resulted in the impulses to destroy her breasts and vagina, whereas the outer-directed "male violence" was intended to keep me, her stepfather in the transference, from getting near her sexually at those times.

As the terrible story of her oedipal victory unfolded, she confessed to one of her deepest secrets, which drove her into a suicidal frenzy—that her sexual involvement with her stepfather continued into adolescence and instead of being able to say no, she actually experienced sexual excitement and orgasm. Apparently, she would relive this dreaded pleasure when "the Admiral" emerged and it was happening more regularly in our sessions. She sobbed incessantly with deep shame as this material eventually came out, a unifying, cathartic release which was a new experience for her. Interestingly, one of the keys to understanding this aspect of "the Admiral"'s inner life was discovering that "he" had "his" own biography which was strikingly similar to her stepfather's own corroborated life story (see chapter 6). "He" believed that "he" had a military background and that "he," too, was sodomized by "his" own father as a child. "He" even reported being involved in a bloody battle, recounting hand-to-hand combat with an enemy soldier where "he" kicked the man into unconsciousness and killed him. "The Admiral" was so convinced of "his" own separate identity that the patient did not just identify with her stepfather, the aggressor, she actually became a facsimile of him in her altered state! It appeared that transmission of the stepfather's own trauma as well as perverse transsexual trends became organizing influences in the formation and conviction of "his" being a separate entity.

A breakthrough occurred when Barbara started feeling rivalrous toward other patients and acknowledged feeling very possessive of me in the transference. When I wondered if she had wanted to be regarded as my favorite, she suddenly exploded in fury. She then got very quiet and switched to "Baby," the 5-year-old. "Baby" then started to hallucinate "the Admiral" 's familiar sounds coming closer, threatening to take her because she said "he" always called "her" "his" favorite. My interpretation apparently hit home with such accuracy that the patient could not tolerate remembering these sexual episodes with her stepfather, so instead relived and enacted them in the session in her "Baby" altered state. I was able to maintain contact with her during this switch, and she eventually "came back" to her usual self, violently sobbing but without knowing the reason why. When she asked why, I quietly mentioned the word *favorite* and she registered a sad, fleeting look of recognition as she choked on her desperate childhood wish for love, to be her stepfather's favorite. In spite of and, at times, perhaps because of the things he did to her, made her do to him, and how it all made her body feel, she longed for him in a most ambivalent way. But, her shame, guilt, and humiliation could not be tolerated for more than a few seconds at first, without lapsing into altered states. Given her conscious hatred for her stepfather, she was appalled to discover a deep-seated empathy for him, for as a young girl she instinctively sensed his own inner pain and just knew that she had to try to make up for it, even if it meant enduring her own pain.

As her efforts at reconstruction accelerated naturally from the catalytic effect of the transference, she gradually began to accept more of her personifications, but they still remained just parts of her, i.e., "It's me, but it's not me." She still had a strong need to remain somewhat removed from the pain, horror, sadness, and what was beginning to feel like the truth about her childhood. Coincidentally, her estranged brother found her, reestablished contact, and began sending her a series of graphic letters about not only his own trauma but also what he helplessly witnessed happening to Barbara. The timing of this corroboration was quite uncanny, but the patient took it in stride, observing that it was not unusual at all for her to feel in telepathic contact with her loved ones (see chapter 9). To her, it seemed as though she needed someone else to verify that she was not out of her mind and this long lost brother helped her out.

Integration

Barbara began to sense a growing closeness between herself and the two young girls, "Baby" and "Susie." Her increased awareness of just how much a part of her they were was becoming undeniable. Her maternal empathy for them, as if they were her own children, enabled her to feel their pain, though still somewhat removed. Her complete coconsciousness when they were out seemed to approach depersonalization, i.e., observing herself at a distance, rather than the separateness that she used to feel. Furthermore, she could remember more of what was said while in these altered states. As a result, after "Susie" began to reveal more of the details of her trips to the cabin, Barbara would "come back" and sob uncontrollably over the pain, fear, and helplessness that was abreacted and still felt in her body. When "Susie" described being forced to ingest a noxious mixture of semen and bodily waste products as part of a perverse group ritual, "she" became nauseated and tried to rid "her" system of the memory of these substances. "Her" revulsion and sense of urgency was so great that "she" just wanted to take a knife, cut "her" stomach open, and remove the toxins as quickly as possible. Because Barbara was more able to listen in at will, she suddenly realized why she had repeatedly stabbed herself in the abdomen during her dissociative periods. Perhaps "Susie" wasn't just a crazy, suicidal girl after all. Barbara could now see that "Susie" was a very frightened and desperate girl who would do anything to try to end "her" misery. And, the more "Susie" could see that "she" was a part of Barbara, that "she" was not alone anymore, the more "she" could differentiate the past from the present, and the more they could work together to protect *their body* from further harm. But, as more memories spewed forth, there seemed to be an endless litany of degradation, humiliation, abuse, and sexual exploitation.

The patient's headlong confrontation with her past overwhelmed her at times, and powerful, conscious urges to cut her arteries and bleed to death seemed like her only way out. Once her personifications started to give up their suicidal urges, i.e., as she dissociated less, Barbara herself had to own these impulses as her own. One memorable day, she planned to secretly buy a knife while on a hospital pass in order to end it all, but much to her surprise, it slipped her mind until she returned. By now she was insightful enough to recognize unconscious motivation, concluding that she was more conflicted over killing herself than she realized, so she decided to tell me of her failed plan. She also revealed that she was experiencing a greater closeness with the younger ones than ever, as though they were almost like one, but something was still in the way. I reminded her to say whatever came to mind, and she reported hearing inside that "the Woman" was feeling jealous of Barbara's new inner closeness with the girls. Until recently, "the Woman" 's role as maternal protector was unchallenged, and now "she" was feeling left out. Apparently it was "she" who made Barbara forget about buying the knife, as "she" reasserted herself to keep the body safe. Barbara then felt very ashamed of herself and started to cry, berating herself for her self-destructive impulses, declaring that more than anything in the world she just wanted to be together with her parts. She felt that "the Woman" was responsible for saving her life and that was a signal that she must be included in any efforts to merge with the younger girls. She then sat up from the couch and looked at me beseechingly, as if to ask, "How do I do this?" I simply said something to the effect that if she truly felt ready to join them and they join her, then she was free to do so. Barbara then spoke to these personifications, asking them to be all together with her and shortly afterward seemed to have a profound affective and revelatory experience. She described a sudden whooshing sensation, as though a huge, powerful vacuum cleaner had sucked these parts inside of her. Once "inside," they merged into her sense of self and she experienced a sublime sense of oneness. She exclaimed, "It's all me! They are all me!" repeatedly and began to sob uncontrollably with a mixture of enormous relief, incredulity, and grief. She truly felt different, like never before, and she could not believe what had happened spontaneously in her mind. She had integrated with these parts! It was like a dream come true, and she could not stop crying from the joy and sadness of it all. Now she finally realized that whatever did happen, happened to her. For the next week, she alternated between sobbing and sleeping more soundly than she ever remembered, awakening only to cry more as the thoughts, feelings, and memories of "Baby," "Susie," and "the Woman" became truly hers. The world seemed more three dimensional to her and clearer. She felt more substantial. Things were changing inside. All she could say was, "It's all me and I never really knew it. Now I feel it and I know it!" It was a though a floodgate had opened and three dissociated alter selves rushed in to fill a psychic void. Barbara's "it's not me!" self was dissolving, and the decision as to who got integrated and when was not a planned strategy. It was a naturally occurring process determined by Barbara's own inner forces.

Over the next month, she repeated this epiphanous experience with her other alters. The impetus for integration seemed to follow new or more deeply felt revelations about herself, as her encapsulated personifications seemed to melt. "Sandy," for example, described more of her high-risk behavior resulting in being raped numerous times; "Bessie" came out with a disclosure about a secret homosexual relationship; "the Admiral" stopped raging, expressing fear and helplessness over "his" fate in being stuck with a woman's body. Barbara would have negotiations with each alter in which the promise of being together required giving up the dangerous or unacceptable behavior for the betterment of everyone. When finally agreed upon, each gave up his or her separateness and joined Barbara. With these subsequent integrations, the patient experienced the same whooshing, suction sensation, and cathartic release afterward. She also had similar cycles of sobbing and exhaustion, but they did not last as long. When "P" finally joined in to become integrated, the patient gave up her plans to kill herself, feeling for the first time that she had a future.

Everything was going smoothly until the patient went AWOL from the hospital and was not heard from for many hours. I felt distraught and wondered if things were happening too quickly. Barbara left me a series of panic-stricken messages but refused to divulge her whereabouts. She was terrified and very secretive, refusing to return to the hospital from her hideout, in a hotel room. When she was finally reassured there would be no punishment, she agreed to return but felt too afraid to leave the building. I had become aware of a countertransference fantasy of picking her up to personally escort her back to the facility, since she was so afraid and probably self-destructive. But, after several more hours, she returned on her own, very shaken up, tearful, and not discussing any details with the staff. Barbara was terribly embarrassed to divulge the details of what little she did remember during her AWOL, but the picture that developed was as follows: The patient was feeling very agitated and had urges to run away. She did not know where to go and checked into a nearby hotel. She then switched, "Tessie" emerged, and in an amnestic state picked up a man in the bar. She invited him up to her room and while there, "Tessie" asked him to have forceful sex with her. He eagerly complied. When they were finished, she gave him some money and sent him away. Barbara then "came back," finding herself naked on the couch, very sore, and feeling absolutely contaminated. She then bathed for several hours, trying to cleanse herself, and not wanting to think why she felt so disgusting and dirty. During our session, she became aware of her sexual interlude. Horrified and tearful, she ultimately confessed that she had had transference fantasies of this exact nature. In an effort to eradicate the feelings, she ran away but lapsed into a defensive altered state and enacted the fantasy with the compliant man from the bar. Barbara vehemently condemned herself for such behavior, but over time began to see that the function of "Tessie" as a seductress was an attempt to master the trauma of rape by turning passive into active.

As she became a bit more understanding of this promiscuity, she could then talk to "Tessie" about her worries regarding this extremely risky form of sexuality. Then she negotiated with her, and they became much closer, as it had been with the others. Barbara then experienced another whooshing vacuum cleaner type sensation, after a promise to give up this dangerous, potentially life-threatening behavior.

I reminded the patient that she was free to express herself through words and feelings in the transference, which was a therapeutic substitute for action. She was enormously relieved after this integration, feeling a new sense of liberation and impulse control. As before, this profound experience was accompanied by days of exhaustion and sobbing, as Barbara realized affectively that it was really her all along doing these things. But, how could she ever live with herself? So, it was imperative to emphasize, as the revelations of her childhood continued, that she never had a chance to fight back or defend herself against her stepfather. Consequently, the creation of an irresistible temptress who could pick up and sexually dispose of men at will gave her the illusion of being in total control of the traumatic situation.

Having been her stepfather's sexual partner from early childhood through late adolescence, Barbara's oedipal victory left her quite scarred and exquisitely vulnerable in the transference. For her to admit that she could not say no to me either, were some untoward move be made, was an astounding confession which reflected a level of trust in me she could never have imagined. Several other integrations occurred following a similar sequence and each time a negotiation or compromise between Barbara and her alter was needed in order to join. Barbara then sensed that all of her parts had become one with her, experiencing a sense of wholeness and authenticity within herself which was unprecedented. Her voices, amnestic periods, flashbacks, and aggressively tinged orgasmic sensations ceased. Her need for medication was greatly reduced, and her sleep improved significantly also. She walked around in amazement for days declaring that "It's all me!" I had the feeling that Barbara's integration was authentic and an enormous psychological achievement, but one that had the consistency of fresh cement which needed time and protection in order to solidify. The hypnotic literature described a minimum three-month period without switching as an indication of successful integration, and the need for extensive supportive therapy afterward (Kluft, 1986a) to reinforce the new mental state. Barbara's arrival at this point followed a dynamic route, and there was no doubt that she was at risk for regression during her working through of these issues.

Consolidation and Working Through

An unavoidable reality of Barbara's life required an interruption in our therapy, and our clinical contact was limited to weekly telephone sessions. She felt abandoned in the transference, despite her intellectual understanding of the reasons for her hiatus. Nevertheless, she did quite well. After almost three months of solid functioning, however, the first anniversary of her mother's not unexpected death made Barbara feel as if she were literally coming apart. It was a delayed reaction to the loss. Overwhelming grief coupled with the news that her siblings had reestablished contact with their stepfather, who demanded to see her, made her feel paralyzed with terror once again. She started losing time, having nightmares, and experiencing massive anxiety, after being symptom-free. Most disturbing, however, was the onset of auditory hallucinations, as she tried to avoid the inevitable conclusion that she was disintegrating. She showed me journal entries which revealed the handwriting of the "young children" personifications, providing written evidence confirming the clinical suspicion that indeed she was dissociating again. In an altered state, she lacerated her arm and "came to" as the blood was spurting out uncontrollably. Out of shame and fear, she had dutifully dressed and cleaned the wounds herself, as she was astounded and completely bewildered by her motivation.

Intensive therapy was quickly resumed, having the quality of a discontinuous analysis (Ferenczi, 1914b), and I asked her to listen inside, while I inquired if "anyone" knew anything or was directly responsible for the cutting. She appeared blank at first but when she heard a voice telling her that it was her lesbian alter, "Bessie," she became distraught and confused. Expecting the more obvious suspect to have been "the Admiral" or "Susie," given "their" history of violence, I, too, was puzzled by this information which nevertheless I took at face value as part of her associations. I tried to discover what may have triggered off this particular reaction, having learned to be more active in potentially life-threatening self-destructive situations.

When I asked about her experience of losing time and "Bessie" 's possible activity during these altered states, a personification suddenly emerged in a hostile and threatening mood, a total change from her demeanor moments before. "Bessie" emerged and made it clear that "she" was completely opposed to talking to me because "she" hated me. Furthermore, "she" stated that "she" tried to sabotage treatment in the hopes that the cutting would have angered me into giving up on "her." The patient had amnesia for the time "Bessie" was out and was quite crestfallen to return at the end of the hour, feeling quite left out and feeling like a treatment failure. I reminded her that her sense of mental unity was reversible and that we simply had a lot more unfinished business than she thought.

Barbara realized that the interruption in treatment was a precipitant to her regression also. Each day, "Bessie" emerged during some point of the session, continuing her hostile, sarcastic tirade against me and men in general. As before, "her" spontaneous appearance had dynamic significance, serving as a defense against remembering and feeling in the transference. This paradigm was dramatically confirmed again after Barbara's tearful description of a recently recalled memory at age 17 when her stepfather entered her room unannounced while she was alone and masturbating. Upon catching her in the act, he reportedly took over and masturbated her to orgasm and then demanded that she perform fellatio in return. Her extreme discomfort in relating this memory was not only due to her being at an age when she "should" have remembered it all along, but "should" have also been able to fight back. Suddenly her intolerable shame disappeared, as she got quiet, rolled her eyes upward, looked away, and apparently "switched" to "Bessie," the hostile lesbian.

The timing of this involuntary autohypnotic event enabled the emergence of a personification to feel anger, defiance, and utter contempt for me as a man instead of the intolerable shame and guilt moments before. I inquired about "Bessie"'s reappearance, but the patient derisively mocked me and the treatment process, angrily spitting out my first name as her eyes were half-closed in hatred. Having no awareness of the aforegoing revelation about her father when "they" were 17, she instead told me that the only reason that she would even continue in therapy was that it gave her a chance to visit one of her former female lovers who lived nearby. After an obstinate refusal to discuss it, she eventually but defiantly informed me that her previous contact consisted of being masturbated and then performing oral sex on this woman, who may have been infected with a disease. I was immediately struck by the similar sequence of sexual activity that was reported by the patient in her flashback at age 17, an event of which the patient was not cognizant in her "Bessie" state of mind. Apparently this regression to the "It's not me!" self was associated with a reciprocal amnesia. After several more minutes of her bravado, "Bessie" then disappeared, leaving the patient with a big headache and a frustrating sense of having been excluded from an important conversation. I confirmed her suspicion that she missed a considerable chunk of time again, and she sank back in despair feeling she was on the verge of total decompensation. I told her I did not agree, and, in fact, was encouraged because at least I was able to communicate with her personification. When the patient expressed curiosity, I reminded her again of the technical options in order to facilitate learning what was going on. For Barbara, becoming conscious of this material was equivalent to increasing internal communication with her alters and becoming "coconscious" again. I also reminded her that her mind kept things separate for a reason, that something was very unacceptable to her. So, we discussed whether I should simply tell her what I learned or whether she should journal in order to be able to "listen in" on "Bessie" once again. She felt pessimistic, but her mood lifted a bit when she assured me how liberal-minded she had become about homosexuality. She then chuckled ruefully, when I gently confronted her by saying that I thought, perhaps, her open-mindedness applied to the rest of the world not to one of her inside people. But, she, at least intellectually, knew that she would have to find a way to come to terms with a facet of her complex sexuality which not only was ego dystonic, but was still being practiced with little regard for her reality.

As we discussed this dilemma during the next session, "Bessie" re-emerged, as angry as ever, trying to scare me away with vague threats of harm. Despite the patient's history of violence, I had been assaulted by "her" "only" once, and that was early in her first hospitalization when I got in the way of an altercation she was having with the staff. I, therefore, felt relatively sure that eliciting her fantasy, if possible, would not precipitate an attack, so I inquired in the same way I might have done with a typical analytic patient. "Bessie" reiterated her hatred of men, and she stated that it was their genitals that particularly revolted her. I then wondered out loud, tentatively, if her wish to do me harm might have anything to do with that part of my body, and she smiled menacingly, verbalizing a wish to bite it off. She could not elaborate on why or how she had this particular fantasy and seemed very much on guard, which did concern me at the time. I said that I sensed a great deal of tension from her and asked her if she felt an attack was imminent. I was intentionally ambiguous about the source of the attack wondering how much projective identification was operative at this time and essentially wanted to assess her sense of danger rather than her ownership of the aggressive impulse. She awkwardly assured me of her control, so I encouraged her to discuss her wish for revenge. Once again, "Bessie" left as spontaneously as she emerged, leaving the patient most distraught and amnestic. That night, she decided to write in her journal, an activity that consisted of several paragraphs alternating between "herself," and "Bessie." In her written dialogue with her dissociated self, they both referred to "the Woman," whom "Bessie" had been unsuccessfully trying to convince to be like her (i.e., "the Woman" was an embodiment of the homosexual conflict itself). "Bessie" had also written about me that she wanted to "bite his dick off," a confession which mortified, but also informed the patient of how the transference was manifesting itself in her altered state.

When the patient arrived at the session the next day, she was obsequious and unusually deferential. She wordlessly handed me her journal, hiding her face and quietly hoping (I learned later) that I would refute what "Bessie" had written. When I confirmed the entry, she tearfully apologized, promising me that she would never, ever do such a thing and wondering how could "Bessie" have been so crudely vicious. While the genetic aspect of her wish for revenge remained a mystery, she did report being able to listen in on "Bessie" once again since the journaling. Specifically, she had learned about the unprotected oral sex, and, as I listened to her description of it in the third person, I sensed that she was shifting from an "It's not me!" to an "It's not me, but it is me!" position. I, therefore, gently drew her attention to the striking similarity between the age 17 flashback and her recent affair with her lesbian lover. In each instance, she was masturbated and then performed oral sex. She was the passive, coerced, albeit gratified victim with her father, while she was the tender responsive, active lover to a woman in the latter. The patient was intrigued by these comparisons, beginning to sense a connection between the two and smiled with insight when she added, "and with a woman *she* is not afraid, but with my stepfather *I* was afraid!'' I responded enthusiastically, suggesting that her fear might have somehow been transformed into ''Bessie's'' rage and wish for revenge against father through wanting to bite off my penis in the transference. The patient began to cry at this point synthesizing aloud and ''forgiving'' ''Bessie'' for her homosexuality.

It then became comprehensible, as though for the first time, that a female who was sexually brutalized by a male, might turn to the ''gentler sex'' for love and affection, as her tremendous longing could easily take on a sexual dimension with a like-minded woman. It appeared as though she were communicating internally with her ''Bessie'' alter, trying to reach out (or ''in'' as it were!) and accept the homosexuality. She then became bewildered and said, ''Something is happening inside. It's like before. We are very close—this far apart (holding her fingers ½ inch apart from each other), but something is blocking it.'' We then discussed how she wanted ''Bessie'' to give up acting on her lesbian urges and how necessary it would be before they could join. I listened carefully and, at this point, simply reminded her that ''It is really all you!'' She looked sad, startled, and then happy to rediscover that the unity of her mind was the missing insight resulting in the block. She then began to cry uncontrollably and deeply, experiencing a catharsis and sensing that ''Bessie'' had indeed joined her again. ''It is me!'' she exclaimed, with understanding, acceptance, and enormous relief. She was horrified at her cutting, her high-risk homosexual behavior, and her threats to mutilate my penis, trying to neutralize these impulses in light of a childhood with a mother who was ineffectual and absent and a sadistic stepfather who abused her at will.

As the ''reintegration'' with ''Bessie'' continued over the next several days, it was similar to her original fusions where she fluctuated between excessive sleepiness and uncontrollable sobbing. This time, however, she did not feel the dramatic, sudden ''vacuum cleaner'' like sensation. Instead, there was a slower, more tentative pace of her ''negotiations'' with ''Bessie.'' Throughout, she was quite aware of a constant inner dialogue with this homosexual personification. It was a more deliberate inner process, as she strove to understand herself better and mediated the coming together of her selves on a deeper level. She was quite surprised to hear ''Bessie'' say that she actually *was* her sexual feelings, quipping to me the next day that she did not know that sexual feelings could talk! But, the patient did acknowledge a longstanding inner deadness during most heterosexual encounters which supported ''Bessie's'' contention. ''Bessie'' was asked to renounce her lesbian activities if she were to ''join'' everyone again, and, in return, ''Bessie'' insisted that the patient call me by my first name. Seemingly a simple request, the patient felt great anxiety over this idea, as it denoted in her mind a change in our relationship, from doctor-patient to friend. ''Bessie'' 's fear and rage of men was intensified by the patient's memory of being molested by her general practitioner when she was a young girl. As a result, from this alter's point of view, a friend relationship with me would make her feel safer. The patient felt required to go along with this demand and began to call me Ira. Each time she did, she felt embarrassed, ashamed, and apologetic, insisting that she would only call me Ira during sessions and not be disrespectful to me in the presence of other patients or staff. I did not object to her plan, and we both became amused at the times she would lapse back into calling me Dr. Brenner, because her neck would snap back involuntarily as she felt a knocking in the back of her head, which she perceived as a reminder from "Bessie" of their agreement.

The patient's anxiety increased as she verbalized her confusion over what it meant for me to be her friend. While she recognized the double jeopardy of my being both a man and a doctor, the conflict over being her friend initially made no sense to her. Her eyes then filled with tears as she exclaimed that she would not be alive today were it not for me. I felt a sense of deep gratitude and love from her, as we both knew that the countless scars on her body were a testament to the bloody inner battle that was nearly lost when we first met. Though far from over, the tide had clearly turned, and how could she ever repay me?

At this point, she became visibly agitated and seemed to become lost in thought. Not knowing if she were dissociating again, I waited for about a minute and then asked her what was going on. She looked quite pale, having just remembered an incident with her stepfather when she was about 7. The fact she did not become disoriented, lose time, or "become" another person was quite significant, but I did not comment on it at the time because she was so disturbed over the memory, which was precipitated by her transferential feelings. With much difficulty, she revealed that her stepfather, in his relentless efforts to completely dominate the family, experimented with many types of behavioral control. He had begun an allowance program which, although short-lived, was devastating to Barbara. All of her siblings were assigned weekly chores which, when satisfactorily performed, would entitle them to their paltry allowance. The patient was neither given specific tasks nor an allowance and felt completely left out. When she mustered up the courage to ask her stepfather about her allowance, he quietly led her into his bedroom and sat on his favorite chair, a chair which resembled the "psychotherapy chair" in my office. (In retrospect, we realized that one of the factors impelling her to use the couch was the relief she felt at not having to sit in "stepfather's chair" during our sessions.) When she looked at her stepfather's cruel smile, she suddenly realized what she was supposed to do in order to earn her allowance, so she dutifully unzipped his pants and removed her underpants. She then sat on his lap allowing him to penetrate her, after which she was promptly paid. Feeling like her stepfather's little whore, she felt utterly disgusted and vehemently condemned herself once again for her compliance. She failed to realize just how conditioned she had apparently become even by the age of 7.

As her rage at her stepfather escalated once again, I pointed out that with her background it was no wonder that she did not quite know what was expected in our relationship. She initially looked horrified but quickly saw the parallels, acknowledging not only that she did not know how she could repay me, but confessing again that she still did not know how to react were such a demand placed upon her. Although she really "knew" the parameters of our relationship, a bolt of uncertainty prompted her to directly ask if I indeed was expecting "something" from her. I empathically reminded her that all she needed to do was to attend the sessions, say whatever comes to mind, and pay her bill—no more and no less.

She sighed with great relief, insisting she already knew that but was very glad to hear it again. Despite her visible relief, I sensed that she was holding her body very rigidly and had become internally preoccupied again. Reminded of the many times when her altered state or flashbacks were accompanied by overwhelming somatic memories and genital sensations, I inquired once again what she was experiencing. Indeed, her account of the sexual incident with her stepfather was overstimulating, and she was trying to suppress her awareness of the orgasmic sensations. Her confusion in the transference was fueled by these feelings and she felt profoundly vulnerable. At this point, we reiterated not only the boundaries of our relationship but also the crucial distinction between thought and feeling versus action. It felt completely bizarre for her to be feeling what she was feeling and to be just telling me about it, rather than acting on it. Her wish-fear of enacting this memory in the transference was the natural result of a lifetime of living out her nightmare of abuse in altered states of consciousness. In her world, whatever came into her mind would become reality. Despite her embarrassment, shame, and guilt, she marveled at this newly acquired sense of control over her mind and body.

I, too, felt a bit amazed, recalling how violently she had reacted to such somatic sensations less than a year before, having needed restraints in the hospital for her protection from self-injury. Her increased ego strength was reflected not only in the impulse control but also in her capacity for self-observation. As we explored the paternal transference further, she commented that she, unlike some of her peers, did not feel possessive or jealous. Nevertheless, she could not imagine saying goodbye to me, as a confluence of abandonment issues and unresolved grief over her mother intensified her feelings. Her mother, she lamented, was unable to protect her and perhaps did not fully believe her, but did promise to stand by her during her testimony against her stepfather. Although she cried bitterly about being forsaken by her mother yet again, she eventually sounded more realistic about her mother's own bleak life. She also mentioned how difficult it was to part with mother's belongings. Shortly afterward she asked me about a certain magazine in the waiting room with a picture of her favorite teddy bear. During my summer break, she had wanted to hold it and in return, lent me one of her child alter's toys for collateral.

Memories of her mother reminded her of this request for a transitional object for her "children." The young girls had apparently also "come apart" during her regression, but the patient reported that she was able to facilitate a reintegration of them on her own. I was quite impressed, but the patient was rather nonchalant about it, perhaps not realizing the significance of her self-analytic accomplishment as she told me about her plan. "Baby" and "Susie" would "join" her again as long as the patient would ask to see the toys she gave to me prior to her interruption. She was initially too anxious to ask to see them again, fearing that if I had disposed of them, it would have been a crushing act of treason. But, the girls were able to comfortably merge with her again as long as the toys remained with me. As though by analogic action (Hamilton, 1974), the knowledge of my acceptance of her gifts enabled her to identify with my attitude and allow her to accept her own disparate parts.

Discussion

The patient's consolidation was an ongoing, long-term process which enabled her to further review her progress, learn more about her mental functioning, and work through more of the transference. Her capacity for self-observation and self-analysis were exemplified by her ability to tolerate further exploration of her sexuality as expressed through "the Admiral" and "Tessie." "The Admiral" 's sadomasochistic rage was associated with intense arousal and mutilation of her breasts and vagina. "He" protested being trapped in a female body. In contrast, "Tessie" 's sexuality was object related, promiscuous, and aimed at mastery and control of the man (father), while putting "herself" at great risk. The patient was a bit astounded to consider how her sexuality was expressed in her various states of mind, sensing that "Bessie" 's homosexuality was her true sexuality. Indeed, "the Admiral" 's maleness also served to legitimize her female object choice. Part of her "negotiations" with "Bessie" entailed giving up her homosexual relationships and learning how to tolerate arousal in the context of a long-term intimate, nonsadistic relationship with a man.

The patient was feeling quite proud of herself until she began to reexperience intense sexual stimulation during the sessions again. It was accompanied by enuresis, a feeling of shameful defeat, and memories of bed-wetting after being with her stepfather. As before, she avoided eye contact and held her body very rigidly, feeling quite confused about her transferential feelings. She reluctantly acknowledged feeling deep love but thought she saw me more as the kind of father she never had, rather than a lover. At the same time, she cried with relief, reiterating her belief that she would have most certainly died without my help. She described how she had felt more or less programmed to respond sexually to her stepfather, starting at a very early age. She then recalled how symptomatic she had become when her own daughter became 5 years old, the age she believed she was when she first had intercourse with him. She lamented how, over the years, she had come to experience sexual gratification with her stepfather but tried not to condemn herself as viciously as before. When she could allow herself to see that, as a helpless child, she had no chance but to submit were she to survive, she concluded that much of her sexual arousal was involuntary conditioning. With this insight, her arousal in the session abated, so the patient felt encouraged that indeed she was becoming better able to take control and ownership of her bodily functions.

She was very apprehensive about having to interrupt treatment again, fearing a recurrence of her symptoms as before. She doubted that she could maintain her gains without me. Her unresolved grief over her mother and her longstanding separation anxiety returned with a vengeance. Having made a "friend," such an absolutely rare achievement for her, she was loathe to let him go, again.

While arrangements were made again to meet every several months for another installment of treatment and to consider telephone sessions if needed, she could not help but feel that she was the one being abandoned. Uncertainty over the hospital's future lent a degree of reality to her plea of "How will I find you?" Relying heavily on her transitional objects (Fink, 1993), she asked again for my magazine, tape recorded my voice, and journaled vigorously, trying to capture the essence of our last sessions and hold onto our last words. Much like the indelible imprint of the "last look" or parting words of the child traumatically separated from the parent during the Holocaust (Kestenberg and Brenner, 1996), these last interactions were to be kept within her as a permanent reminder and guide. And, as time went on, this cycle was repeated many times in her efforts to work through her traumatic past. Having shed her chameleonlike, dissociative skin, her "it's not me!" self gave way to a more solid sense of identity.

Chapter 9
THE LIMITS OF MEDICATION

> I feel like an Alka Seltzer dissolving in a glass of water
> and nothing helps! [A severely traumatized, "medication
> resistant" patient].

THE LIMITED RESPONSE TO MEDICATION

The morbidity of severely traumatized, dissociative patients may, at times, warrant the prescribing of psychoactive medication, offering another challenge to clinicians trying to work with them analytically. While there is no medication of choice (Barkin, Braun, and Kluft, 1986), and the benefit may be limited at best, sometimes it can make a significant difference and enable treatment to proceed. Other times it may be a great interference and source of resistance. Given the complexity of some of the agents used and the need for constant monitoring during crises, the value of using a consultant to do the prescribing needs to be weighed in light of the dynamic cost of his or her presence during times when transferential issues may be most intense. For this reason, I have found it most expeditious and beneficial to prescribe the medication myself. I feel comfortable, competent, and up-to-date in this area, so it has come to feel more natural for me to incorporate this function into my role than to delegate it to a colleague. Working with such patients in this way would, therefore, be the domain of M.D. psychoanalysts who have both

Portions of this chapter were presented at the 19th Annual Conference of the Regional Council of Psychoanalytic Societies of the Greater New York area and Philadelphia on June 5, 1993, Montauk, N.Y.

the expertise and authorization to employ an integrated, pharmacologic approach to this "widening scope" population (Stone, 1954).

When medication is employed in dissociative patients, it is usually prescribed to treat the manifestations of depression and/or anxiety. Because of their efficacy and relative safety, even during an overdose, antidepressants of the selective serotonin reuptake inhibitor (SSRI) category such as Prozac, Zoloft, and Paxil, seem to be those most popularly prescribed. Depressive and suicidal symptoms often are a chief complaint which brings the patient to treatment in the first place. But, with the intermittent panic and severe anxiety which accompanies profound "unassimilable trauma" (Baranger, Baranger, and Mom, 1988), it may be so paralyzing at times, as to appear psychotic in nature. Auditory hallucinations, bizarre conversion symptoms, depersonalization, and emotional inaccessibility may further be part of a clinical picture which adds to diagnostic confusion. Interestingly, the number of reports of "multiple personality" in the literature declined significantly after the introduction of Bleuler's term *schizophrenia*, and it has been postulated that many such cases, including some very highly publicized psychotherapeutic triumphs, were, in fact, misdiagnosed cases of severe dissociative pathology (Rosenbaum, 1980). Consequently, many patients with "multiple personality" have been inadvertently treated with high doses of major tranquilizers such as Thorazine, Mellaril, and Stelazine, generally with unsatisfactory results or intolerable side effects. Because their symptoms are generally minimally responsive to antipsychotics, it may have led to the erroneous conclusion that they were refractory schizophrenics with a dismal prognosis who needed chronic institutionalization. I will describe such a case below. In such facilities, they have not infrequently reported retraumatization (Kluft, 1990) which further complicates treatment when and if the proper diagnosis is ultimately made. Under these circumstances, these patients may temporarily reconstitute or "pull themselves together," much to the surprise of their institutional guardians, and appear to make a surprising recovery. This temporary abatement of gross symptoms may then lead the clinicians to conclude that such patients have a bizarre, episodic mood disorder or schizoaffective disorder. This problem was graphically demonstrated to me by a chance meeting I had with a patient many years after she had been lost to follow-up.

Case 1. Multiple Personality Refractory to Antipsychotic Medication

Ms. K had become somewhat notorious at a facility due to her record number of admissions. She was very well known for her florid psychoticlike symptoms, her seeming immunity to all dosage ranges of all the prominent major tranquilizers available at the time, and her propensity for self-directed violence which regularly required physical restraints. Yet, there was something quite likeable and mysterious about Ms. K, who, at times, seemed to have a very mischievous twinkle in her eye, who could be quite engaging and endearing between her abrupt episodes of head banging, and who could even seem quite "normal" when she was not feeling absolutely possessed by her inner tormentors. The staff felt especially helpless about this young woman's prognosis, as there seemed to be little correlation between her clinical course and her treatment. The intensity of her self-directed rage seemed to be boundless, while her parents, a rather cold and forbidding couple, were becoming progressively more frustrated with her and the hospital for not curing their daughter. The patient was quite secretive about her life and seemed to vaccillate between an apathetic or euphoric indifference and inconsolable rage. Quite often following a hostile confrontation between her and her parents, a very serious discussion ensued over whether to proceed with commitment to the state hospital. Then, an abrupt reversal would take place, and the staff would frequently be left feeling aghast or baffled when she would demand to go home with them. Her parents would then assume complete responsibility for her, turning against the staff, and threatening to fight any efforts to send their daughter away. Concluding that it was a "borderline" family who used to "split the staff," she would then be lost to follow-up for weeks, only to repeat this cycle over again. This pattern continued for several years until she did go to a state hospital, and it had a dramatic impact on the whole unit.

A number of years later, after I became "educated" about dissociative disorders and started reflecting on all the patients with whom I had contact and whose diagnosis may have been "missed," the elusive Ms. K came to mind. I had had no idea what happened to her and had not thought about her until I went through this clinical inventory, but her enigmatic mental status and her psychoticlike symptoms, which seemed immune to the medication that only obtunded her, made me question if she were an undiagnosed "multiple."

Much to my surprise and curiosity many years later, I passed her in the hallway of another hospital which had opened up a specialty unit for the treatment of dissociative disorders. I felt happy to know she was still alive and wanted to know if she indeed were on that unit. I did not think she recognized me, and I did not want to intrude on her privacy, but when we passed each other again several days later, we made eye contact and smiled. I told her I remembered her from the previous hospital, and she, too, recalled me as one of the familiar old faces in that distant landscape. We chatted briefly, and she smiled mischievously once again when she said that she was, indeed, on the Dissociative Disorders Unit. We nodded knowingly to each other, and I said, "I guess we finally figured out what was really going on with you!'' She chuckled, as though her secret was finally discovered, saying that for the first time she felt understood and optimistic about her treatment. I walked away feeling enlightened by such a rare moment when my retrospective clinical suspicion had been verified by this chance meeting. In this regard, Ms. K seemed to exemplify the "medication resistant" schizophrenic who is later rediagnosed with a severe dissociative disorder and begins to respond to a more psychotherapeutic approach.

In addition to the "medication resistant" schizophrenia misdiagnosis, patients may present as intractable manic–depressive or bipolar patients. At such times, lithium carbonate and, more recently, other mood stabilizers, such as Tegretol or Depakote, have been added to little avail. In either case, the possibility of years of inappropriate treatment seems to have provided much empirical data about the limited value of these drugs and to be another potential source of iatrogenic complications. More commonly these days, however, the well-publicized concern over "implanting false memories" has eclipsed the more longstanding and possibly more widespread problem of misdiagnosis and institutionalization for the wrong condition. In the following vignette, I will describe such a case in which mood stabilizing medication was ineffective, but where other medications were then continued throughout treatment and had important implications.

CASE 2. MULTIPLE PERSONALITY REFRACTORY TO MOOD STABILIZING MEDICATION

Laura, a woman in her late twenties, was referred for treatment in an acutely suicidal state. Over the previous six years she had had a downhill, deteriorating course characterized by multiple, extended hospitalizations, the interruption of her promising professional career, and the breaking off of her engagement. Yet, in between her decompensations, she appeared "normal" and functional. Having been diagnosed as a rapid cycling manic-depressive, or bipolar disorder, her overt symptoms were characterized by short episodes of maniclike symptoms such as euphoria, hyperactivity, and shopping sprees. These states might last hours or several days and then would suddenly be punctuated by alcohol abuse, hopelessness, self-hatred, and progressively more serious attempts to take her life. Several times, in seemingly manic episodes, she would drive her car for days, ending up in psychiatric hospitals over a thousand miles away. She would report intermittent amnesia for most of these fuguelike spells, feeling forced by some deep inner compulsion to just keep going, despite claims of being assaulted and raped along the way. These latter details were kept secret until shortly before her referral, after therapeutic doses on virtually every known mood stabilizer proved "ineffective." Treated with tricyclics, MAO inhibitors, SSRIs, lithium carbonate,

Tegretol, Depakote, Calan (a calcium channel blocker), and Neurontin, Laura's "moods" seemed impervious to these medications. Major tranquilizers only obtunded her, while minor tranquilizers in high doses, most notably Klonopin and Ativan, seemed most effective in helping take the edge off of her impulse-ridden panic states. A rather secretive woman with a tendency to deny any problems with a falsely reassuring smile, Laura's capacity to enter into a therapeutic alliance was only on a most superficial level, thereby leaving her therapists frustrated and unable to help, let alone really know what was going on in her mind. Indeed, Laura was too scared to admit to herself, let alone to others, that despite her outward facade, she felt absolutely insane and possessed.

As the oldest of three children from three brief, stormy marriages of her unavailable mother, who lived in fear of her impulsively violent ex-husbands, Laura grew up as the peacemaker and sacrificial lamb. A competent and well-endowed child, she was expected to excel in everything and be perfectly behaved at all times. She felt she could not complain about anything, even when she was sent away to live with her father so her mother could be unfettered by a young child. Outwardly, Laura's development seemed unaffected, although she was frequently observed by her teachers to drift off and daydream excessively. Although she would come back from her father's house with bumps and bruises, she minimized them to her mother, attributing them to accidents or horseplay with her friends. As a young teen, she would accompany him to parties and other evening activities, assuming the role of a date more than a daughter. Interestingly, her mother insisted she be called by her first name, seemingly wanting her as a friend more than a daughter. Consequently, Laura's confusion over generational roles and boundaries were apparently perpetuated in both households until she left for college. As might have been expected, she did not adjust well to an independent life at school, and following a series of ambiguous, unreported date rapes, she dropped out for a year. She then resumed her education with renewed zeal, throwing herself into a challenging career which she was able to successfully negotiate for a number of years.

Things seemed to be going well until her father's second divorce, a breakup with a woman not much older than Laura. He became much more available and wanted his grown daughter to move in with him, an invitation that filled her with panic and confusion. Since that time, her "rapid cycling" disorder manifested itself as described above, but one of her therapists began to suspect a dissociative disorder. She reported hearing voices, and it became evident that her "cycling" was accompanied by amnesia as well as identity changes more consistent with "switching of alters" in "multiple personality." Being refractory to treatment for the affective disorder, she was eventually referred for definitive diagnosis and treatment.

Laura, initially apprehensive about revealing not only the true nature of her inner life but also her abrupt discharge from her previous therapist, was extremely uncooperative and demanding. Insisting she would not talk to me unless I promised never to leave her and to be her doctor forever, it became immediately clear, not surprisingly, that there were profound separation and abandonment issues. Furthermore, she tried to break treatment in her acutely agitated and suicidal state, thereby testing me immediately. This behavior had a more characterologic and dissociative feel than a manic quality as she did not manifest pressured speech or flight of ideas, but rather seemed to fluctuate between outrageousness, tearfulness, and a peculiar childlike state. In addition, she seemed very forgetful, although she did her best to cover it up and emphatically denied hearing voices, with an inappropriately cheerful and reassuring smile totally inconsistent with the gravity of the situation. The quality of her intense engagement with the staff and her past history did not seem psychotic in nature, nor was there any evidence of organicity, further raising the index of suspicion of a major dissociative disorder.

Developing an alliance with Laura was like trying to hop aboard a runaway train. Between her secrecy, her alcohol abuse, her overdoses, and her self-mutilation, the patient's provocative testing of limits betrayed a desperate infantile wish for a benign parent to take charge of her life. Repeated hospitalizations, threatened involuntary commitments, and constant renegotiation of safety contracts required very small prescriptions of medication, sometimes on a daily basis. Even then, she was prone to hoard some for her next overdose, as her "self-destructive alters" tortured her with hallucinatory commands to drink, take the pills, and bleed to death in order to end her lifelong anguish. The medication became the medium of our power struggles, as the amount prescribed became equated with how worthy of trust and love she felt. More important than the efficacy (at best, she experienced a reduction in anxiety and impulsivity on high doses of benzodiazepines) was the ritual of my writing out the prescription, which became a major event in our three to five times a week therapy. After several years of this rather tedious protocol, which, at times, significantly enough, become a source of tension-relieving humor between us, Laura began to realize that she was not going to wear me down. Instead of giving in to her incessant demands for more, I made the writing out of her prescriptions for Klonopin, Prozac, and a small dose of Stelazine the centerpiece of many of our sessions, often spending much of the time discussing every possible detail of the transaction in order to convey to her that it all had potential meaning.

Her psychopathology unfolded not unlike the other cases described throughout this volume, as there was a very strong sadomasochistic trend and dissociated memories of repeated early sexual abuse by her father and others which continued throughout adolescence. Significantly, there were also never forgotten memories which she was just unable to reveal to me early in treatment (see chapter 5 on dreams and negation). In the transference, I was seen as an unavailable but desperately longed for, all-purpose object who treated her with stingy amounts of medication. A crisis in treatment eventually developed as she incurred a very large debt owing to the complexity of her perpetually inept insurance company. While I was not convinced she was doing all she could to facilitate the reimbursement to me, and, indeed, she may have unwittingly contributed to the problem, I felt fairly sure that eventually it would all get straightened out. In my own countertransference monitoring, however, it became essential to be aware of my growing impatience over the ever growing debt, the extremely fragile nature of her psyche which resulted in suicidal crises over feared rejection or abandonment, as well as my sense that she was deriving vicarious, sadistic pleasure through the insurance company's withholding of payment to me (revenge for my parsimonious dealing out of medication?). I began to feel, at times, that I was being held hostage and taken advantage of by her, suspecting that I was resonating with some of the horrors of her childhood. It became difficult to find a comfortable balance with her, and I suggested we temporarily cut back the sessions until some payment arrived. I offered this compromise, in lieu of an interruption in treatment, which I felt would be utterly catastrophic at this time, but Laura felt nonetheless that the cutback was a prelude to the inevitable.

In her mosaic transference (see chapter 9), she, in different states of consciousness, reacted to the situation differently, from being reasonably understanding due to the size of her debt, to wanting me to treat her for free, to wanting to pay me through sexual favors, to being absolutely convinced that she would die without me, to becoming violently enraged at my greed. These disparate, seemingly separate states of mind left her feeling more out of control than ever, and one day she arrived for her session uncharacteristically intense. She eventually revealed that she was so hurt and outraged with me that she had collected every last pill that she had hidden in her apartment over the years and had planned her revenge through her grand finale—a truly lethal overdose. She had not planned to tell me, but one of her child alters who was afraid of dying, "popped out" and blurted out the secret. I told the patient that it had become difficult for me to walk that fine therapeutic line between not getting provoked into giving up on her, because I was starting to feel abused and taken advantage of by her. I explained, in what I hoped was comprehensible language, how her projective identification was inducing me to want to interrupt her treatment, and I was fighting hard not to give in to it. Yet, I could not allow her to build up the debt at the rate it was proceeding, which was not only unfair to me, but placing a potentially insurmountable burden upon her. I told her that I was getting a first-hand experience of what it had been like growing up for her—with a sense of helplessness, of being trapped, of feeling unprotected by her mother, and of being at her father's mercy, physically and sexually. For the first time in years, she began to cry and had an uncontrollable urge to scream. All of her "inside people" felt like yelling at the top of their lungs, but making any noise was absolutely forbidden by her father and others, as it would have brought attention to her plight in the past. She looked at me helplessly, and I did not discourage her or try to shut her up, much to her surprise in the transference. And, indeed, she let out blood curdling screams until she lost her voice.

Her cathartic release was apparently an integrative experience for Laura, which heralded an important phase of treatment, characterized by her becoming more "real," more able to "own" the different parts of her mind, and her being more honest with me. Interestingly, her amnesia improved, also. She immediately contacted an attorney who helped resolve the problem with the insurance company and a cutback in treatment was averted. Significantly, she also felt that her need for medication had decreased in the aftermath of this profound affective experience, and we gradually tapered it without major regression. She was maintained on a low dose of Klonopin subsequently, and treatment evolved into a more typical analytically oriented mode characterized by further analysis of transference, reconstruction of her childhood, and much less self-destructive aggression.

Discussion

In Laura's case, it appeared that the prescribing of medication was where the "action" was in treatment. Oral, anal, narcissistic, and transitional themes were woven into every facet of the pill-giving relationship, as she measured her desirability, self-worth, and sense of control in terms of what and how much was given to her. Inasmuch as truly life and death issues were at stake here, the intensity of every transaction required the utmost thoughtfulness. Interestingly, a countertransference enactment coupled with the disclosure of my dilemma and the feelings being induced in me culminated in and eventually resolved a potentially lethal regression. I revealed my difficulty in walking the clinical tightrope so as not to feel abused due to the buildup of a serious debt nor masochistically held hostage by her veiled threat of suicide if I were to "dump" her. This series of interventions seemed to catalyze a significant, cathartic integrative experience for the patient in the transference. Subsequently, there was considerable decrease of amnesia, anxiety, aggression, and need for medication. She was essentially able to stay out of the hospital afterward, also, enabling treatment to evolve along less chaotic and more typically analytic lines.

Incorporation of Medication into Analytic Treatment

But, does the use of medication in psychoanalysis (Sarwer-Foner, 1960; Ostow, 1960, 1962, 1966; Hayman, 1967; Mandel, 1968) truly reflect one of the major directions of the "widening scope" (Stone, 1954), or does it reflect problems in countertransference (Levy, 1977), in case selection, or in succumbing to the pressure of the times? Does the dichotomy between the "biological" and the psychological lead to arbitrary conclusions (Wylie and Wylie, 1987) about what is not analyzable about the patient? Does medication take the edge off, just enough, to reduce the patient's motivation to delve deeper?

Against this backdrop of uncertainty is the uniqueness of each case and the various ways in which medication may be incorporated. Informal polling of analysts suggests that this practice is more widespread than reported, but there are still few paradigms or theoretical models to utilize. What is striking about combining dynamic psychotherapy with drugs (Bellak, 1966; Gabbard, 1990; Beitman, 1992; Kessler, 1992; Klerman, 1992) is the ambiguity that arises in the areas of initiative, control, and ownership of the medication as it becomes an extension of the therapeutic relationship. While the limits of this treatment and the severity of the pathology may preclude a thorough analysis of the transference and working through in a number of cases, transference phenomena are nevertheless operative.

I have found it helpful in conceptualizing the pill-prescribing relationship to borrow from the psychology of inanimate objects, especially transitional phenomena (Winnicott, 1953; Kafka, 1969; Adelman, 1985) and Kestenberg's intermediate objects (1975), which refer to the food and bodily products involved in the object relatedness of each level of psychosexual development. The incorporation of psychotropic medication into the analytic situation requires the careful consideration of a number of factors. Factors such as the indications for prescribing, the psychotropic effect itself, side effects, and fantasies about the medication are obvious. In addition, issues such as the point in the treatment process when the medication is being introduced, who is prescribing it, the monitoring process, the frequency of renewal of prescriptions, and compliance need to be considered also. Finally, and most important, are the issues pertaining to the effect of the medication on the analysis itself. What, for example, might be intended as an adjunctive, temporary measure in order to maintain the continuity of the treatment may become a larger issue in the transference, which if not fully addressed may increase an already powerful resistance. On the other hand, if the medication is seen as necessary for a rather disturbed patient, there may be an implicit assumption that what would have formerly been an unanalyzable situation, might then become analyzable.

However, the extent to which this psychopathology would be amenable to the analytic process is controversial, as some writers seem convinced of a dichotomy between "biological" and psychodynamic symptoms. But, since it is believed that very early conflicts may result in somatic compliance resulting in the development of psychophysiologic symptoms (Alexander, 1950), if the affected organ system happens to be the brain, then one may consider that a mental condition has psychodynamic determinants but may seem to develop a biologic life of its own. As a result, one may employ defensive operations and have symptoms which may not respond to interpretive efforts until possibly there is some medical intervention. But, that does not mean they do not have meaning. Due to the early and deep nature of the issues, analysis may be long and uncertain, but not necessarily impossible.

The use of psychotropic medication in, for example, patients whose depression (Azima, 1959; Bellak, 1966; Modell, 1966; Klerman, 1992) becomes so severe that they cannot function, may enable us to analytically treat many who would have been unsuitable in the past. In this type of patient, finding a way to analyze the transference may require flexibility, creativity, support, time, and additional parameters. In my view, the question that such cases raise is how much of an analytic experience can be made available to the patient rather than "is it really analysis?" In the following case of a severely traumatized woman who converted to analysis, I will focus on certain aspects of her treatment to illustrate many of these points.

CASE 3. CONVERSION TO ANALYSIS OF AN "INTERMEDIATE LEVEL" DISSOCIATIVE CHARACTER

Julie, a young woman, converted to a four times a week analysis after several years of treatment, continuing on up to 60 mg of Prozac and up to 50 mg of PRN Thorazine per day. I prescribed the medication and was able to appreciate the significance of it with her as treatment progressed to an analytic plane.

The patient was initially referred for hospitalization following a nine-month deterioration, which had been diagnosed as a major depression. Neither lithium carbonate, several antidepressants, nor psychotherapy were effective, so it was hoped that this downward spiral could be reversed with vigorous inpatient intervention. I had been recommended, but as a committed feminist, Julie was opposed to having a male psychiatrist. However, she felt broken, defeated, helpless, and unable to make any decisions, so she accepted the arrangement until she was stabilized, believing that at the very least, I was competent. In a counterphobic way, she rationalized the situation by thinking that if she could ever learn to relate to someone as foreign to her as a Jewish, male physician, coming from her Irish, Catholic background, then she would be able to relate to anyone.

The precipitant to her decompensation was the breakup of the love of her life, a manic–depressive woman who was also on lithium. Julie was devastated and found herself emotionally isolated and without support. She had been alienated from her mother because of the latter's tendency toward deception, secrecy, and emotional unavailability. Julie spent much of her early life questioning her perceptions about life at home, feeling dominated, controlled, and overstimulated, yet deprived and devalued at the same time. She was terribly troubled about and chronically enraged with her mother, but as yet could not articulate the problems, leaving her feeling "crazy." As a preadolescent, her father all but disappeared from her life, remaining a distant, elusive, and secretly longed for figure. The younger of two children by almost a decade, her brother also had little to do with her.

Julie had sought help several years before this crisis when she first questioned her sexual orientation but felt she got nowhere. At the time, she found a woman psychotherapist with an analytic couch who was able to engage her. She began to discuss her burgeoning homosexuality, but, as things intensified in therapy, she experienced flashbacks from an all but forgotten experience, a vicious rape at age 15. Memories and anxiety overwhelmed her and her therapist, who referred her to a male psychiatrist for medication. Julie had fears of being alone at night and car headlights reminded her of the flashing lights at the party where she met a man who took her to a field, ravaging her at knifepoint. Because of her symptoms of insomnia and racing thoughts, she was prescribed lithium, which seemed to help her at first. She saw the male psychiatrist once a month, did not speak to him, and could not remember his name. He was another distant, elusive man in her life who did not have enough time for her. Eventually she became terrified of what lithium was doing to her insides and would forget to take it from time to time.

Julie moved, and she replicated her arrangements with another woman therapist and a male psychiatrist to monitor her medication from afar. In an effort to stave off the hospitalization, this psychiatrist made several medication changes which alarmed her. She refused MAO inhibitors due to fear of a hypertensive crisis, became oversedated on benzodiazepines, and experienced disturbing anticholinergic effects on tricyclic antidepressants. She continued to decline, feeling she had no choice but to kill herself or swallow her pride and ask her mother for help. It was in this state of mind that I met her.

During her hospitalization, I had the impression that it might have been prevented if she had been in intensive therapy all along. She had strengths and a desire to get well. Despite her despair and utter hopelessness, she had never acted on suicidal impulses and generally had taken good care of herself. Interestingly, she was punctual for every session, even in her regressed state. In addition, she had no history of substance abuse or promiscuity, and seemed to have a deep sense of integrity. She was quite verbal, extremely intelligent, and was very successful throughout her education. However, her separation anxiety and terror over abandonment reflected serious preoedipal pathology, which was complicated by her trauma.

As a voluntary inpatient, Julie was free to leave at any time, but she refused to budge, even though most of our sessions were consumed by her inconsolable wailing about her incarceration. Much later, in analysis, she said, "I was locked in and you were making me do something I didn't want to do." At the time, she felt retraumatized but could not connect it to the rape, which she would have me believe was a minor footnote in her life. She mentioned it with a bland, distant affect and rationalized her amnesia for it as it not being important enough to remember. She gave the impression of it being an ambiguous "date rape" which she did not pursue legally, leaving her feeling mildly confused and annoyed at the whole situation.

Pharmacologically, I offered to add Thorazine for her agitation and recommended stopping the lithium, which had suppressed her thyroid functioning. Despite its toxicity and apparent lack of benefit, Julie tenaciously clung to the lithium, as it seemed to link her to her lost lover. I suspected that she questioned my judgment also, not wanting to give up anything else unless she had to. After her vehement protest and a bit of grieving over the loss, she eventually did agree to stop taking this mood stabilizer. I tried to be as unauthoritarian and democratic as possible, keeping in mind that the reality of her situation accentuated the power differential between us.

As with the medication, I was low key about the duration of her stay, too, trying to make all decisions in collaboration with her. So, when Julie felt ready to leave, I simply discharged her. She wanted to see me as an outpatient, despite her intense ambivalence, and that was a pleasant surprise for me. She decided to see me weekly until she felt ready to change doctors. The hospitalization seemed to provide a holding environment, and she did not want to leave whatever comfort or protection she derived from it. She wanted to hold onto it for as long as possible until ready to venture out on her own again, and I suspected that she experienced masochistic gratification, also. Despite her numerous overtures to quit, she rarely missed appointments and continued to be punctual. She begrudgingly felt indebted to me for switching her antidepressant medication to Prozac, which gave her objective relief from her renewed crying spells. Her gratitude over this rather simple pharmacologic decision brought to mind an off-handed comment I had heard several years before from a pathologically narcissistic and grandiose "depression expert," who took great personal delight in the accolades of his "cured" patients: "Once you find the right medicine, they are your slaves for life." Indeed, her gratitude made her feel uncomfortably obligated and masochistically bound to me. She then began to feel that I knew "too much" about her after I learned the true nature of her rape. She became terrified of increasing closeness, dependency, and neediness as though she, too, would become hopelessly entangled in a murky maternal transference. We then, unexpectedly, ran into each other at the movies during the showing of a controversial film about rape. She had spent weeks getting mentally prepared for this attempt at self-healing with her friends, but I, of course, knew nothing of these elaborate plans until she was "caught" at the theater. Two years into treatment, this encounter catalyzed a more open discussion about her felt need to keep secrets from me. She even kept secret her progressive promotions at work which betrayed her hidden competence.

She was successful in her field but continued to feel miserable. Her relationships were doomed to fail, and she continued to question her sexuality, but she wanted to be a mother. As a result, she was unsure where to get the semen. Should she seek artificial insemination, get impregnated by a willing gay friend, or wait and see if she would "change" to become heterosexual? After realizing the depth of her confusion, the limits of her current treatment, and her request for more help, we decided to discuss more intensive treatment options before she pursued her quest for semen. At this time, she was only dimly aware of the preoedipal determinants to her wish to have a baby (Gedo, 1965) and redo her own childhood. Regarding therapy, she revealed an old fantasy of being in analysis and had been intrigued by the former therapist's couch. Once again, we discussed her seeing other mental health professionals, and I explained to her, in layman's terms, that her rape may have intensified her early developmental struggles, especially her apparent rapprochement conflict. I further pointed out that her hospitalization and medication had become major issues between us which might complicate an analysis with me. However, she reminded me that her previous unsuccessful treatment had always been split and would not consider analysis with anyone but me. It was clear that she had developed a profoundly ambivalent transference, but whether it could be analyzed and the extent to which it could be resolved was unclear. I concluded that she had enough ego strength at this point to at least consider a trial of analysis, and shared this impression with her.

As further evidence of her determination to get well, she found a better paying job and reached the point of reviewing her finances with me in order to arrive at a realistic fee. We were to continue on this topic the next hour, but, interestingly, she had complete amnesia for the extensive financial discussion and was shocked at the idea of analysis! It seemed preposterous to her, as though she were hearing about the idea for the first time. She then reported a series of fuguelike experiences, such as finding herself in strange places she had never been before. I told her that this seemingly new behavior might be her way of telling me, before we started analysis, there was much more going on than I realized. She ruefully agreed.

The Analysis

Julie was punctual and consistent in keeping her analytic appointments. She was consumed by the perceived demand that she lie down immediately, although she acknowledged I was really not coercing her. By this time she had a rudimentary awareness of the illusory nature of transference. She spent hours working on an epic entitled "The countless reasons why I should not use the couch." Most of these reasons had to do with variations of her fear of lying on her back. She, at times, however, did not always remember that she was engaged in this project, sheepishly acknowledging that some of it was in different handwriting. In fact, she kept a diary in which many entries were in different handwriting, which she often did not recall writing, either. The increased frequency of our visits enabled me to see the discontinuity in her memory and moods which she also kept secret.

I also thought it might be useful to try to analyze as many aspects of her use of the medication as possible, so I asked her how much of a supply she wanted. After several years of weekly visits, weekly prescriptions, and repetitive discussions, she was puzzled by this change. I told her that since she was in analysis now, I hoped that we could collaborate better on her medication and could understand it more fully if she made more of the decisions herself. She opted for a two-week supply but often did not request refills for three weeks, thus betraying her erratic compliance. On several occasions, she would go to the bathroom after a session and absent-mindedly leave her prescriptions by the toilet. They would be discovered later and brought to my attention by others. Apparently, she left her bodily wastes and her prescriptions behind before she went home. She admitted with some embarrassment that her problem of forgetting was out of her control but could not tell me earlier for fear that I would think she had truly lost her mind.

Julie's anxiety escalated at work, as her new boss, a woman, terrorized her with unpredictable moods, demandingness, and favoritism to others. She had taken this new job to pay for analysis and now felt trapped. I made an extratransference interpretation, pointing out how she imbued her boss with traits of her mother, and, following this intervention, her anxiety diminished. Encouraged by evidence of "the talking cure," Julie then weaned herself off the medication, hoping that analysis was all she needed. I, too, was aware of similar idealistic wishes for a drug-free analysis but recognized that at times, such feelings may have mirrored her own denial of the seriousness of her problems. With this idea in mind, I was able to maintain as much neutrality about the medication as possible. Her anxiety skyrocketed again prior to a vacation, and she wanted to resume her Prozac, which she did. Again, the symbolic importance of the pill as a transitional object was not easily teased

out from the severity of her symptomatic regression. So, in addition to interpretation, she was free to resume her medication. She continued to feel a
sense of impending doom, and, upon returning, Prozac was titrated up to 60
mg per day. During that summer, she developed a photosensitivity reaction,
which angered her and made her feel betrayed. "Why didn't you warn me?"
she implored. I suspected her rebuke was multiply determined, and we pursued other feelings of betrayal, as the transference deepened and broadened.

Julie felt the need to keep analysis a secret from others, fearing their
disapproval over her growing dependency, which was a progressively terrifying issue for her. "Suppose you are sick and demented and I don't know it?"
she asked, as fragments of the rape emerged. She had an image of the knife,
memories of the cuts on her thighs, and sensations of abrasions all over her
body from the thick brush in the field. She then mentioned her history of
asthma, which, as a child, resulted in a number of emergencies, including a
life-threatening event requiring hospitalization. She sadly wondered why her
parents would encourage her from time to time to expose herself to known
allergens in the vain hopes that she might have "outgrown" her asthma,
despite her violent medical reactions. Apparently nobody ever warned her of
the danger, then or now, and she saw me as a sadistic mother trying to
"toughen" her up.

Julie acknowledged that she was looking for protection in her life, and
a crisis in her medical coverage exemplified her plight. A reviewer requested
my records and a detailed summary justifying treatment. It felt like another
unexpected violation, a rape, and she was paralyzed. She wanted to quit but
eventually mobilized to take action this time, appealing this intrusion and
managing to have her benefits continue without documentation. But, she
experienced an upsurge of anxiety again, exclaiming, "These drugs are not
working!" Julie then became disillusioned and confused over drugs versus
analysis as she observed, "Sometimes I think you are the only one who can
help me." In general, however, she preferred to see me as merely the pre-
scriber of her drugs, although it was perplexing to her because she began to
see the converse also, i.e., how taking pills could legitimize her unacceptable
wish to continue seeing me: "I can't do this alone but what needs are you
really meeting? . . . I hate you sometimes. You are in my way."

Julie then became obsessed over the notion of genital mutilation and
female circumcision practiced in certain African cultures to ablate sexual
pleasure. Around this time, she found a written account of her rape but did
not remember writing it. The handwriting was unusual, also. It seemed like
it belonged to someone else, i.e., it was hers and not hers. She insisted that
the rape was not sexual and could not remember the pain of the intercourse.
She recalled, sadly, how, when freed by the rapist, she did not know whom
to call or what to say, "I just wanted to cry and be held. It wasn't my fault,

but maybe it would have been different if I hadn't reacted with such shock and horror.'' She then reported images of a man on top her, whom she was slashing with the same type of knife that cut her. She could not sleep without Thorazine at this time. Interestingly, she misplaced her medication again, which seemed to reflect not only a conflict over symptom relief, but also her ambivalence in the transference: "You are my best friend and my worst enemy! You are a reminder of the pain. . . . I hate you for having this knowledge.''

Julie became afraid to quit treatment and felt she needed to control me by staying my patient, believing that I would follow the rules as long as I was in the office. She dare not think what I might be like outside. The rapist was charming and safe while at the party, but he suddenly changed outside the safety of the room. But Julie was confused about his motivation because he said he wanted her to experience pleasure. So, was there a chance that she misinterpreted his intentions and judged him too harshly? However, he threatened to kill her, so how could she doubt herself under such dire conditions? The fact that she felt such uncertainty despite her intellectual awareness infuriated and demoralized her. She described growing up doubting her own perceptions and this problem obviously continued. She needed to get distance from the rape and from the analysis. Though she remembered his name, she simply referred to him as "Rapist" and her analyst simply as "Brenner." "I hate you for being in that movie theater. . . . You are just a man sitting behind me with a pen and paper annoying me,'' she said. I pointed out that she must have trusted me, at least enough to tell me that, and she eventually revealed that she felt absolutely vulnerable on the couch.

Soon after, she reported a dream: "I ran into you at a movie theater. You put tape over my mouth.'' Julie lamented that the rapist did not gag her to muffle her screams. Instead, he threatened to kill her if she made any sound, so she had to squelch everything all on her own. Now she wanted to scream—she wanted Primal Scream Therapy, as she described her ordeal in a depersonalized way. She commented on a burning sensation and the pain of their pelvic bones colliding during his violent thrusting, as she lay paralyzed and mute: "I turned into a statue.'' She began to feel mean and angry as her view of the assault became clearer. She wanted to expel me again, asking, "Do I really need you or are you just in the way? . . . I don't need my mother anymore, either.'' She wanted to flee treatment, uncharacteristically canceling an appointment, becoming very anxious again, and complaining that the drugs were not working. She felt that she was incurable and would drift off into trancelike states once again.

Eventually she became able to explore the autohypnotic nature of her dissociative withdrawal in the sessions, how she would fixate on an object or listen to the monotonous background noise and lose track of time. She would initially block out reality at will and then would become very distant from a process that was no longer under her control. At such times she felt like a spinning top when her feelings became intolerable, and she would be swept away into a dissociative reverie, feeling very unlike herself. Her conflict over having a baby soon reemerged, as she glumly concluded that, "It must be horrifying for me to want a man, or at least his semen to provide a baby. . . . Babies and rape, that's it all along," She then became convinced that the medication was dangerous and making her sick, so she wanted to stop it. She was afraid for it to be in her body. Julie then became confused, wondering if she had stayed on it in order to justify not getting pregnant, since she worried about fetal abnormalities. (I was reminded of the deterrent effect of antabuse for alcoholics.) She then felt very unsafe, becoming nauseous at the thought of any parallel between the rape and analysis. But, there she was on her back again, feeling forced to do something—this time it was to talk about things she did not want to talk about and to allow medication to enter her body.

Having relived some elements of the rape in the transference and survived, her analysis progressed. Several weeks later, she dreamt of her great uncle and recalled, longingly, how he would stroke her hair from behind. She adored him and still grieved for him, too. She made no comment this time about what the analyst was doing behind her. She then described her mother's handling of her hair, too, and became quite anxious. Everything had to be perfect, and she must sit completely still or her mother would go into a rage. She recalled feeling forced to sit everyday in very uncomfortable positions for long periods of time, paralyzed with fear while her hair would be combed, braided, and styled. She felt like a mannequin as she described her mother's ceaseless obsession with her hair and other parts of her body. She could not bear to think that this was the tip of the iceberg, as fears of recalling memories of incestuous touching made her feel "crazy" and very impulsive. Julie noted almost offhandedly how her old phobia to birds had improved over time, but their unpredictability, like her mother's, still terrified her. A bird could fly and land on top of her when she least expected it, and she wanted to deny the obvious symbolic significance.

Julie knew how imperative it was to talk about her "odd" relationship with mother, but her voice trailed off, and she could not continue. Once again, she was tormented by not being sure if I were helping or hurting her as she got deeper into treatment. She then reported a terrifying dream: "I was my age, sitting in my mother's old house. We were on the couch, but she was too close and was touching me. Someone said, 'Stop it!' and then mother went on a tirade." Julie felt haunted by this dream and cried about not being able to tolerate any physical closeness without having an urge to violently push her away. "It is as though she is all over me. . . . Was I abused?" she finally asked, incredulously. Julie was shocked and outraged by her suspicion, feeling terribly guilty and disloyal to finally share such fears with her analyst. Such things were to stay family secrets between mother and daughter, only. But she could not even dare to think that she might be blocking out horrible memories, even though it was a possibility which seemed more and more likely over time.

Julie then became angry that her mother wanted to share her Prozac. She felt like mother's little doll once again and had to obey her, knowing that she, too, was going through a personal crisis and needed her support. But Julie felt invaded and unable to even keep her pills as her own. Her mother wanted to hug her, also, and Julie passively let her, feeling depersonalized, helpless, and unable to resist. "I had to do it right, but why?" she asked, ambiguously. She agonized over new memories and flashbacks of the rape, once again, as though there was a layering of this trauma upon earlier violations of her body. "When you speak to me, it is like a chisel against a hard surface," she protested, alluding to her autohypnotic facade of stone which was starting to crack. She thought that her medicine was a crutch, as it provided her with comfort, soothing, and protection, while it kept her memories somewhat away from her consciousness. Everyone always wanted something from her—her mother, the rapist, and now her analyst. She, however, was sure that she only wanted one thing: "I want nothing from you, just your pills."

Again she noted how "our relationship is safe in this room . . . if it leaves it gets bigger . . . there are boundaries in here . . . out there, you are like anyone else." Julie initially thought that it was absurd that the medication might have psychological, not to mention sexual, implications, although she conceded that taking it did legitimize her attachment to me. She thought it was a strange kind of dependency. She then began to visualize a marble version of herself being raped, lying there rigidly with her mouth wide open, making no sound. She knew she must have been in pain, but she was encased in stone. "Until yesterday I kept sex away from the violence and pain." This connection overwhelmed her, feeling she needed more medication as she warned me, "I want you to stop thinking I want sex with you." She reported a dizziness which lasted for several days and was anxious about an upcoming break, predicting that when I returned she would feel depressed but would not miss me when I was gone.

Thereafter, she reported the following dream: "I was in my lover's apartment with my mother, my pets, and my little brother, who was a small child. There were huge blankets on all the walls. My lover was weaving the blankets from huge spools of yarn. I was lying on the bed naked, while the animals were getting tangled in the yarn. The pattern in the weave was of a fetus, like an ultrasound pattern. There were pieces of fruit like watermelon rind and bananas all over the sheets. The animals and my brother were getting into everything, and I was exasperated.'' It was rare for Julie to remember such a vivid dream, and she initially could not comment on her sexual vulnerability in the midst of the chaos, temporal confusion, and the presence of her mother. However, she was struck by the two kinds of colorful fruit neatly cut in circles. She wondered if bananas had seeds. ''Watermelon seeds, black specks, the fetus looked like a seed, an embryo . . . babies, children . . . all the seeds were so prominent in the dream.''

Several days later, when she asked for a renewal of her prescriptions, she was unusually defensive. ''It's become such a big deal to ask you for medicine. Though you have never told me to try it without medicine, you want me to make judgments I'm not capable of. When you say that my feelings about the medicine are a byproduct of our relationship, it annoys me.'' I then asked her what color her medication was. ''Green and ivory, the Prozac. Thorazine, a reddish pink, usually, with tiny black printing. That is a really stupid question, and I'm annoyed. What is your point?'' I quietly said, ''Colors . . . ,'' and Julie was startled. ''My dream! The fruit on the bed was that color!'' she exclaimed. ''You know, I'm curious why I haven't really tried to go off of it. Have I succumbed to it? Don't I want to deal with it? I could get more depressed if I have to go back on it and concluded that I really need it. But I am frightened about the idea of having children.'' I reminded her of the seeds in the fruit. ''Hhhhmmm . . . '' she said, ''I do think it's time to stop the medication!''

Shortly after the ''seed'' dream, she had an hour in which she acknowledged how it might not feel inappropriate to have erotic feelings, but not between a patient and her doctor. A sequence of anger, sex, sadness, and pleasure came to her mind as she agonized over how a traumatic event of such a short duration (i.e., her rape) could have had such a long-lasting impact. The next hour she reported decreasing her medication, having trouble sleeping, getting nervous, and being scared of ''getting more sad again.'' She was afraid of having to take medicine all the time. Here are some excerpts from that session:

J: I don't like coming here lately. I am very anxious. Sex is a hard thing to talk about. I don't want to talk about it, but it keeps coming up. I am not sure how or why. Your suggestion is that I'll never know. There is always something. Do I need drugs or was it the difficult issues? I'm pretty pessimistic . . . such a catch-22. It's odd taking medicine in order to sleep. Is it sleep deprivation that makes me deal not as well? But it's a difficult subject no matter what. I fear going off the medication and sinking into a great depression, but I'm not depressed right now. I didn't think I had a great concern; I never thought of the rape as sex before, but it seems ironic to me now

A: I wonder how you understand this change in your views.

J: Well . . . I can't bear the fact that I might look, find, feel any pleasure
        in it. And, if sex is pleasurable, which I thought it was, then it seems
        like I'd have to get to it. But the thought of it makes me really sad
        (crying). . . . I don't know what to do with that or what it has to do
        with anything. It was a really painful thing (silence). . . . I don't know
        what the point of it all is (very long silence). . . .

A: You have gotten silent. . . .

J: (She sounds distant and superficial) There is a speck of dirt up there
        that is driving me crazy . . . I don't know . . . I have nothing to say. . . .

A: At times like this, I get the impression you feel it would be easier to
        say nothing and just medicate it away (a recurrent issue that is very
        familiar to us, as the medication seemed to fortify her autohypnotic de-
        fenses).

J: (defensively and indignantly) I am "not" medicating it away, "but"
        I refuse to believe that it is just a screen. If that were the case, I would
        want to be drugged all the time. This really makes me angry!

A: Anger is part of that sequence you told me about. . . .

J: Anger, sex, and sadness . . . yes, but how do the drugs fit in? I've done
        the best I could for years with all that and it doesn't go away or get
        hidden by the medication. (During this denial, and her justification of
        her need for the pills, I associated to my young daughter's whining
        protests, clinging, and continued insistence on her need for her night-
        time pacifier.) And I still don't know how it is connected with my "se-
        quence."

A: It seemed like you got upset and your mind might have clicked off
        earlier when you got silent. And I know you get huffy whenever we
        talk about your medication.

J: You annoy me and I feel intruded upon, like with my mother. I don't
        want to talk about it. I don't know how. And, why would I want to
        talk about it with you? I don't even talk about it with myself . . . I am
        getting sad again . . . I can't really imagine it all . . . this sequence of
        feelings. I really don't know why I keep talking about this! I needed
        to go away . . . all this fear and pain . . . more fear and more pain
        . . . and what I might have been left with is that it might have felt
        good . . . I was just left there . . . lying there . . . I went through all this
        pain and fear . . . and then I have this orgasm . . . and it must have felt
        good . . . and then I was just there alone . . . that's what I ended with
        when it was over. That's a lot to take . . . I suppose it's hard to live
        with . . . pretty contradictory feelings . . . pleasure and pain . . . it's
        harder to live with the pleasure . . . I remember the pain easier . . . (it
        is now in the closing seconds of the hour) . . . Oh! I had a dream about

you last night. You had three boys . . . they were very little children, 5, 2, and a baby! But I don't remember the context. . . .

Subsequently, she became medication free for the next several years, and she did not become disabled from either depression or anxiety. Although she was prone to crying more, she was better able to tolerate it. Initially, she kept asking, "Am I going to have to feel all this sadness in order to work it through?" She felt as though there was a little child inside crying "I need my mommy. . . ." At this point, she seemed more prepared to explore her defensive altered states and could learn about them without the added confusion of sorting out the medication effect.

SUMMARY AND CONCLUSION

All three patients were on medication prior to intensive therapy and this pharmacotherapy assumed a central role in their earlier treatment. At best, their dissociative pathology was only partially ameliorated through the reduction of anxiety due to these agents. As described in case 1, medication and treatment for psychosis can be a dismal failure. In cases 2 and 3, medication was continued, adjusted, and monitored in accordance with good psychiatric practice, while engaging the patient in the development of a therapeutic alliance. Over time, as transferential phenomena arose and were addressed, the medication could be seen as an extension of this relatedness, serving as an intermediate object (Kestenberg, 1975), a transitional object (Winnicott, 1953), and a perceived expression of love. As treatment progressed, the patients were able to tolerate and "own" more of their psyches, resulting in integrative ego strengthening experiences derived from the working through of past traumas in the transference. In addition, developmental fixations appeared to be freed up, and crucial acquisitions, such as object constancy, seemed to be possible, decreasing the need to incorporate a piece of the analyst through ingesting of medication.

It is plausible to consider that such severely disturbed patients might not have been amenable to this form of therapy were it not for the use of psychoactive agents. However, the extent to which this population can approximate an analytic experience and resolve a transference neurosis seems to be highly individual and, at times, limited. The use of medication in the earlier, stabilizing, "preparatory" phase of treatment may last several years or continue intermittently throughout the course of an extended treatment lasting beyond a decade.

Chapter 10

INTERSUBJECTIVITY AND BEYOND

> Have I given you the impression that I am secretly inclined
> to support the reality of telepathy in the occult sense? If so,
> I should very much regret that it is so difficult to avoid
> giving such an impression. In reality, however, I was anx-
> ious to be strictly impartial. I have every reason to be so,
> for I have no opinion; I know nothing about it (!) [Freud,
> 1922, p. 220].

I have started and stopped writing this chapter numerous times. I quickly
realized how difficult it would be to write about working with traumatized
patients who seem to manifest that facet of mental functioning that pertains
to the realm of psi phenomena—clairvoyance, telepathy, out-of-body experiences, precognition, and other paranormal experiences. It is a subject that
has fascinated psychoanalysts since Freud (1899, 1901, 1919b, 1922, 1923a,
1925c, 1933) and, to a certain extent, has been demystified by our increased
understanding of the unconscious communication between analyst and analysand (Hitschmann, 1924, 1933; Deutsch, 1926; Roheim, 1932; Hollos, 1933;
Hann-Kende, 1933; Zulliger, 1934; Saul, 1938; Eisenbud, 1946; Pederson-
Krag, 1947; Fodor, 1947; Devereux, 1953a,b; Servadio, 1955). But, despite
the "minor epidemic" (Ellis, 1947) of papers in the literature in the post
World War II years, it has not been a subject of mainstream psychoanalytic
inquiry, and like other elusive, transient occurrences it is extremely difficult
to "prove."

It has been my observation, however, that when such incidents are reported in anecdotal form in case conferences, younger participants sit in
amazement while the more senior clinicians smile knowingly and quietly to

themselves. But, because many of the earlier papers had titles that included terms such as *occult* and *telepathy,* it may not be readily apparent that much of this work has laid the foundation for what is currently known as intersubjectivity. Recognizing this link, Mayer (1996) has recently attempted to rekindle interest by bringing to our attention the impressive body of research on "information transfer" that has been collected over the years by the Princeton Engineering Anomalies Project (PEAR) and by the Ganzfield Studies. She suggests that perhaps these findings need to be taken more seriously if we are to gain a fuller understanding of what is jointly created by the analytic dyad, i.e., "the central and defining features of what makes for a clinical psychoanalytic fact" (p. 711).

In my work with severely traumatized individuals, I have been struck by the frequency with which dissociative patients report such phenomena. Although considered by many to be further evidence of their "craziness" and often another area of their mental functioning which is concealed from the outside world, long-term therapy provides an important forum in which this "anomalous communication" emerges. In my experience, well over 50 percent report paranormal experiences, the most frequently being an autoscopic, out-of-body sensation which may or may not be associated with forms of information transfer. Interestingly, these "symptoms" bear a resemblance to what has been well-described in near death experiences (NDE) (Pfister, 1930; Stratton, 1957; Hunter, 1967; Moody, 1975; Kletti and Noyes, 1981; Greyson, 1981a,b, 1983a,b, 1997; Ring, 1981, 1982, 1988, 1991; Kohr, 1982, 1983; Sabom, 1982; Gabbard and Twemlow, 1984; Raft and Andresen, 1986; Groth-Marnat, 1989; Sutherland, 1989; Spiegel and Cardena, 1991; Irwin, 1992, 1994; Owens, 1995). These reports come from such people who, for example, have had cardiac arrests and have been resuscitated, or those who have even been pronounced dead and somehow were spontaneously revived. The generally accepted components are a pervasive sense of peace or euphoria, a belief of returning to life, an out-of-body experience, movement through a tunnel, contact with unearthly beings, and a review of one's life. In some instances, out-of-body experiences have also been reported during severe pain, such as in childbirth, where there was no life-threatening crisis (Ring and Lawrence, 1993; Lawrence, 1995). When these phenomena, which may be inseparable from or in fact may be merely "symptoms," emerge in the treatment situation, they may evoke strong feelings in the analyst.

Analysis of one's countertransference, an indispensable component of any treatment, is especially important in this population (Devereux, 1953a, b), since the "paranormal" would be the result of those mutual influences affecting both analyst and analysand. But, while the literature is expanding with contributions about intersubjectivity (Stolorow, Brandchaft, and Atwood, 1983; Jacobs, 1991; Aron, 1991, 1996; Ehrenberg, 1992; Bader, 1993;

Renik, 1993, 1995; Greenberg, 1995; Levinson, 1996), I suspect that many authors will continue to tread lightly around this outer edge of the realm of unconscious communication. But, patients severely traumatized in childhood may manifest autohypnotic hypervigilance (Shengold, 1989), an exceptional awareness and sensitivity to external stimuli. And, this hypervigilance in an altered state may be on a continuum with what has been considered extrasensory perception. Although this propensity may seem to have great survival value in a world of danger, it may not be experienced by the patient as a desirable capacity that can necessarily be turned on and off at will. Indeed, it may have been felt as a loathsome curse. There may also be a genetic component, as seen in generations of women in the same family (Orloff, 1996). Its manifestation within the transference can be a profoundly intense experience, especially when the patient's perceptions of the analyst are highly personal, accurate, and seemingly in the realm of the uncanny.

Many technical dilemmas arise, which I will describe in my work with a patient with "multiple personality." A differential diagnosis of delusions of grandeur and paranoia versus hypnotic suggestion and mutual regression, versus dynamically significant extrasensory perception were all considered. Through reconstructive work and countertransference analysis, it was then hypothesized that this patient experienced a near death experience at the age of 6. A condensation of this trauma was thought to have become incorporated into a child personification who seemed to display these "special powers." I will address some of the issues that accompanied the challenge of working with such an individual, especially those pertaining to boundaries, neutrality, personal disclosure, and the need to be open-minded but not naive. This type of intercommunication provided an important opportunity to put the more mundane aspects of transference–countertranference nonverbal communication into a broader context (Stein, 1965; McLaughlin, 1981).

CASE REPORT

Initial Presentation

MaryLou, a biracial woman in her late twenties, was referred to me in a suicidal crisis. She had a history of longstanding sexual abuse by her stepfather and had recently won a legal decision against a physical therapist for sexual misconduct with her. It was an ordeal which had completely depleted her. Despite the admiration of women's groups, close friends, and family members who lauded her heroic effort to get justice, she was left feeling that she had totally destroyed a man who had proclaimed his love for her. Because of severe and mysterious medical symptoms which took several years to diagnose due to fluctuating endocrine, autoimmune, and autonomic symptoms,[1] she consulted many specialists, was subjected to extensive, painful testing, and had had several operations. During this ordeal, she became sexually involved with one of her team of consultants and decompensated. Counseling was of no help to her and she rejected any more professional help. But she further deteriorated and had a traumatizing psychiatric hospitalization, which left her even more hopeless. After a period of time, she felt she simply had no choice but to die. In deference to her family and as an expression of the last chance she would ever give the medical profession, she flatly stated that she wanted help either in the form of real psychiatric care or physician-assisted suicide. I was surprised, given the history, that after only one meeting she confidently said she thought she could work with me and would give a safety contract not to harm herself until our next appointment. Aside from the obvious acute distress she was feeling, I was impressed by her very engaging nature and her very high intelligence. I felt quite empathic to her plight and was extremely aware of the enormous challenge that her situation presented.

As the history initially unfolded, MaryLou cited the onset of her problems in adulthood to the birth of her son and his life-threatening perinatal complications. This crisis totally consumed her while her stepfather was dying of a degenerative neurologic disease. As though one had to die in order to make room for one to be born, she felt there was a link between the birth and death of these two people who were so vital to her. She insisted on bringing her newborn back home before the doctors thought it was safe, as she was convinced that he would die of neglect, unless she were able to be by his side twenty-four hours a day. She recalled feeling strange at the time, staring off into space, somewhat depersonalized, and, in retrospect, overly identified with her baby. And, while she was sitting vigil for him, her stepfather's condition rapidly deteriorated, and he died much sooner than she imagined possible, leaving her in shock. In fact, she did not allow herself to accept the prognosis that he had been mortally ill, despite what she had seen and heard from the doctors. As a result, she felt that if only she had been there during his terminal event that somehow she could have prevented his demise and therefore blamed herself for his death. Her guilt became all-consuming, and she was not able to stop grieving for her stepfather, the only father she had ever known.

Persistent insomnia, nightmares, and tremendous anxiety accompanied a pathological grief reaction which may have been the initial presentation of

---

[1]This constellation of symptoms is quite prevalent among patients with severe dissociative psychopathology, and I, at times, have seen them in more than 60 percent of the population on a Dissociation Disorder Unit.

her dissociative disorder (Putnam, 1989). But, her psychophysiologic symptoms prevailed and she got caught up in a modern medical nightmare of endless diagnostic workups. Her vulnerability and desperate need for loving forgiveness were exploited during this helpless time. I felt sickened by her account of the seduction, which began with undue curiosity about her sexuality and progressive physical comforting during her physical therapy. There was no doubt in her mind about what had happened, but much doubt about *why* it happened and whose "fault" it was. She was confused to think that a health care provider, rather than trying to help her, fell in love with her instead. Or was he lying about his love and in reality the opportunistic predator that many perceived him to be? Was she irresistible to certain men and, if so, what was she doing wrong? How could she ever make up for all the damage she had caused without fully realizing it? After all, she seemed able to live essentially two separate lives, "knowing and not knowing" about her absolutely dedicated family life while being unable to resist this man's overtures. She even told him about her never forgotten incestuous relationship with her stepfather, crying and begging that she be freed from his domination, yet feeling a sense of life-threatening abandonment at the thought of his breaking off their affair. Mercilessly trapped and hopelessly repeating her secret enslavement by her stepfather in this progressively destructive involvement, she eventually started to unravel. Amnestic periods, auditory hallucinations, wild mood swings, suicidal impulses, a sense of impending disaster, and an exacerbation of medical symptoms brought her to a series of new doctors who tried to make a correct diagnosis but did not grasp the significance of her dissociative symptoms. She was eventually hospitalized where the diagnosis of multiple personality was made, and while there was reportedly exposed to a number of patients who claimed to be victims of various kinds of organized abuse. She was not sure if the therapists were planting these ideas in the patients' heads but felt a bizarre sense of belonging despite her abject terror. Having attributed her own survival to a rebelliousness and stubborn streak that was rarely totally extinguished, she marshalled her strength to bring charges against her former perpetrator and to extricate herself from this treatment system. She was reverberating from all of these issues when we first met.

Initial Intersubjective Response

The opportunity to undo the harm that had been visited upon her by the professionals, to help her find the strength to live, and to successfully treat what, by the history, sounded like a rather severe dissociative disorder, evoked many feelings within me. By the time I had met this patient, I had already worked intensively with a number of severely traumatized individuals, but each time I experienced the uniqueness and overwhelming magnitude of their problems, it would sadden and unsettle me. I wondered if I could truly help them or indeed how much they could be helped at all by our usual treatment methods. And certainly here, I could not help but wonder if she could ever work through such a breach of professional trust which had been heaped upon what was beginning to sound like a profoundly disturbed childhood. While I tried to be realistic about my own limitations, I also felt that I had at least as good a chance as anyone I knew to be of help. Working with a suicidal victim of cruelty and exploitation, who is exhausted, depleted, hopeless, in supreme mental pain, and does not think she can survive another day is an utterly profound experience. I have become quite aware how it elicits my rescuer identifications, and I find myself intensely involved, immediately trying to make contact with the patient's ego in order to bolster her waning will to survive. The utmost priority becomes the development of an alliance with the life-preserving forces in the mind while being mindful of those aspects of my own psychology which draw me into helping someone to fight on and live even when she sees no meaning in life. Without making false promises or being an idealistic cheerleader, I nevertheless do try to reason, bargain, encourage, or otherwise convey a sense that there might be another way out besides death by one's own hand. When appropriate, I incorporate a "safety contract," eliciting a promise not to give in to self-destructive impulses without informing me and giving us a chance to discuss it first. If necessary, this contract is ratified at each session, and if not able to be honored, may result in an emergency hospitalization if our work is to continue. I would then see the patient throughout the hospital stay, ensuring continuity throughout the crisis. My initial meeting with MaryLou brought up these feelings to a great degree, and they were a harbinger of things to come, as her preoccupation with loss and death were all pervasive.

Clinical Course

Our work for the first several years was stormy. Chaos and anxiety prevailed with literally scores of hospitalizations lasting anywhere from overnight to several weeks at a time. A profound rapprochementlike transference reaction of clinging and darting (Mahler, 1967) was enacted in this exhausting way. Tremendous inner turmoil was experienced as countless inner people screaming at her to be heard, such as terrifying voices instructing her on how to kill herself, others telling her she was a crazy liar, still others criticizing her in most degrading ways, and most prevalent of all, the inner crying of young children. She brought in a "map" of her alters which was drawn up prior to our work, in which an exceedingly complex inner system of over a hundred selves existed in various strata of her psyche. These personifications had various functions which included holding onto certain traumatic presumed memories in order to protect MaryLou, "herself," from their knowledge. In addition, they were of all different ages, both sexes, and some even had apparently specialized functions or attributes, such as mathematical ability, artistic talents, gourmet cooking, delivery of childcare, and knowledge of foreign languages. Internal drive and affective states seemed to be localized or tolerated by some and not others, resulting in frequent "switching" which often left the patient feeling as though her mind were like a slot machine with the lever pulled—she never knew how she would end up. Her observing ego and insight were quite variable, so that sometimes she could comprehend that her altered states were all manifestations of her own mind. At other times, however, the need to keep things separate and disowned was so great that she felt genuinely possessed by demonic spirits. One of the most frightening, mysterious, and unreachable of these parts was "the dead child," who we did not learn more about until much later. Significantly, numerous neuroleptics had been tried, all of which did not stop these Schneiderian First Rank symptoms (Kluft, 1987b) and usually caused dysphoric side effects. She had been diagnosed with a so-called "polyfragmented" type of multiple personality disorder. This variant implied such a degree of disintegration that any thoughts of treatment based on the then in vogue notion of hypnotically fusing her parts together would have been as challenging as trying to glue a shattered glass back together. In contrast, however, I thought I sensed a hidden ego strength in MaryLou's insistence that she did not believe in a hypnotherapy cure, and in her fleeting but confident awareness that "everyone" was essentially "all her" even though it did not feel like her most of the time. It was as though, despite the prevailing wisdom of the times that she had a rather dismal prognosis, the fleeting presence of what I have come to think of as a type II "it's not me!" self (see chapter 8) was a ray of good news. I, however, did not delude myself or her into thinking that treatment would be easy, short term, or even necessarily successful, but I did think that it might be possible if given the chance.

Development of a therapeutic alliance was the initial challenge, which continued to be the single most important aspect of the treatment process throughout. Because of her perceptual acuity and the boundary violation in a previous treatment, she was exquisitely sensitive to any comment, body movement, facial expression, gesture, or change in the tone of my voice, wondering what it might have meant. Not infrequently early on, I was confronted by her in a panic to try to explain why I had said what I did the way I did or why I would have asked about certain issues. I was aware at times of feeling as though I were undergoing a cross-examination and believed that unless she received as full an explanation as possible for my behavior, she would not be able to tolerate the anxiety of her justifiable apprehension. While I certainly realized that perhaps she had many other underlying reasons for her curiosity and her at times defiant insistence on answers, I sensed that we would never get to that point unless I could openly and nondefensively address her questions. I was able to maintain an empathic position by reminding myself of her disastrous life experiences and at times felt like I had become a spokesman for the whole medical profession. Whenever she sensed that I might have become impatient with her incessant need for reassurance about this or any other issue, our hard fought and very fragile alliance seemed to evaporate instantaneously. Repairing what she perceived as my many lapses in compassion was a major theme of our early work, as her gaping narcissistic wounds were just under the surface of "whoever" might have been out at any given moment.

Given the profound injury she sustained with a former caregiver, Mary-Lou, once again, undoubtedly felt entitled to know as much as possible about me in order to feel safe. Despite her initial leap of faith, which eroded quickly, she felt she needed to know about my personal and professional background in order to make sure that I was reasonably satisfied in my life, and experienced enough to truly help her.

Anything short of directly answering her questions was liable to shatter our rapport, despite my repeated attempts to explain and her intellectual understanding that indeed I might just have a clinical rationale not to disclose certain things to her at that time. Her sense of deserving and expecting access to any information about me was profound. At the time, she felt there simply should be no secrets from her. She worried that there was perhaps a manipulative, underlying motive on my part, and this suspicion needed to be addressed along with her very deep insult over feeling excluded or not trusted. She was not always amenable to reason in this state of mind, so when I felt strongly enough about setting a limit and maintaining a boundary on whatever the issue was at any given moment, there was often an explosion of her rage, after which she frequently became contrite within a few days. I postulated that her insatiable need for access was related to both repeated early deprivation with an unavailable but intrusive mother and her incestuous world with her stepfather where she was privy to all of his secrets. Her earliest memory was of being in her crib crying in terror for her mother who left the window open while she spent time next door. The patient's exhausted screams reassured her mother of her well-being, and mother would periodically yell back and tell her to shut up.

The intensity of her transferential feelings as well as her commitment to treatment waxed and waned as she continued to wrestle with deep issues. Object constancy at times seemed nonexistent, such that our five times a week schedule did not provide enough continuity for her to believe that I would really be there the next day. It was necessary at such times to speak to her on the telephone. Aggressively derived affects and altered states left her feeling totally abandoned, hated, unloved, and in desperate need of reminder that I would still be there for her. Her conviction that she was hated by her mother, had killed her stepfather, and had destroyed her former lover made her feel that anyone she had become close to would be destroyed.

Material eventually emerged in various altered states accompanied by deep visceral responses and searing affects which enabled her to piece together a macabre jigsaw puzzle. With the help of medical records, she confirmed a deep-seated fear that she had become pregnant by her stepfather and undergone a late-term abortion in adolescence. She was convinced that the baby was alive at birth and died shortly thereafter, which lent absolute certainty in her mind that she was indeed a murderer. She understood her decompensation over her newborn's health problems much better but was tortured with guilt, nonetheless. Not only could she never repent for her "misdeeds," but how could she protect her loved ones from her destructiveness yet get the loving nurturance she desperately craved? Any wish for a loving response in treatment filled her with such mortal dread that she sought to end treatment as soon as possible.

After a period of adequate functioning, she was convinced that she was better. She thought perhaps that she had been the victim of a well-intentioned therapeutic regimen which nevertheless implanted a belief system about multiple personalities. Since "they" were not in evidence once she broke free from our daily sessions, it must have all been a mistaken diagnosis. I was pleasantly surprised but somewhat puzzled at her apparent capacity to seal over the difficulties and carry on with her life; I did not push too hard during our progressively infrequent meetings, as her functioning was a primary goal at this time. All seemed to be well until her son had an accident which could have been life-threatening and she decompensated again. By her own admission she "broke apart" and desperately wanted to resume intensive treatment. Furthermore, there was something about her mind that she had not told me before.

REVELATIONS OF EXTRASENSORY PERCEPTION

I know things about you I shouldn't know! I don't want to invade your privacy, but someone is telling me all about your childhood. I must be crazy, please tell me I have delusions of grandeur, that I do not have this power—it terrifies me! I can't stop it, now—I am getting images of your childhood—there was a death; you as a young boy crying out reaching for your mother; so sad; where is your father? A certain melancholy that you lapse into. Am I right? *Am* I right? Tell me if I'm wrong. Please tell me. I am going crazy. It is as if I can peer into your soul! All of a sudden I am finding out things about you. I know you are a private person, but it is as if someone inside me is saying, "You have been afraid, knowing that you can do these things all your life and now I will prove it to you. This is really the source of your problems." Am I crazy? And there are other things I have not wanted to tell you about. I have dreams of murders and other violent events in great detail before they reach the newspaper. My family will verify it. I know about. . . . Can this be for real or is someone inside playing tricks on me, trying to drive me crazy? Tell me if I am right, please? There are these things, too—I can make things happen . . . appliances and lights at home turn on without my touching anything, especially when I'm all pent up with frustration and get it out.

The next hour during a time of such difficulty articulating her bewilderment, she made an exasperated hand gesture at nearly the same time the lights in my office got very bright due to a momentary power surge. She was sure her hand gestures preceded the power surge. The two events were so close in time and happened so quickly that I told her I really wasn't sure which I noticed first, although I thought I sensed the power surge first. At this point I felt slightly disappointed that I could not confirm the temporal relationship she experienced, and was even tempted to ask her for a demonstration of her psychokinetic powers. I was struck by the choice of items that I contemplated asking her to move with her mental energy—a box of tissues on the table—would they move closer or farther away from her. I mused, as I realized that my fantasy was related to her difficulty in crying which usually manifested itself as a surge of affect, percolating up from deep inside of her in the closing moments of the hour, when she would have to rush out of the office before having to use any of these tissues.

My initial doubts notwithstanding, I was struck again when my lights surged brighter during a time she had frantically tried to call me and got a busy signal. When she eventually got through, she said she had been trying to reach me, and was feeling very pent up again. Knowing that, of course, there was "no proof" of any cause–effect relationship to these events, I was concerned about feeding into her overinterpreting these confluent events if I shared all my observations with her (Devereux, 1953b). Nevertheless, I made a mental note of such not infrequent occurrences.

MaryLou's revelation about these "powers" did not come until several years of treatment, after a tumultuous and extended initial phase characterized by her desperate flight to avoid becoming attached. She was terrified also, that she would have been certified totally insane if this secret were to come out and had hoped to completely avoid it. The family myth was that her great grandmother was psychic, and she trembled at the prospect of such an inherited predisposition (Orloff, 1996). She recoiled at the notion that she indeed had special "powers," feeling more cursed and tortured by her nightmares, visions, and voices instead. She never quite knew what it all meant until bad news confirmed her sixth sense. I noticed a pattern in our sessions in which this aspect of her psychic functioning seemed to get activated. The first time it happened, she was describing her progressive feeling of weakness, infirmity, and helplessness during a recent medical hospitalization of life-threatening urgency. Were it not for her husband's presence and his assertiveness, she feared she would not have been taken seriously and might have died. The second time she described how exposed, humiliated, and naked she felt when her mother would berate her in front of others. In the midst of her descriptions of each of these ordeals, when she was feeling so completely weak, helpless, and at the mercy of others, she stopped abruptly and seemed to go into an altered state. Then, as though she were possessed and listening to her internal voices, her dazed look was abruptly transformed into a fixed piercing stare, making eye contact with me for what felt like a very long time, as she "peered" into my soul. Initially, I felt uneasy with the intensity of her most unusual look suddenly fixed upon me, wondering what in fact she could or would learn about me. I felt as though it were against my will, as if I were being penetrated by a powerful force that could almost extract things from within me. My neutrality and analytic anonymity seemed like a flimsy, silly, and useless "protection" from this woman who seemed to switch from being in a weakened state to one exuding a remarkable strength, sudden energy, and an air of knowing things about me that she "should not" have known. But, what did she really know or was there something I wanted her to know?

The abrupt reversal of her mental state was quite striking, resulting in amnesia and derailment of her thought processes. I, therefore, was mindful of the defensive aspect (Saul, 1938) of this involuntary deployment of her telepathic gaze, which I pointed out at a later time. For the moment though, I let myself regress as much as I could at the time but wondered if I were being manipulated in some way. If so, what did she want me to think she knew? Why was I reacting so peculiarly to her shifting ego state? Was I succumbing to a hypnotic suggestion that she could read my mind?

While I was caught off-guard the first time it happened, I sensed a certain dread when I anticipated it happening again. MaryLou sensed my uneasiness and asked me if I had become afraid. Not waiting for an answer, she reassured me in a very loving, maternal way, that it really was "okay." I felt somewhat shaken up after the first hour, reflecting on the experience and found myself ambivalently associating to her vision of me as a very sad young boy. While I realized that what she "saw" was so general and would have undoubtedly applied to anyone's childhood at some point, I also realized that I was resisting my own self-analysis at that moment out of a fear of confirming that she was indeed psychic!

When I recognized this resistance, I was then freely able to associate and found myself reflecting on the hot summer night as a boy, when my maternal uncle, a young man in his twenties, died of an inoperable brain tumor. The anguished grief we all shared that night welled up in me again as it has at various times throughout my life and in my analysis. While I had "dealt with it" already, I was reminded quite abruptly of how much unresolved grief I still had for him. It was the worst day of my mother's life, and my father, while certainly upset, did not grieve to the same extent that she did. In a sense, he receded at that moment, when I cried in my mother's arms. What, if anything, did it mean for my mind to be drawn to the senseless death of my uncle at such a young age? What I might have been resonating with and how it might further my understanding of MaryLou was rather unclear, so I let it go for the time being.

I then felt I regained my analytic equilibrium and was ready to see the patient the next day. I had no idea whether she would have had any recollection of what had transpired in the previous session since she had lapsed into an altered state and was often hazy about such sessions. She was apprehensive, tentative, and apologetic, desperately wanting a diagnosis regarding her sanity or her psychic ability. She insisted that validation of her telepathic insights was essential, not just out of curiosity but for her own reality testing. Once again, her need for access came to the fore and now it appeared that there was another factor contributing to it.

I carefully considered what she said and told her that there was some accuracy to her reading, but decided not to elaborate for fear of burdening her with my own story at that time. She then proceeded to tell me that certain electrical devices would activate in her presence and how these appliances would turn on or off before she went to operate them. Sometimes, just the intent was enough to make things happen. At such times, it was quite understandable that if she believed in these occurrences, she would be terrified of the power of her thoughts. This omnipotence of thought made her feel quite insane at times and she was utterly horrified to disclose this information, which was a mundane occurrence for her family by this point. Some peculiarity in the wiring of her home was thought to be the reason. Unable to elaborate any further, she identified with the main character in a movie about a man who had undergone a transformation, developing superintelligence, telepathic, clairvoyant, and psychokinetic abilities. Sounding quite paranoid, and even more crazy to herself, she became too self-conscious about proceeding, but was tormented by an inner voice belonging to that most mysterious alter known as the "dead child."

I had heard about this inside dead child early on in the patient's treatment, during some of her most regressed moments in the hospital. At those times, the patient seemed especially frightened, confused, and unable to consider letting me know more about this part of her mind. It took little prodding for me to remember that very turbulent time where grief, enormous anxiety, and uncontrollable lapses into altered states propelled the patient through the revolving door of the hospital as she tried to run away before getting too entrenched in therapy. While I was reflecting on this early time in our work, I became aware of the coincidence that the man in the movie who developed special powers died of an inoperable brain tumor just like my uncle, and I wondered if I would ever understand what meaning, if any, all this had.

But, apparently there was more to come as it was time for me to learn about the "dead child." MaryLou strongly felt that this personification had died a long time ago and did not let herself dwell on the seeming contradiction of being alive herself and having a dead person living inside. As we spoke, however, she realized that since the "dead one" was talking to her and making her presence known, then she, too, must be alive. Also, in order to reconcile the confusion, MaryLou then wondered if it meant that she has been dead and then came back to life. It made no sense to her, but it was clear that the dead child was different from all the others in ways that absolutely terrified her. She apparently was the one who knew about what was in others' minds, had visions about the future, and could even move things. It was too bizarre to be true and no wonder this aspect of her mind had to be kept the most secret of all. As we were in the midst of her disclosures, a short, planned break was imminent.

I had asked MaryLou to meet a little earlier the day before this interruption, and she complied without any hardship on her part. As we were in the midst of a discussion of a very frightening, nightmarish experience involving airplanes and getting lost as a very young girl, she abruptly stopped and listened intently inside. She then turned to me with that piercing stare and declared that she was just told that I was about to catch a plane. Furthermore, she stated that I was going north and going to talk to a group of doctors about "multiple personality." By this time, I was more accustomed to her sudden revelations about me, but I nevertheless was a bit taken aback (Hollos, 1933; Devereux, 1953a) by her accuracy, which I confirmed to her this time. Admittedly, she could have logically deduced a lot from our meeting a little earlier, my being dressed a little better than usual, and my possibly being a bit preoccupied during our session (Hann-Kende, 1933), but she took it a step further. She reportedly "heard" about my imminent mode of transportation, destination, and purpose from an inner voice belonging to her "dead child" alter.[2]

MaryLou then went into an uncharacteristically detailed description of how she sensed that I clear my mind in the beginning of our sessions, listen evenly and openly to what she tells me, and then allow my own thoughts to emerge. It was those emerging thoughts that the "dead child" was able to discern at certain times. She also told me that I, too, was like her in this regard, but since our lives were different my powers did not develop the way hers did. I listened very carefully to her. MaryLou just "knew" that I was leaving immediately after our session for the airport and feared for my safety, although she had no premonitions of disaster. She then went back to her earlier thoughts about some very bad and frightening experiences as a young child. As we ended the session, she pinpointed a certain time, the summer before entering first grade, when her mother gave birth to a set of twins. For reasons that were never remembered or explained to her, she started school several months late and discovered that fact many years later when coming across her old report cards. The "dead child" told MaryLou that she died at that time. I felt puzzled and quite aware of the patient's anxiety over the interruption in treatment which I thought might have been expressed in this cryptic way.

As MaryLou anticipated, I did leave for the airport immediately after the session, and while I was sitting on the plane, I calculated that the mysterious period of time in MaryLou's young life corresponded to the same summer that my uncle had died! I then realized that the main character in the movie that haunted her was a condensation of my uncle and MaryLou's "dead child" alter, i.e., a man with an inoperable brain tumor who developed extrasensory perception and tragically died as a young man. While these connections were obviously my own creation, given the nature of our communication at this time, I was reminded of Jung's notion of synchronicity and the possibility of the importance of that summer for MaryLou, also. During this time, I had a dream in which the patient was very, very worried about the mental condition of one of her cousins. The cousin was thought to have manic–depressive illness, but I reassured MaryLou that it was a misdiagnosis and that she was not that seriously ill. I had recalled the dream prior to her hour, wrote a brief notation about reassuring her, and went about

---

[2]These occurrences were not rare. For example, prior to another break several months later, she believed that I was going to "Stanford" or "Sanford" because she saw a black and white sign with the name on it. I did not refute this prediction although that was not my destination, and when I arrived at the ticket counter at the airport I encountered a rather inept agent whose slowness began to annoy me. As I was about to exhort him, I noticed that he was wearing a black and white name plate, "Mr. Sanford," and just smiled to myself, wondering if this were the sign that MaryLou had "seen."

my clinical work. At the appointed hour, MaryLou arrived in an agitated state. She blurted out that her niece had developed obsessive–compulsive symptoms which had greatly worried her sister. Numerous telephone calls had taken place the night before, as the patient was drawn into this crisis. MaryLou was overwhelmed and deeply worried herself, seeking reassurance from me that her niece was not afflicted with a major ailment. Feeling that I somehow had anticipated this conversation, I did not know whether a disclosure at this time would further confirm her belief that I, too, had some of this "thing," but I needed more time to self-analyze what it all meant. What I did know at the time was that it seemed as though we were tuned into each other's "wavelengths," so I felt I needed to be mindful of this additional dimension to our communication and mental constructs.

More material emerged about her childhood which centered around heightened maternal neglect and obliviousness after the birth of twins. Already feeling like the ugly duckling of the family, her brand new brother and sister bore the desired familial traits, and she was totally eclipsed. With the exception of her stepfather's drunken rages and beatings following ever more sexual demands, she felt she had no acknowledgment of or purpose for her existence.

The patient became progressively more preoccupied with death again and reported several episodes of nearly falling from heights, cutting herself quite severely, and almost swallowing handfuls of pills while in altered states. She then reported a dream in exquisite detail which left her with a sense of revelation, profound understanding, and a vision of the future. In the dream, she was driving at night and had a serious accident with a large green truck, where she went over an embankment. She was carried from the car but protested because she did not get a chance to say goodbye to her family. She was told it would be a year before she could see them again. She seemed to be flying above the accident scene and was taken to a place where a council of men asked her many questions about her life which she answered honestly. She felt she passed the test and was ushered through one of two doors where she went to a place of great beauty, light, and peace. She felt no pain or sense of her body, experiencing a sense of freedom, acceptance, and total love. When she awoke, she felt she had been on an indescribable journey beyond life and was shown the mysteries of God and the afterlife. She experienced a most unusual serenity and tranquility, as though a certain inevitable path had been shown to her in which everything was the way it was supposed to be. Her dream was remarkably similar to the description of a near-death experience, and she spoke with such conviction that it seemed to drown out my being able to listen for the usual dynamic themes (Devereux, 1953a,b). Because MaryLou was convinced that it was prophetic in some way, we were not able to go any further than the manifest content, and after several days it was forgotten about in the midst of more painful childhood reminiscences.

About two weeks later, she reported the onset of an ominous symptom—reckless driving. As though someone else would come out and take over the wheel, she felt depersonalized and almost possessed while driving at a very high rate of speed. She would come back to "herself" just in the nick of time in order to avoid a collision, but felt that her luck was running out. In an effort to help her gain some understanding and hopefully better control of this increasingly dangerous situation, I told her that I thought perhaps it was related to feelings about her childhood she was as yet unable to express in any other way. She reported hearing voices of children crying out for help and was told that the "dead child" was behind this frightening symptom. I decided it was imperative to address this "dead child" directly at this point, feeling that the risk of reifying a personification was outweighed by the risk of a self-fulfilling prophecy (Merton, 1949).

I told the "dead child" that I was very aware of her presence and desperate need to express herself, hoping that if she knew she could participate in therapy, then she perhaps could slow down and drive more carefully, having already drawn attention to her plight. Essentially, I reminded MaryLou that she was free to express herself in any altered ego state that she experienced but that the same ground rules still applied, i.e., communication in words and feelings, but not self-destructive action.

Apparently, whatever material was related to this "dead child" evoked intense internalized aggression which MaryLou disowned and relegated to this mysterious personification. The "dead child" acknowledged having heard my invitation and told MaryLou that she would think about not interfering with her driving. I was feeling slightly optimistic about this intervention and suddenly remembered her dream about the car accident, which on one level seemed like a dissociated suicidal wish. I debated with myself whether to remind her about it, not knowing once again, if I were merely feeding into some quasidelusional belief about her having precognitive ability. Having considered this possibility, I did decide to remind her, hoping it would help her regain control by pointing out the existence of an unconscious, self-destructive wish in her dream two weeks before the onset of her reckless driving. MaryLou heard me but said little at the time, and the session ended uneventfully. An hour later, I received a frantic message that she narrowly avoided smashing into a pile-up of cars but was okay and would tell me more tomorrow. The next day, she reported that when she left the session something very strange had happened. While driving home, she ran into an unexpected downpour, and it became very dark—almost like night time. A large green truck suddenly sped by her, and a few moments later a car in front of her lost control, resulting in a series of rear-end collisions. Were she not driving slowly and carefully this time, she would not have had the time to react and avoid joining the wreckage. As she swerved away in horror, she noticed that the pileup was at the edge of an embankment.

MaryLou was convinced beyond the shadow of a doubt that she had visualized this accident scene in her dream. The green truck, the embankment, and the darkness were identical. The obvious major difference was that she was not a casualty, having seen one version of the future in her dream (Freud, 1899; Zulliger, 1934; Servadio, 1955) but creating an alternate scenario after our discussion in the session. MaryLou credited me with saving her life and expressed such profound gratitude that I was quite moved. She was absolutely certain that she was to have died in that accident but had actively altered her fate (Ring, 1988; Punzak, 1990; Litton, 1990) by driving cautiously that day. Her preoccupation with death continued unabated, however. She pledged appreciation and love, feeling forever indebted to me for my assistance in helping her see a dream of the future just in time to change it. At this point, she allowed the slim possibility that she might have a future and thought that she could trust me enough to use the couch. Up until this point, I had answered her questions about the use of the couch and was neutral about her own interest in it for her treatment.

From then on, MaryLou used the couch, permitting herself to say whatever came to mind with a freedom and openness which was unprecedented in our work. As I got to know this "dead child" part of herself better, we kept coming back to that fateful summer where it sounded more and more as if she might have sustained a life-threatening injury as a child. I had heard bits and pieces of several stories which were consistent with neglect and accidental injury. She had made several references to falling into her neighbor's pool, after which she awoke in a hospital. This even became part of the family folklore which was told nonchalantly and apparently was known by her neighbors, also. Her own "memory" had first emerged in piecemeal fashion in various altered states of consciousness and was expressed with a peculiar blend of disconnected numbness and terror. She described an out-of-body experience in a hospital where she was on the ceiling watching a doctor and a nurse trying to get her to breathe and apparently giving up on her. She tried to call out to them, but they did not hear her as they walked away from her lifeless little body connected to tubes, wires, and an I.V. At this point, she made the link between this dreamlike revelation of herself at age 6, with her panic over seeing her newborn son connected to monitoring equipment, and her insistence that he would die in the hospital unless she went against medical advice and took him home immediately. In addition, she intuitively felt that her mysterious medical problems were linked also. Following these connections, I offered the reconstruction that perhaps she had experienced a near-death experience at age 6 as a result of the life-threatening drowning. And, as a result she, as is known to occur in children, too (Bush, 1983; Gabbard and Twemlow, 1984), may have felt as though she left her body and experienced something similar to what she reported in the car accident dream. Furthermore, I hypothesized, after she got revived and recuperated perhaps she was left with a "dead child" alter who encapsulated some of these sensations and memories. In addition, maybe the "dead child" also became the repository of whatever familial tendency there was for extra-sensory perception, which may have become potentiated by an early brush with death. In addition, I supported her impression that there was reactivation of early trauma in her later medical crisis. As a result, her very mysterious and seemingly supernatural little inside creature may have been borne of trauma and was essential to the treatment process also. MaryLou, along with the "dead child," listened very intently and seemed to agree with this formulation.

After many weeks of working through memories, feelings, and a deeper consideration of this possibility, the "dead child" decided that she indeed must truly be alive and must, therefore, be a part of MaryLou. They gradually became "closer" and less dissociated from each other. The "dead child" preferred to be called "young MaryLou" from then on, and, interestingly, the telepathic experiences diminished greatly, except during times of great anxiety in the transference or in anticipation of ominous events affecting her loved ones. Significantly, a most intense, ambivalent paternal transference then came to the fore in which boundary and incest issues emerged in excruciatingly poignant detail. MaryLou's reliving of her oedipal victory with all of its attendant dangers intensified due to unresolved preoedipal trauma, then became the central paradigm in her treatment.

Many Months Later

An example of the evolution of her capacity to do analytic work was seen in a session which started in the waiting room with her reading an informational pamphlet about psychoanalysis. She thought it would be helpful in explaining to her friends what she was doing five days a week and asked if she could borrow it for a day to make a copy. I consented and chose not to inquire further at the moment about her interest in the pamphlet, as such direct inquiries were often met with an impatient plea that we were digressing and not dealing with the central issue of treatment. She was very upset from the night before when she dissociated again and lost about two hours while she was attending to her new pet, a very fragile baby, furry creature. When she "came to," she found herself in an absolute rage, yelling at her husband for leaving her there as she felt abandoned because everyone had gone to bed. She realized that her outrage was grossly out of proportion with the situation, as she felt that she or someone "inside" was feeling sexually used and *then* abandoned with her baby. Her baby pet apparently triggered off memories of her fragile baby who died after the late term abortion, and she was quite shaken up.

She had enough observing ego at this point to recognize that another part of her mind had come out, but was perplexed and anxious when she fell asleep. She then reported a dream in which she was with a number of couples on vacation in which everyone was hypersexual. There was sex going on in all the rooms in the hotel. A very good friend who had since moved away was there, too, and the patient confided in her that she was overwhelmed and had to get away quickly. As she reported the dream, she insisted a little too vigorously it was unimportant but was curious that her dreams included old friends who had either broken off their relationship or who had moved away. My initial associations were to the intensity of the erotic transference and our efforts at understanding it in light of her incestuous relationship, the pregnancy with her stepfather, and her enactment with her physical therapist. I was also reminded that considerable work had been done in exploring and clarifying issues related to the nature of transference in general, especially its illusory nature and the need to tolerate its ambiguity (Adler, 1989). Her "parts" experienced intense fears and wishes over repeating her disastrous affair but this time with a happy ending. The themes of boundaries, the compulsion to repeat, the difference between thought and action, tolerating impulses without acting on them, the omnipotence of thought, etc., dominated our sessions for many, many months.

It appeared that her growing comprehension about the concept of transference in and of itself was a reflection of increased ego strength and a maturational step which enabled her to make more of a distinction in her mind between the past and the present, and between memory, fantasy, dream, and reality. It was a very painful, bittersweet experience for her, to be permitted to experience profound longings of the deepest, most loving nature only to be reminded, often at her insistence, that she was in therapy and no matter what she felt or said and no matter what I may or may not feel and no matter "what if . . . " or "if only . . . " (Akhtar, 1996), that the boundaries would not change. Once she got over her hurt, disappointment, and confusion, she was greatly relieved to know that she had the freedom to say and feel whatever she needed to without having to worry about the repercussions, i.e., that she could be free to love without having to give anything in return. For her to create a loving father in the transference who could aid in her disengagement from a suffocating maternal dyad, who could be an oedipal object who would reject her in a developmentally healthy way, and one who would encourage the development of her feminine identity without exploiting it for his own sexual needs, was too good to be true.

It was in this context that when her passion would threaten to overwhelm her, she truly needed clarification due to her confusion over whether our relationship permitted a sexual consummation. As she became more able to tolerate and accept that our domain was limited to the realm of fantasy, then her "inside people" slowly began to merge. The anxiety, however, would become unbearable and she would retreat into her internal world. I sensed, therefore, that one facet of her dream was a representation of her efforts to ward off intense sexual arousal through a dissociative walling off in the form of various other people fornicating in the different rooms. But even this measure was not successful, so she had to take flight from the dream and awoke in a confused state.

Interestingly, she was particularly vexed over the presence of her very good friends who had moved away. She concluded that having recently invited them to a family celebration was probably the day residue. She then began to agonize over an impulsive decision she had made several days before, unbeknownst to me, regarding a pamphlet she created for the occasion. I then wondered if her interest in the psychoanalytic pamphlet was an unconscious allusion to her own pamphlet. What disturbed her was that she gave in to pressure from some of her voices to make a reference to her deceased stepfather. She knew her mother would have been delighted, for it would show the world that all was forgiven between stepfather and daughter or that nothing ever happened in the first place. She did not realize how much it had bothered her, even though she had been quite upset very recently over revealing that she knew certain things about her stepfather's erotic life that her mother did not.

This privileged, oedipally victorious position repeated itself in her affair and in a recent transference dream where she overheard intimate details of a session between my wife and me. She concluded that she could be a better mate, had hated herself for feeling that way, and became overwhelmed with foreboding and guilt. In that dream, I became furious with her and banished her from my home despite her best efforts to be perfectly compliant and obedient. The idea, however, of resurrecting her dead stepfather and including him in family milestone events filled her with more dread and anger than loving forgiveness because she felt it would contaminate the day as he had contaminated her life. She heard a cacophony of voices in favor of removing his name which then bolstered her sense of being in touch with *her* feelings. The patient marveled at how much she was bothered by something she had literally put out of her mind and relegated to her unconscious. Through the therapeutic process of allowing everything and everyone to come to mind, she was able to analyze what was really disturbing her. MaryLou concluded that she did not need to put her stepfather in the pamphlet since she had a good father in the transference, and sighed with relief at the knowledge that there was time to revise the priority. I ended the session by reminding her that she had started the hour by asking about my pamphlet and thereby alerting us, unconsciously, about the issue without even realizing it. We both were amused by this signal from deep within and how she was really believing that she could do analytic work.

Unfortunately, the sense of satisfaction we felt in our analytic collaboration was short lived. MaryLou had several other vague dreams in which her former friends appeared, leaving her in an agitated state. These friends all had one thing in common—they all left her around the time of her devastating relationship with the health professional. Some even scorned her for her "scandalous" behavior wanting to distance themselves from her, and broke off the friendship. Until the dream, the patient thought very little of these women whose self-righteous attitude added to her sense of total degradation. She could not understand why they started appearing, and she did not accept a psychoanalytic formulation relating to the representation of guilt or shame. At the end of the session, when she got up from the couch and exited the office, she became terribly troubled by what she perceived as a very sad look on my face. I was reflecting on the material which related to her stepfather's death and how, in his dying words, he asked for the patient and not his wife. Her painful oedipal victory, her fear of mother's jealousy, and unresolved grief were the major themes, which undoubtedly could have left a contemplative look on my face. However, MaryLou insisted something might have been terribly, terribly wrong with me. Was I okay? Was something *really*, really wrong? I assumed that through mutual regression, projective identification, and a primitive maternal transference, she was made to feel that I was so upset with her that I would do something bad to her, and terminate therapy as her punishment. This paradigm was frequently enacted and beginning to be understood by her.

But this day, she insisted, it was different. Was she "peering into my soul" again? About an hour later, she left a message stating she was having another one of her ominous forebodings, which was an omen of very bad news. She checked with all of her loved ones who reassured her that they are all well, but she became helplessly paralyzed with dread and her whole body felt overheated as though it were being wrapped in plastic. Several hours later, I received an even more frantic call from her, sobbing uncontrollably as she tried to explain that she now knew what her premonition was about—she received a totally unexpected letter in the mail, informing her about the status of the complaint against the provider and what she was required to do next. She oscillated between feeling cursed by her precognitive foreboding and feeling terrified that her perpetrator would come get her again.

Over the next week, her regression was so profound that hospitalization was narrowly averted, as she retreated into a fetal position and wailed uncontrollably. She could barely walk out of the office and spent hours in the waiting room, trying to regain her adult parts in order to go home. Extended sessions were needed during this time, as she regressed in the transference, viciously accusing me of being just another man who used and discarded her. She insisted I mishandled the situation and demanded reparation from me in a most relentless way. Anything short of a total admission of responsibility on my part was seen as a cover-up and a manipulative ploy on my part. She was inconsolable, and I felt her helplessness, realizing that nothing I could say would make a difference, except that I would see her through this crisis and that we would find a way to work out the problem. She experienced a complete reversal of her perceptions of me, having seen me in an idealized light as the only one who could ever understand, tolerate, or help her, but her disillusionment did not last as long as it had before. She was eventually receptive to a review of the sequence of events leading up to her current state and surprisingly regained her synthetic functioning in a matter of days, instead of weeks or months as before.

I told her that I felt anger and a wish for revenge against her perpetrator, as though by proxy I was expressing what she could not let herself feel (Renik, 1995). Perhaps my wish not to acknowledge these feelings to her was perceived as insensitivity and holding back something from her. I wondered out loud if this contributed to her sense that I had made a big mistake in therapy. MaryLou listened very intently, crying and apologizing for bringing me into this most horrid period of her life—her mental and sexual enslavement. I reminded her that it was not her fault and that she was a "sitting duck" (Kluft, 1990). I felt an almost instantaneous reconnection as she "came back" and saw me once again more realistically as one who cared about her welfare. As we further analyzed what had transpired between us as a result of what was going on in her mind, we kept coming back to that aspect of her recent dreams which left her with the sensation—the appearance of her former friends. Her conviction of having had a premonition was so strong and unshakable that challenging it or trying to analyze it away would have been felt as a major lapse in my empathy. So, if we were to take her premonition as a manifestation of an extrasensory perception, then was it possible that former friends were an early warning sign of news about that time in her life? And even if we were to tentatively consider that hypothesis, how could we try to incorporate it into a dynamic model? I wondered out loud about such questions and reiterated the idea that perhaps her premonitions could have first entered her mind unconsciously and contributed to the day residue, along with transference issues, traumatic elements, and genetic material. Could it be that "extra" sensory input got represented there too at times?

But if this were so, how could we know, except retrospectively, when psi phenomena were part of the stimuli for the dream? These issues continued to be worked on throughout her treatment.

CONCLUSION

I do not presume to have a full explanation for MaryLou's symptoms, mental functioning, and the nature of information transfer that occurred between us. It does seem to me, however, that after considering and ruling out the many factors described earlier, I am left with the distinct impression that she possessed some psychic abilities. However, our mutual regression related to unresolved grief which was associated with fluctuating states of consciousness, her amnesia, her shifting sense of identity, auditory hallucinations, profound separation anxiety, boundary problems, projective identification, fluctuating moods, and psychophysiologic symptoms were probably responsible for much of what she ascribed to the "curse" of her special powers. There were times when she would become aware of bits of knowledge suddenly, as a result of a shifting dissociative ego state. As though hearing about it from the inside for the first time, even though I myself may have recalled it from an earlier conversation, she experienced it as though it were information from a telepathic source (Freud, 1899). In addition, there were times that she was so sure she knew how I felt about something, that unless I agreed with her projection or intuition, I was not believed or thought to be out of touch with my own unconscious. While the latter is certainly a possibility from time to time, her defensive air of certitude at those times left little room for discussion (Saul, 1938). Conversely, the times when it most appeared that information transfer was apparently the realm of the extrasensory, she often related with initial fear, doubt, and uncertainty.

The relatively brief period of time examined here covers a significant but narrow aspect of a very complicated long-term treatment, when psi phenomena seemed to emerge as a major issue in treatment. As such, it seemed to require an appreciation of theories that we analysts do not generally confront on a regular basis. It is a lot to consider not only near-death experiences and the reported increase in paranormal events afterwards (Kohr, 1982, 1983; Greyson, 1983b; Sutherland, 1989; Ring, 1991; Sabom, 1982) but also their presence in patients with "multiple personality" (Kluft, 1985; Wilbur, 1988). It is difficult enough to understand how communication takes place in one dissociated mind, let alone to formulate how information transfer occurs between two minds given the limits of our scientific knowledge at this time. And, because psychoanalysis aspires to have a rational basis it cannot accommodate more than one unquantifiable energy, besides libido, in order to explain these phenomena. As described earlier with the major controversy over the death instinct (see chapter 7), which even Freud himself could not get fully accepted, there is no doubt that we are not ready to contemplate the vicissitudes of any other "far out" energy (Sanella, 1976) which may have been invoked to explain psi phenomena. As a result, we must clearly do our best to explain what is reported in near-death and extrasensory experiences on the basis of what has long been known and on our growing understanding of the dissociation of trauma. But, we may be left with a small but significant realm of the unknown, and the failure to consider the possibility of a form of unconscious communication not yet registered by the "analyzing instrument" (Isakower, 1938; Balter, Lothane, and Spence, 1980) could trap us in an intellectual prison (Goldberg, 1990). We are just beginning to appreciate the myriad ways in which severe early psychic trauma may influence the potentials of the human mind as the young child traverses the "channel" of development (Volkan and Akhtar, 1997), and more exploration of these outer reaches may further demystify our mental processes.

Chapter 11

THOUGHTS ON TERMINATION

It ain't over 'til it's over [Yogi Berra].

It may sound a bit antithetical, but I do not think that terminability need be a major factor in determining whether the work with victims of severe early trauma "should" follow a psychoanalytic course. In my experience, so many of these patients have been through numerous therapists who have employed a gamut of approaches, and they see no options left by the time they get to an analyst. For them to even find a therapist around still willing to work with them and see them through their crises over time is in itself often seen as too good to be true. And, for there to be any ray of hope that there could be substantive intrapsychic change borders on a miracle. Assessment of progress due to the enormous resistances involved may necessitate viewing treatment in terms of decades, not years. Therefore, the analyst must be prepared to work with such a patient over a sizeable portion of his or her career and to consider the possibility of hospitalization along with adjusting the degree of intensity as circumstances may dictate. The need for flexibility, creativity, and the reasonable expectation of being in practice for at least ten years after starting treatment might be taken into consideration also. Paradoxically, the enormous complexity and countertransference challenges call for a well-seasoned analyst at the helm, yet the stamina required may be more readily found in a younger clinician. Consequently, the "fit" between analyst and patient in these cases is at least as important here as in any.

With these provisos in mind, the decision when to terminate may present itself more in the form of whether, ever to terminate. The likelihood of not completely resolving the transference neurosis may deter those analysts who see a "clean break" as the ideal (Hartlaub, Martin, and Rhine, 1986), but such an approach may limit the expansion of the "ever widening scope" by not offering analytic therapy to what may be seen as a refractory population. However, Anzieu (1987) cautions that the analyst may be "cathected as an absolute and permanent part object" (p. 15) which increases the risk of an interminable analysis, whereas Klauber (1977) maintains that such analyses are "probably fairly rare" (p. 473). Nevertheless, instead of a more classical two-step process of deciding to terminate and then setting a termination date (Freud, 1937; Glover, 1955; Firestein, 1978), the issue of what *form* a termination would need to take may arise instead. From this perspective, I have found the notion of a "natural termination" to be very useful (Goldberg and Marcus, 1985), an extension of Ferenczi's (1927) ideas about not pushing or structuring the termination. In addition, the very active dream life in which many dissociative patients dwell provides the opportunity to monitor the process through the evolution of "termination signal" dreams (Cavenar and Nash, 1976). Countertransference dreams (Whitman, Kramer, and Baldridge, 1969) may be very useful, too. Because of the recurrent, almost cyclical nature of the patient contemplating a break from the analyst, coupled with the analyst's awareness of the possible interminability of analysis, compounded by the progressive exhaustion of both members of the dyad (Ferenczi, 1927; Margolis, 1996), there may be no "right" time in which to terminate, in my view. There can always be a little more working through, reconstruction, or integration of the psyche with each round of "this time I really *am* going to leave!" As these recurrent episodes of imminent termination may reverberate with slightly less intensity each time, the analyst cannot necessarily know when it is truly time. Therefore, I do not rush the process and, on more than one occasion, have been angrily challenged by the patient, or by proxy from a family member (e.g., "my husband can't believe how long I have been coming here"). When appropriate, I have responded to that protest with a comment to the effect that I would rather be criticized for being seen as having someone in analysis "too long" than be seen as one who has "put the false idea" in someone's mind that something bad happened in childhood when it didn't (Baranger, Baranger, and Mom, 1988; see the section on negation in chapter 5, for further discussion).

To illustrate these points, I will focus on aspects of the protracted termination process that occurred in Samantha's analysis, a treatment that extended well beyond a decade (see chapter 2 for a description of her dissociative character pathology and her clinical course in analysis; see chapter 5 for a description of one of her hypnagogic states later in treatment). A series of seven dreams and a countertransference dream are described which appeared to have clinical value in gauging the inevitability of the termination.

CASE REPORT

As Samantha's analysis proceeded, she became able to stay awake, to develop a sense of continuity of consciousness and of herself, as well as becoming able to "own" her childhood sexual trauma. There were times, however, when she still doubted herself, her memory, and her judgment. Overall, her cognitive abilities improved in the area of reading comprehension, attention span, and ability to think through complex problems. Her confidence in doing a job increased, and she was able to seek employment commensurate with her education and potential. In order to do that, she had to master the job interview situation, a high anxiety interchange usually occurring with an older man who expected a type of performance from her. She was amazed at her ability to self-analyze on the spot, allowing her to recognize how her relationship with her uncle would get activated under such circumstances, which then enabled her to remain composed and not regress anymore. Yet, she was dismayed that she was not totally cured, most notably evidenced by her not having found the "right" man in her life. Although by now she was aware of the differences between life goals and analytic goals (Ticho, 1972), how could she know how she would function under real life, intimate circumstances unless she were with the man she loved in reality? Analysis had become a proving ground and unless she had fully tested herself under all conditions, she understandably had doubts about being able to fly alone, as it were. After all, she had spent much of her young adult life in treatment, a situation which dismayed her until she recognized that she may not have survived were it not for analysis. Working through a complex, eroticized transference which spanned all levels of development had been a longstanding goal, and she did not want to leave analysis just to run into the arms of another man. This well-known scenario had colored our breaks from early on and she had painfully come to realize the transference implications of her impulsive and, at times, high-risk sexual behavior. This time, she wanted to wind down, experience the grief over the loss of analysis, and then enable herself to be emotionally available for any opportunities that might present themselves in her newly resurrected life. I could certainly appreciate her caution, but I also sensed a subtle wish that perhaps I should have pushed her out of the nest by now. In the previous two years, she had set several termination dates which had come and gone with varying degrees of regret and relief. She was feeling frustrated yet comforted that I did not do more to ready her for her life journey without me. Instead, I continued to function as I had all along, maintaining the analytic position, while being quite interested in learning how she was hoping to extricate herself from her maternal symbiotic bondage which had shackled her to her uncle's incestuous bed in the transference.

Eventually, Samantha became very disillusioned with me and, after several months of deliberating, decided to seek consultation with another analyst. Initially, she was obsequious, tentative, and careful about not wanting to hurt my feelings, insisting she was urged on by friends and family who were dismayed by the length of her treatment. Since I did not protest, become defensive, punish, or retaliate, it was an enormous relief for her. And so, emboldened by her newfound freedom, the patient, on her own, sought out a "very famous" senior analyst in another city, one whose opinions she expected to be based upon the wisdom handed down by Freud himself. Her devaluation of her analysis with me then intensified prior to the meeting, as she fortified herself for the barrage of anticipated criticism of our painstaking and tedious work. "If only" she had started with someone as renowned as this fabled consultant she lamented regularly, then perhaps she would have made more progress sooner and finished analysis a long time ago. Yet, it was undeniable that she felt she had gained much. As the long awaited day arrived, I, too, found myself a bit curious about his "judgment," as I sensed her eagerness for some type of a grade for our psychoanalytic performance.

Seeking consultation was a decisive move on her part and a significant departure from her usual passive, masochistic stance. So, prior to her visit, I offered little analytic speculation about any deeper motivation, as in many ways it seemed like a developmental step as much as an enactment. I assumed that there would be ample time to analyze her actions afterward, so for the most part accepted her decision to see a consultant at face value, discussing with her what it was she wanted to learn.

Essentially, she felt ready to finally get some "answers" from someone who would tell it like it was, a courageous wish from a woman who spent most of her life in a mental fog. Her idealization of the fabled psychoanalyst propelled her through several weeks, as her anticipated meeting came to represent a definitive step toward her emancipation, one way or another. Interestingly, her consultation did not interfere with any of our scheduled appointments, and it was a nodal experience for her. She reported a very cordial meeting in which he listened carefully to a condensed but forthright account of her life, her analysis, and her reconstruction. She expressed her concern over the duration of treatment and her continued difficulties in intimate situations, but the consultant apparently chose to emphasize the extent of her progress instead, given the severity of her problems and her traumatic past. Samantha's reaction was delayed but definite, as her initial awe over being in his presence gradually gave way to a more realistic appraisal of the consultation.

The legendary analyst ultimately disappointed her too, as he did not fully appreciate all the nuances of her situation, and in her view, minimized the severity of her ongoing problems. He was not omnipotent, clearly fallible, and could not humanly grasp everything in their one meeting. She stated that he did not offer a second session, essentially telling her that nobody can be perfect, and that perhaps she should be satisfied with how well she was doing compared to where she had been. She was not sure if he were patronizing her, but he clearly was telling her that she had worked hard in analysis, that her analyst was competent, and that she could continue to grow following her termination. The idea that she might have the capability for maturation after leaving analysis was at odds with her wish to be a totally "finished product" before we parted company, and this prospect filled her with trepidation. How could she really know for sure she was ready, and what if she made a mistake? The consultant seemed to help further soften her harsh perfectionistic superego, but she felt annoyed that this psychoanalytic guru did not know everything. Yet, it made her feel proud and feel that she could disagree with him without a fear of repercussion. By confronting a giant, she had slayed one of her own dragons.

Back in analysis, her processing of this meeting went on for several weeks, as she wondered if this time for sure she would succeed in extricating herself from the quicksand of the transference. As the famous analyst continued to tumble off his pedestal, her own analyst's prestige increased in her mind. Perhaps they really had accomplished something durable which would persist after termination, but she had been unable to believe it out of a regressive fear of individuation and leaving her all-purpose parental object behind. In the past, she could not envision how she might structure her departure, feeling that after all these years, to just set a date and stop abruptly one day would be intolerable. She had asked whether she should wean herself from five to four to three to two to one session a week over a period of weeks or months. She then wondered if she should continue with regular "maintenance" visits on a monthly or quarterly basis just to make sure she was doing okay and not falling back into her old ways. She had also suggested converting from analysis to twice a week psychotherapy for an indeterminate period of time and then deciding from there what to do.

When these ideas initially came up, I listened neutrally, trying to analyze the meaning of her wish never to say good-bye. I did imagine, however, that since Samantha's young adult life had been spent in analysis there would be no "ideal" uncomplicated way for her to leave. Like the rest of her analysis, her departure would need to be individual and unique to her, so I told her that I was open to any ideas she had, hoping my open mindedness would help her see that she was free to do whatever she wanted.

Again, her tendency to lapse into rigidity and a black or white way of doing things made her feel quite anxious, thereby leading her to conclude despairingly that she was not ready each time her deadlines arrived. And, wondering if she would ever be able to go without my explicit direction and blessing, she angrily protested that she was being held back and thwarted by my indecision. After several rounds of such tirades associated with abortive termination plans, I was tempted to take over, as her mother had in times of her panic, and tell her what to do, but I did not. It became obvious to her that her decision to seek consultation was an outgrowth of this frustration.

We also discussed how her seeking consultation was an identification with me, alluding to a time several years before when her depression and anxiety nearly disabled her for several months. At that time, she begged for medication and, much to her surprise, I referred her to a colleague for a pharmacologic consultation. Although I felt quite comfortable prescribing medication myself, I thought that the severity of her symptoms and the possibility of an insoluble negative therapeutic reaction, out of a wish not to know (Renik, 1991) after years of analysis, justified another opinion. Interestingly, the consultant prescribed a medication that I did not think would be particularly efficacious. As it was a benign choice, I did not countermand it at the time and continued to analyze, but it did little to help. Significantly, what did seem most beneficial about this consultation was the implicit message that I believed her and took her pain so seriously that I was willing to forego the theoretical purity of analysis for the sake of trying to help alleviate her pain. Although this perception alternated with the fear that I was giving up on her, sending her away, and feeling that she was a total failure, it seemed that her predominant feeling was of vindication.

A period of rededication to analysis followed in which she came to terms with the conviction that she could trust her own judgment about her sexual relationship with her uncle. An intensification of erotic longings in the transference occurred which was then followed by the sad realization that a "healthy rejection" was more likely to occur in analysis. Nevertheless, she felt she could never be sure if something would ever happen between us, and I wondered if part of the difficulty she had in leaving was because she was giving me every possible opportunity to make a sexual advance toward her. She ruefully agreed, acknowledging that she could not imagine ever giving up that wish and that she wanted to stay with me indefinitely. Consequently, her decision to seek consultation was her own way of trying to get beyond a potentially interminable state. I subsequently concluded that if I had endorsed her wish to cut back to twice a week therapy then I might have unwittingly played into this scenario of a never ending therapy, also. To paraphrase Mahler, she appeared to need a paternal analyst of individuation to help her separate from analysis.

With all of these issues swirling about, I was struck by a dream she reported shortly after the consultation:

> Dream 1. My landlord kicked me out of my apartment because I left the lights on.

Samantha's associations were about wanting to leave analysis but not knowing how. She needed to set a date, and insisted that it was time to trust her
judgment. She wondered if she had to provoke me to throw her out. She
wasted the landlord's electricity, and her passion, like the light, still burned
brightly after so many years. She then declared, once again, that she would
leave in six months to a year. (This time she did terminate about eight months
later.) Several days after this dream, she reported a more extensive dream:

> Dream 2. My best friend, her boyfriend, and I were rushing to the train
> station, but I forgot my ticket. I ran to the ticket counter and I thought
> we were late, but the ticket taker said "No, we were waiting for you."
> I couldn't find my ticket, but he was very patient. He gave me a form
> to sign, but I signed in the wrong place. He said it was no problem and
> gave me another form which I still did not sign in the right place. The
> next time I did it correctly. I was hesitant to get on the train, but my
> friends urged me, and I'm glad I did. I had a friend working behind
> the counter who held up the departure, treating me specially, and break-
> ing all the rules. But, when I finally left, I had a great time.

Samantha saw me as the ticket taker, and her associations were to being
ambivalent about leaving analysis, feeling ambivalent about me, and wanting
to blame me for why her analysis had taken so long. Then she finally admitted
that she had to be silent for many years for fear of revealing secrets and
destroying the illusion of being from a normal, happy family. We came back
to this dream repeatedly as it came to symbolize her passivity and conflict
over termination, as the ticket agent-analyst had to delay the train departure
and practically sign the ticket for her in order to help her take her trip. She
even felt treated specially by her friend behind the scenes who broke rules
to help her make her train. In subsequent dreams, she took more responsibility
for action and decisions, as the time approached this latest deadline.

Samantha reported the following dream two months later:

> Dream 3. I was in the home of my best friend from childhood, but I was
> a grown-up. It was oddly decorated, like from the 1970s, but somehow it
> was redone. She was moving away, and, although we never stayed in
> touch, I loved her so much and never forgot about her. I remember the
> fun times we had and how loved I always felt by her parents. Then, I
> was having sex with two old boyfriends who were making my body
> feel good.

Her associations were about trust, as she wondered whom she trusted
more, her analyst or an old boyfriend who loved her so much but whom she
hurt so deeply because she could not return his love back then. She also felt

happy that she allowed her body pleasure as she was not depriving or punishing herself anymore. She declared that analysis was not over, but that this time she was really leaving. She felt a deep sense of loss and did not want to part. I, too, began to think that this time she indeed would leave me, as her psychological house was remodeled with a unique mixture of the past and the present. I also wondered if her loving her best friend, whom she kept in her heart but whom she chose not to stay in touch with, was expressing her ideal wish for no posttermination contact or ''follow-up'' which she so often talked about. I chose to say nothing about it at the time, not wanting to influence or burden her with any expectation or reminder about the ''open door'' to my office.

Four months later, Samantha reported this dream:

> Dream 4. I am in an area where there are many beautiful homes. I am working with a woman in one of these homes. Then I find myself among rows of cots, like in an army base. I left my shoes in one of the bunks and went to the main part of the base, but the woman said she or I could go back to get them. I was about to go back for my shoes but then ended up on a train back home. It was not a smooth trip, and even though I had to get off while it was moving, it was going very slowly, and I made it safely home. Then I didn't want to go back to the cots for my shoes.

Samantha's associations were of not being ready to leave, i.e., jumping from a slow moving train. She wondered if she left without her shoes. Quite often she would walk out of the office leaving one of her belongings behind, and felt like leaving a piece of herself behind. But then she gleefully revealed that she really loved not wearing shoes. When barefoot, she felt happy and free. She was not even sure whose shoes they were anyway. Were they the woman's or hers? She didn't wait for her to get them and decided not to retrieve them herself. She said there was no confusion in our relationship anymore and that it was a safe boundary. But she was confused if they were her mother's shoes or hers. She sadly concluded she could not have a relationship with her uncle anymore. She would panic if she got too close, but she was reliving her past less, although she was constantly reminded of the pressure she felt over what she had to do in order to be ''good'' in his eyes. The army base reminded her of concentration camps. She was fascinated by the Holocaust, wondering if I were born in the camps and if something traumatic happened to me, also. (She had learned of my writing on the Holocaust and became intrigued by it, wanting to analyze me up to the last hour.) ''You have such a deep understanding, it is something deep in your heart. It must come from trauma. My intuition tells me I'm not wrong. I will miss you a lot. I want to hold your hand when you die and pray for you. We will reunite in heaven. One day I will see you again. You see sunshine and a beautiful rainbow only after a storm.''

I was impressed by Samantha's attunement to me and her approaching readiness to leave. As symbolized in her dream, she was not sure if what was left behind really belonged to her, but in either case, was not inclined to go back to the cots (couch) to find out. Even though she anticipated somewhat of a rough ride, she knew she would ultimately be safe and would have to tolerate life without her analyst. She also made it quite clear that she knew how to find me if needed. Subsequent to the dream, she more confidently began to feel that this time was for real, and she set a specific date about two months hence, almost coinciding with my winter break. She wanted to be the one leaving me so she decided to terminate two days before my vacation, but I needed to be prepared for any eventuality. Having convinced herself of very limited time left, this self-imposed deadline (Orens, 1955) pressured her into analyzing as much as possible. She became emboldened, knowing that she had a planned escape from the inevitable pain of dredging up more of her past. She discovered that she could alleviate her excruciating anguish on the couch merely by sitting up and catching her breath. This maneuver, although very rarely used, renewed her courage enough to submerge into the depths of her childhood confusion once again in her inexorable quest for the truth about her self (Grinberg, 1980).

Somatic sensations which reminded her of bodily secretions sticking to her anus, vagina, and thighs convinced her definitively that her uncle had ejaculated on and inside her orifices. A reemergence of nausea and urges to vomit prompted her to move the trash can to the side of the couch, and she used tremendous amounts of tissues cleaning up her tears and dripping mucus. Memories of cleaning up "the evidence," his semen, reemerged with crystal clarity, adding more weight to her conviction that things really did happen with her uncle. Genital excitement, convulsive hip movements, and an acknowledgment of her longing for him led her to conclude that she must have experienced orgastic pleasure as she got older. She then admitted to continued involvement with him after he moved out of her home when she was 9. This secret made her feel like an absolute criminal who would get caught at any minute and be mercilessly punished by her mother. As this oedipal victory, which was enacted with her uncle, became clearer than ever for her, she then acknowledged that with the dwindling time left she must get some peace of mind about the last area left—her erotic longings for her mother.

Although convinced that her mother did not actively seduce her, Samantha's memory of having her head stroked lovingly while nuzzling her face deep into her mother's lap was both a comforting and a painfully overstimulating experience. At times she would feel utter revulsion at the memory of her odor. Revelations of secret masturbation fantasies of mutual cunnilingus overwhelmed her with shame and guilt reaching near self-destructive proportions. She recalled sleeping in bed with her mother which had evoked strong urges to suck her breasts, and she further regressed. Fighting off a decompensation that would preclude her termination, Samantha experienced me similarly in the transference, as a mother who overstimulated her but never had sex with her. Her observing ego remained intact this time, however, as she recognized that she needed a "healthy rejection" from me in the positive as well as negative oedipal transference. She contemplated postponing the termination date, once again, given the onslaught of all the new material, but then went into a rage declaring, "I have to get the fuck out of here!" She then reported the following dream:

> Dream 5. I was in a family orgy which lasted indefinitely and I couldn't get out.

She associated to this dream and feared being in analysis forever, endlessly dredging up the muck from her childhood with no chance for a respite. She resolved that she must stick to her deadline or run the risk of staying masochistically entrenched in these nightmares interminably. She thought that life would be so much easier with a clitorectomy, as mutilation fantasies reemerged as both a punishment and a flight from her sexuality. Now she could easily see how her childhood was one of overstimulation and little comfort. With an absent father, she ran from her uncle back to her mother for soothing, only to get more aroused with nowhere to go except deeper into her altered states. She felt there had been no protection in her life until analysis, and now she was trying to convince herself that she truly was leaving. Each day was an obsessional litany of leaving and not leaving. In her anxiety, she reopened the question of cutting back to twice a week for an indefinite period of time as more memories of her mother's daily ministrations became eroticized torture. Abandonment fears in the transference escalated as she felt the only way to keep "me" from leaving her was through sexual seduction. Being the active aggressor was a desperate last ditch effort to hold on.

Once again, she confronted her uncle who did not "remember" anything inappropriate happening between them. This time, she told him that she remembered everything, and she knew the truth (Grinberg, 1980). Interestingly, he was much less sure of himself than before, absent-mindedly complaining of always being blamed for things. Samantha was not as devastated after this meeting. She saw him more realistically as a very troubled man who, too, probably had a great need not to know. She also discussed her childhood with her mother again, experiencing a bubbling up of rage and disappointment at her limitations but seeing her more realistically, too. She was able to stay very present and not drift off anymore. Throughout the last several months, despite what certainly felt like a massive regression, she excelled at work and was in line for a promotion. She then reported this dream:

> Dream 6. There was an obstacle course, like a steeplechase race. I was doing trials. I thought that I was really going to practice and be prepared for this race. But then the coach said, "Well, the race is tomorrow!"

Samantha awoke from the dream in a giddy panic, insisting she was not ready to leave, as she was shocked to hear the coach announce that tomorrow was the big day. She misplaced important belongings and feared that her mind was malfunctioning again. Samantha was panic-stricken by this dream which so succinctly represented her postanalytic life as a race for which she had been preparing a long time but one whose actual date had snuck up on her as a big surprise. We doubted if she would ever feel ready. Once again, she bargained for time, offering new termination dates ranging from several weeks to several months. With less than two weeks remaining until her "official" termination date, I was not at all sure what would be. I had found long before that I could tolerate her indecision much better by simply trying to accept that I just might not know when her last day would be. I needed to reconcile myself to the fact that I could not offer "her" times to a new patient wanting to start treatment until the hours were actually available. This uncertainty made planning my schedule next to impossible. The accompanying countertransference and financial issues involved (Goldberg and Marcus, 1985) could have been transmitted to Samantha, so when I found myself feeling any discomfort over her "natural" way of terminating, which to a certain extent is out of an analyst's control, it was useful to reflect on the progression of her dreams. Consequently, I could attend to her apparent, unchanging, obsessional deliberating but at the same time be mindful that she very clearly knew that the "day of the race" was rapidly approaching. Although at least one of us was likely to be surprised when it actually would occur, it was evident that in her own way she was getting prepared.

Then, several days later, I had a dream.

> Countertransference dream. I was riding a bicycle along a familiar and popular path which was fairly crowded. There I met Samantha who was out riding also. We greeted each other in a friendly way, not completely surprised to see each other, and rode together for a while. We were having a pleasant and enjoyable time when I suddenly remembered that she might still be in analysis! Then, I became confused over whether

she actually still was in analysis or had long since terminated. I thought that we should stop riding together until the situation was clearer in my mind, so we parted company amicably and went our separate ways.

It occurred to me upon awakening that my conflict over our mutual bicycle ride was not only a reflection of my uncertainty of her status but also a wish to see her as a peer. Most significantly, however, the ride together seemed symbolic of our many years of collaborative analytic work which I had unconsciously wished would finally come to an end. I had somehow resolved my own confusion and was ready to "let" her go (Klauber, 1977). The following hour, interestingly, Samantha talked about wanting to leave and calling me in six months to let me know how she was doing. She knew she had to let go of her love affair with her uncle now that she could remember much of what had happened between them. She thought she could continue to do more of the work on her own and knew she could return if needed. She mourned and cried intermittently for several days, feeling confident she would be safe. She fantasized having sex with me to say thank you and two days before her departure reported the following dream:

> Dream 7. I was at the library studying for a final exam which was tomorrow, but I hadn't bought the book. The librarian lent it to me so I read it and then I gave it back. I took extra readings home with me, but I couldn't decide if I would take the exam or not. I can't remember if I ever did take it, but I was just so glad to get out!

Samantha was determined to get out whether she was fully completed or not, knowing that she was able to live without the life and death anxiety which had crippled her for so long. Ready or not, she was going. She now had her "extra reading" which she could take home with her, i.e., her capacity for self-analysis, and she felt more able to "study" herself on her own. The next day, Samantha reviewed the years of our work together and how she felt we both had changed. We both had become older, more experienced, more relaxed with each other, and now she could see me and my role more realistically. She acknowledged how difficult it must have been for me to reach her, how rude and insensitive she had been, but how I did not let her abuse me. She wanted a tangible artifact to take away with her, a souvenir, but, anticipating yet another disappointment from me, she quickly pointed out that now she could rely on herself. She expressed gratitude that I did not give up on her, nor take advantage of her sexually.

Quite significantly, she could also see how important it was that I never told her I thought she was sexually abused because she was so susceptible to being brainwashed. "You could have made a big mistake with me," she cautioned. Nevertheless, she was sorry it took so long and objectively wondered if someone else would have been able to connect with her more easily. I acknowledged that possibility as I had before, but this time she was not blaming me, but rather matter of factly and almost humorously describing her months of sleeping and years of being in a dissociated, inaccessible "other world." To complicate matters, she wondered if her sadism, rage, and years of wanting to truly hurt me had pushed my countertransference "buttons," resulting in excessive silence on my part.

Samantha broached the issue of countertransference withdrawal while under siege, a topic which she had become quite interested in of late. She was intrigued by my self-disclosure that indeed there may have been a time when she had pushed my "buttons." Knowing that she had "gotten" to me helped her gain more confidence in her perceptions, allowing her to consider that it might have been valid to feel that my reticence was more like giving her "the silent treatment" at certain times. She declared, "I couldn't see how hard your job was. But, I'm trying to understand you, and I do. You are just a person. I see you better, now."

The last hour, Samantha sat up and enthusiastically predicted that she would have a great ending. She announced that she was going to leave several minutes early, a compromise which enabled her to end on her announced day yet be a bit spontaneous. Perhaps it also kept her from losing her resolve. She proudly declared that she trusted her intuition about her decision to terminate, and I said that I had come to trust her judgment, too. She was very touched by my comment and presented me with a small gift which symbolized her appreciation that I had given her the ability to think and speak up. I told her that perhaps we both had acquired that ability, and she was delighted. Once again, she reminded me that it was so hard to reach her and that she was so mean to me. But, she gently chided, that she pushed my buttons, and I was too silent at times. She assured me she would be okay and that she would contact me in about six months. In order to walk out, she needed to renounce her desire for me, and give up her masochistic gratification. That day, she preferred to be admired but sexually rejected and did not want me to want her anymore. That day indeed was to be the last day, as she alluded to the coach and the librarian who helped prepare her for the race and the final exam. She felt jittery and sad but hopeful, proud, and very happy. Happier to leave than to stay. She then continued with her analysis of me, stating that I, too, must have been traumatized but somehow turned it into a gift, a sublimation, to help others. She assured me that she was going to be okay because now she could trust her mind. She smiled, got up, shook my hand, gave me a quick hug, and walked out. I felt tears of joy for her beginning to form; she did not look back and sauntered out.

Six Months Later

As promised, Samantha contacted me about six months after our last visit. She sent me a letter and photographs, describing and depicting some of her happy moments in her new life. She was quick to point out how much she missed me and our work but that she was doing quite well. Clearly her life was not perfect, as she had her moments of despair and anxiety, but she knew she would come out of it as she took time to self-analyze, which helped. At the time, she said she felt no need to come see me even though she wanted to very much. She restated her option to contact me at some point in the future, but for now, she wanted to see how well she could handle things on her own.

I felt as though I was reading a very cheerful letter from someone, like a daughter, who was having such a good time playing outside that she did not want to come back inside the house and get bogged down by the drudgery of her homework. But, since she had become such a good student, analytically, she knew the material well anyway. Samantha assured me that if she needed me, she would know when and where to find me. Here are excerpts from her letter:

> I'm not panicky and feel I can really take care of myself. . . . I actually feel like I am living. . . . Our work has really given me a completely new lease on life. . . . It's funny how you are alive in me. . . . I was tempted to call you to make an appointment, but I decided I'm not ready yet. I still need to work on dealing with my past and our ending myself. You have given me so much faith in myself that at times it is overwhelming.
>
> I'll be in touch,
> Samantha

Discussion

Samantha, as her dreams seemed to indicate, preferred to go it alone after termination. Like the dream of her best friend with whom she lost contact, she carried her analyst around in her heart and was quite content. And, as the dream of the cots in the army base suggested, even if she left something behind, she did not want to return for it, especially if she was unsure if it was hers. She was ready to give up her mother's shoes and live her own life, freer and happier than before. Even if the trip was bumpy and uncertain at times, as in her train ride dream, she felt confident enough in herself to know she could get through it by herself. Samantha habitually overstudied for tests throughout her life, and as she prepared for her final exam in analysis, i.e., termination, she never quite felt prepared. But, now she had her "extra readings," her self-analytic capacity, and could do it on her own. Even though her coach, the analyst, caught her by surprise by telling her the day of the race was "tomorrow," she had been practicing all along and was about as in shape for the event as she could be. And, she was so glad to know that she could walk away from the endless family orgy of overstimulation which she relived on the couch each day. She reached a point where she owned her mind, her body, and her past. Samantha had a higher level dissociative character, and her "it's not me!" self was more in the "it's me and it's not me" position instead of the fully disowned "it's not me!" position (see chapter 8 on integration) seen in the bona fide multiple personality. So, for her to ultimately conclude that "it is me!" afterward, i.e., to acknowledge, feel, and own her past incestuous experiences with her uncle, was not as dramatic as in more dissociated cases seemingly with fully formed separate identities or selves. Nevertheless, her analysis was quite lengthy as preoedipal, separation–individuation issues fueled a deeply entrenched masochistic resistance which required extensive working through in order for her to acquire object constancy (Blum, 1987a; Emde, 1988a,b).

Knowing that she had had an impact on me also seemed to be vital in order for her to terminate. For her to have her perceptions validated that she had induced feelings in me helped her trust her judgment. If she could trust her judgment about what she may have sensed in me at times, then perhaps she could trust her judgment about what came to her mind about her troubled childhood. In addition, for her to realize that she could affect people emotionally would mean that she indeed could have influence or power over others. It also meant that she had some role or responsibility in what happened in her encounters with them. She had apparently dissociated any knowledge of her effect on others in order to defend against her deep guilt over her incestuous relationship with her uncle, especially when she was older. So, she vacillated between self-destruction, guilt of unknown or displaced origin, and her style of pseudostupidity, which was a blend of negation, denial, projection of guilt, and a great difficulty in learning, all of which was facilitated through defensive altered states of consciousness.

She could not allow herself to know anything well, for to know anything well meant having to acknowledge, remember, and accept responsibility. She simply could not fathom how susceptible and faultless she had been as a young girl because she mercilessly berated herself for not knowing better when she got older. Her vicious superego needed to be tamed so that she could eventually "see" how it could have happened and forgive herself. Along the way, she needed to learn the difference between guilt, involvement, culpability, and responsibility as a mature adult.

Samantha's self-imposed pressure by setting termination dates (Orens, 1955) gave her a way out, while at the same time may have also replicated the build-up of explosive erotic tension as a child. Each cycle of increased stimulation was followed by relief, gratification, and the anticipation of yet another build-up. And, although she was able to further the process in this spasmodic way, she knew she had more work to do. But, she was able to free herself up enough to learn, which was a liberating triumph from her mental bondage, and she was elated.

Interestingly, an incomplete analysis, according to Kantrowitz, Katz, and Paolitto (1990) was found to be less important than the acquisition of the self-analyzing function as a predictor of posttermination functioning. Samantha's six-month report indicated that she was relying on her self-analytic work to help her struggle through the demands of posttermination life. And, just as she was tempted to call me for an appointment but did not, I, too, was tempted to contact her for a follow-up appointment and did not.

As was discussed at the panel at the American Psychoanalytic in 1987 on postanalytic follow-up (Panel, 1989), contacting the patient for research purposes and outcome data may be at cross-purposes with the analysand's best interests. It may interfere with the necessary work of separation, mourning, and subsequent emotional growth, especially if the treating analyst and the follow-up analyst are the same. I felt that this caveat was especially relevant to this case, and since follow-up was not discussed at the beginning of treatment, I did not want to introduce a new variable during her termination.

In Samantha's words, she said the same thing: "I think when I have all (well, not all, I want to see you before I'm 90!) this stuff sorted through, I'd like to visit you." In the meantime, she is living her life and is proud to be able to do so. It is not in the spirit of analysis to do anything other than respect her wishes and look forward to hearing from her when she sends me an annual update on the anniversary of her termination.

REFERENCES

Abraham, B. (1986), *The Angel of Death—The Mengele Dossier.* Brazil: Sherit Haplieta.

Abse, D. W. (1974), Hysterical conversion and dissociative syndromes and the hysterical character. In: *American Handbook of Psychiatry,* ed. S. Arieti & E. B. Brody. New York: Basic Books, pp. 155–194.

——— (1983), Multiple personality. In: *New Psychiatric Syndromes: DSM-III and Beyond,* ed. S. Akhtar. New York: Jason Aronson, pp. 339–361.

——— (1987), *Hysteria and Related Mental Disorders,* 2nd ed. Bristol, U.K.: Wright.

Adair, M. (1993), A speculation on perversion and hallucination. *Internat. J. Psycho-Anal.,* 74:81–92.

Adelman, S. (1985), Pills as transitional objects. A dynamic understanding of the use of medication in psychotherapy. *Psychiatry,* 48:246–253.

Adler, G. (1989), Transitional phenomena, projective identification, and the essential ambiguity of the psychoanalytic situation. *Psychoanal. Quart.,* 58:81–104.

Akhtar, S. (1992), *Broken Structures.* Northvale, NJ: Jason Aronson.

——— (1995), Aggression: Theories regarding its nature and origins. In: *Psychoanalysis: The Major Concepts,* ed. B. Moore & B. Fine. New Haven, CT: Yale University Press.

——— (1996), "Someday" . . . and "If only" . . . fantasies. *J. Amer. Psychoanal Assn.,* 44:723–744.

——— Brenner, I. (1979), Differential diagnosis of fugue-like states. *J. Clin. Psychiatry,* 40:381–385.

Alexander, F. (1929), Need for punishment and the death instinct. *Internat. J. Psycho-Anal.,* 10:256–269.

——— (1950), *Psychosomatic Medicine—Its Principles and Applications.* New York: W. W. Norton.

——— French, T. M. (1946), *Psychoanalytic Therapy.* New York: Ronald Press.

American Psychiatric Association (1994), *The Diagnostic and Statistical Manual of Mental Disorders,* 4th ed. (DSM-IV). Washington, DC: American Psychiatric Press.

Anzieu, D. (1987), Some alterations of the ego which are interminable. *Internat. J. Psycho-Anal.,* 68:9–19.

Apprey, M. (1993), The African-American experience: Forced immigration and transgenerational trauma. *Mind & Human Interact.,* 4:70–75.

Arlow, J. A. (1959), The structure of the déjà vu experience. *J. Amer. Psychoanal. Assn.,* 7:611–631.

——— (1966), Depersonalization and derealization. In: *Psychoanalysis—A General Psychology: Essays in Honor of Heinz Hartmann,* ed. R. M. Loewenstein, L. M. Newman, M. Schur, & A. J. Solnit. New York: International Universities Press, pp. 456–478.

——— (1969), Fantasy, memory, and reality testing. *Psychoanal. Quart.,* 38:28–51.

——— (1992), Altered ego states. *Israel J. Psychiatry Relat. Sci.,* 29:65–76.

——— (1996), The concept of psychic reality—How useful? *Internat. J. Psycho-Anal.,* 77:659–666.

Armstrong, J. (1991), The psychological organization of "multiple personality" disordered patients as revealed in psychological testing. *Psychiatric Clin. N. Amer.,* 14:533–546.

Aron, L. (1991), The patient's experiences of the analyst's subjectivity. *Psychoanal. Dial.,* 1:29–51.

——— (1996), *Meeting of the Minds: Mutuality in Psychoanalysis.* Hillside, NJ: Analytic Press.

Azima, H. (1959), Psychodynamic alterations concomitant with Tofranil administration. *J. Amer. Psychoanal. Assn.,* 4:172–176.

Back to the Future (1985), Universal City, CA: Universal City Studios.

Bader, M. (1993), The analyst's use of humor. *Psychoanal. Quart.,* 62:23–51.

Bak, R. C. (1968), The phallic woman: The ubiquitous fantasy in perversion. *The Psychoanalytic Study of the Child,* 23:15–36. New York: International Universities Press.

Balter, L., Lothane, Z., & Spence, J. H. (1980), On the analyzing instrument. *Psychoanal. Quart.,* 49:474–504.

Baranger, M., Baranger, W., & Mom, J. M. (1988), The infantile psychic trauma from us to Freud: Pure trauma, retroactivity, and reconstruction. *Internat. J. Psycho-Anal.,* 69:113–128.

Barkin, R., Braun, B. G., & Kluft, R. P. (1986), The dilemma of drug therapy for multiple personality disorder. In: *Treatment of Multiple Personality*

Disorder, ed. B. G. Braun. Washington, DC: American Psychiatric Press, pp. 107–132.

Barrett, D. (1995), The dream character as prototype for the multiple personality alter. *Dissociation,* 8:61–68.

Beitman, B. (1992), Medications during psychotherapy. Case studies of the reciprocal relationship between psychotherapy process and medication use. In: *Integrating Pharmacotherapy and Psychotherapy.* Washington, DC: American Psychiatric Press, pp. 21–43.

Bellak, L. (1966), Effects of antidepressant drugs on psychodynamics. *Psychosomatics,* 7:106–114.

Bergmann, H., & Jucovy, M., Eds. (1982), *Generations of the Holocaust.* New York: Basic Books.

Berman, E. (1981), Multiple personality: Psychoanalytic perspectives. *Internat. J. Psycho-Anal.,* 62:283–300.

Berzoff, J., & Darwin, J. (1995), Treatment of character or treatment of traumas? In: *Dissociative Identity Disorder,* ed. L. Cohen, J. Berzoff, & M. Elin. Northvale, NJ: Jason Aronson, pp. 447–466.

Bibring, E. (1941), The development and problems of the theory of the instincts. *Internat. J. Psycho-Anal.,* 22:102–131.

——— (1954), Psychoanalysis and the dynamic psychotherapies. *J. Amer. Psychoanal. Assn.,* 2:745–769.

Blank, A. S. (1985), The unconscious flashback to the war in Viet Nam veterans: Clinical mystery, legal defense, and community problems. In: *The Trauma of War: Stress and Recovery in Viet Nam Veterans,* ed. S. M. Sonnenberg, A. S. Blank, & J. A. Talbott. Washington, DC: American Psychiatric Press, pp. 293–308.

Bliss, E. L. (1986), *"Multiple Personality," Allied Disorders, and Hypnosis.* New York: Oxford University Press.

Blum, H. (1986), On identification and its vicissitudes. *Internat. J. Psycho-Anal.,* 67:267–276.

——— (1987a), Analysis, terminable and interminable: A half century perspective. *Internat. J. Psycho-Anal.,* 68:37–47.

——— (1987b), The role of identification in the resolution of trauma. *Psychoanal. Quart.,* 56:609–627.

——— (1997), Seduction trauma: Representation, deferred action and pathogenic development. *J. Amer. Psychoanal. Assn.,* 44:1147–1164.

Boesky, D. (1969), The reversal of deja raconte. *J. Amer. Psychoanal. Assn.,* 17:1114–1141.

Bollas, C. (1987), *The Shadow of the Object: Psychoanalysis of the Unthought Known.* New York: Columbia University Press.

Braun, B. G. (1983), Neuropsychological changes in multiple personality due to integration: A preliminary report. *Amer. J. Clin. Hypn.,* 26:84–92.

—— (1984), Towards a theory of multiple personality and other dissociative phenomena. *Psychiatric Clin. N. Amer.*, 7:171–193.

Brenneis, B. (1994), Belief and suggestion in the recovery of memories of childhood sexual abuse. *J. Amer. Psychoanal. Assn.*, 42:1027–1054.

—— (1995), On Brenner's "The dissociative character." Letter to the editor. *J. Amer. Psychoanal. Assn.*, 43:297–300.

Brenner, C. (1982), *The Mind in Conflict*. New York: International Universities Press.

Brenner, I. (1988a), Unconscious fantasies of the selection in children of Holocaust survivors. Presented at the first Jerusalem International Conference of Children of Survivors, Dec.

—— (1988b), Multisensory bridges in response to object loss during the Holocaust. *Psychoanal. Rev.*, 75:573–587.

—— (1991), The unconscious wish to develop AIDS: A case report. In: *The Homosexualities and the Therapeutic Process,* ed. C. Socarides & V. Volkan. Madison, CT: International Universities Press, pp. 251–275.

—— (1994), A twentieth century demonologic neurosis? *J. Psychohistory,* 21:500–504.

—— (1995), Letter to the editor. *J. Amer. Psychoanal. Assn.*, 43:300–303.

—— (1996), On trauma, perversion, and "multiple personality." *J. Amer. Psychoanal. Assn.*, 44:785–814.

—— (1997), Letter to the editor. *J. Amer. Psychoanal. Assn.*, 45:1285–1287.

Breuer, J., & Freud, S. (1893–1985), Studies on Hysteria. *Standard Edition,* 2. London: Hogarth Press, 1955.

Buck, O. D. (1983), Multiple personality as a borderline state. *J. Nerv. Ment. Dis.*, 171:62–65.

Bush, F. (1994), Some ambiguities in the methods of free association and their implications for technique. *J. Amer. Psychoanal. Assn.*, 42:363–384.

Bush, N. E. (1983), The near-death experience in children: Shades of the prison-house reopening. *Anabiosis,* 3:177–190.

Calef, V. (1972), "I am awake": Insomnia or dream? An addendum to the forgetting of dreams. *Psychoanal. Quart.*, 41:161–171.

—— Weinshel, E. (1981), Some clinical consequences of introjection: Gaslighting. *Psychoanal. Quart.*, 50:44–65.

—— —— Renik, O., & Mayer, E. (1980), Enuresis: A functional equivalent of a fetish. *Internat. J. Psycho-Anal.*, 61:295–305.

Caul, D. (1984), Group and videotape techniques for multiple personality. *Psychiatr. Ann.*, 14:43–50.

Cavenar, J., & Nash, J. (1976), The dream as a signal for termination. *J. Amer. Psychoanal. Assn.*, 24:425–436.

Chasseguet-Smirgel, J. (1976), Freud and female sexuality: Blind spots in the "dark continent." *Internat. J. Psycho-Anal.,* 57:275–286.

—— (1978), Reflexions on the connexions between perversion and sadism. *Internat. J. Psycho-Anal.,* 59:27–35.

—— (1981), Loss of reality in perversions—With special reference to fetishism. *J. Amer. Psychoanal. Assn.,* 29:511–534.

—— (1988), A woman's attempt at a perverse solution and its failure. *Internat. J. Psycho-Anal.,* 67:23–42.

Clarey, W. F., Burstin, K. J., & Carpenter, J. S. (1984), Multiple personality and borderline personality disorders. *Psychiatric Clin. N. Amer.,* 7:89–99.

Clifft, M. (1986), Writing about psychiatric patients. *Bull. Menninger Clin.,* 50:511–524.

Coons, P., Bowan, E., & Milstein, V. (1988), Multiple personality disorder—a clinical investigation of 50 cases. *J. Nerv. Ment. Dis.,* 176:519–527.

Danieli, Y. (1980), Countertransference in the treatment and study of Nazi Holocaust survivors and their children. *Victimology,* 5:355–367.

Davies, J., & Frawley, M. (1994), *Treating the Adult Survivor of Childhood Sexual Abuse.* New York: Basic Books.

Deutsch, H. (1926), Occult processes occurring during psychoanalysis. In: *Psychoanalysis and the Occult,* ed. G. Devereux. New York: International Universities Press, pp. 133–146.

—— (1942), Some forms of emotional disturbance and their relationship to schizophrenia. *Psychoanal. Quart.,* 11:301–321.

Devereux, G. (1953a), A summary of Istvan Holos' theories. In: *Psychoanalysis and the Occult,* ed. G. Devereux. New York: International Universities Press, pp. 159–203.

—— (1953b), The technique of analyzing "occult" occurrences in analysis. In: *Psychoanalysis and the Occult,* ed. G. Devereux. New York: International Universities Press, pp. 391–417.

Dickes, R. (1965), The defensive function of an altered state of consciousness: A hypnoid state. *J. Amer. Psychoanal. Assn.,* 13:365–403.

—— (1967), Severe regression disruptions of the therapeutic alliance. *J. Amer. Psychoanal. Assn.,* 15:508–533.

—— Papernik, D. S. (1977), Defensive alterations of consciousness: Hypnoid states, sleep, and the dream. *J. Amer. Psychoanal. Assn.,* 25:635–654.

Ehrenberg, D. B. (1992), *The Intimate Edge: Extending the Reach of Psychoanalytic Interaction.* New York: W. W. Norton.

Eisenbud, J. (1946), Telepathy and problems of psychoanalysis. *Psychoanal. Quart.,* 15:32–87.

Eissler, K. R. (1971), Death drive, ambivalence, and narcissism. *The Psychoanalytic Study of the Child,* 26:25–78. Chicago: Quadrangle.

Ellenberger, H. F. (1970), *The Discovery of the Unconscious: The History and Evolution of Dynamic Psychiatry.* New York: Basic Books.

Ellis, A. (1947), Telepathy and psychoanalysis: A critique of recent "findings." *Psychiatric Quart.,* 21:607–659.

Emde, R. N. (1988a), Development terminable and interminable: I Innate and motivational failures from infancy. *Internat. J. Psycho-Anal.,* 69:23–42.

——— (1988b), Development terminable and interminable: II Recent psychoanalytic theory and therapeutic considerations. *Internat. J. Psycho-Anal.,* 69:283–296.

Epstein, H. (1979), *Children of the Holocaust.* New York: G. P. Putnam.

Erickson, M. H., & Kubie, L. S. (1939), The permanent relief of an obsessional phobia by means of communications with an unsuspected dual personality. *Psychoanal. Quart.,* 8:471–509.

Estabrooks, G. H. (1945), Hypnotism in warfare. In: *Hypnotism.* New York: E. P. Dutton, pp. 185–205.

Exetein, I., & Bowers, M. D., Jr. (1979), State and trait in psychiatric practice. *Amer. J. Psychiatry,* 136:690–693.

Faimberg, H. (1988), The telescoping of generations. *Contemp. Psychoanal.,* 23:99–118.

Fairbairn, W. R. D. (1952), *An Object-Relations Theory of the Personality.* New York: Basic Books.

Fayek, A. (1981), Narcissism and the death instinct. *Internat. J. Psycho-Anal.,* 62:309–322.

Federn, P. (1932), The reality of the death instinct, especially in melancholia. *Psychoanal. Rev.,* 19:129–151.

——— (1952), *Ego Psychology and the Psychoses,* ed. E. Weiss. New York: Basic Books.

Fenichel, O. (1941), *Problems of Psychoanalytic Technique.* Albany, NY: Psychoanalytic Quarterly.

——— (1942), In "Symposium on neurotic disturbances of sleep." *Internat. J. Psycho-Anal.,* 23:49–68.

——— (1945), *The Psychoanalytic Theory of Neurosis.* New York: W. W. Norton.

Ferenczi, S. (1914a), Falling asleep during the analysis. In: *Further Contributions to the Theory and Technique of Psychoanalysis.* New York: Basic Books, 1952, pp. 249–250.

——— (1914b), Discontinuous analysis. In: *Further Contributions to the Theory and Technique of Psychoanalysis.* New York: Brunner/Mazel, 1980, pp. 233–235.

—— (1927), The problem of the termination of the analysis. In: *Final Contributions to the Problems and Methods of Psychoanalysis,* ed. M. Balint. New York: Basic Books, 1955, pp. 77–86.

—— (1929a), The principle of relaxation and neocatharsis. In: *Final Contributions to the Problems and Methods of Psychoanalysis,* ed. M. Balint. New York: Basic Books, pp. 108–125.

—— (1929b), The unwelcome child and his death-instinct. *Internat. J. Psycho-Anal.,* 10:125–129.

—— (1933), Confusion of tongues between adults and the child. In: *Final Contributions to the Problems and Methods of Psychoanalysis,* ed. M. Balint. New York: Basic Books, 1955, pp. 156–167.

Ferguson, M. (1990), Mirroring process, hypnotic processes, and multiple personality. *Psychoanal. & Contemp. Thought,* 13:417–450.

Fine, C. G. (1991), Treatment stabilization and crisis prevention: Pacing the therapy of the multiple personality dissociative patient. *Psych. Clin. N. Amer.,* 14:661–675.

—— (1993), A tactical integrationalist perspective on the treatment of multiple personality disorder. In: *Clinical Perspectives on Multiple Personality Disorder,* ed. R. P. Kluft & C. G. Fine. Washington, DC: American Psychiatric Press, pp. 135–153.

Fink, D. (1993), Observations on the role of transitional objects and transitional phenomena in patients with multiple personality disorder. In: *Clinical Perspectives on Multiple Personality Disorder,* ed. R. P. Kluft & C. G. Fine. Washington, DC: American Psychiatric Press, pp. 241–252.

—— Golinkoff, M. (1990), Multiple personality disorder, borderline personality disorder, and schizophrenia: A comparative study of clinical features. *Dissociation,* 3:127–134.

Firestein, S. K. (1978), *Termination in Analysis.* New York: International Universities Press.

Fisher, C., & Joseph, E. D. (1949), Fugue with awareness of loss of personal identity. *Psychoanal. Quart.,* 18:480–493.

Fliess, R. (1953), The hypnotic evasion: A clinical observation. *Psychoanal. Quart.,* 22:497–516.

Fodor, N. (1947), Telepathy in analysis. *Psychoanal. Quart.,* 21:171–189.

Fogelman, E., & Savran, B. (1979), Therapy groups for children of Holocaust survivors. *Internat. J. Group Psychother.,* 29:211–236.

Frankel, F. H. (1990), Hypnotizability and dissociation. *Amer. J. Psychiatry,* 147:823–829.

Freud, A. (1936), The Ego and the Mechanisms of Defense. In: *Writings,* Vol. 2. New York: International Universities Press, 1966.

—— (1954), Problems of technique in adult analysis. In: *Writings,* Vol. 4. New York: International Universities Press, 1968, pp. 377–406.

Freud, S. (1891), Hypnosis. *Standard Edition*, 1:103–104. London: Hogarth Press, 1966.

—— (1899), A premonitory dream fulfilled. *Collected Papers*, 5:70–73. London: Hogarth Press, 1950.

—— (1900), The Interpretation of Dreams. *Standard Edition*, 4. London: Hogarth Press, 1953.

—— (1901), The Psychopathology of Everyday Life. *Standard Edition*, 6. London: Hogarth Press, 1960.

—— (1905), Three Essays on the Theory of Sexuality. *Standard Edition*, 7:123–243. London: Hogarth Press, 1953.

—— (1913), On beginning the treatment. *Standard Edition*, 12:121–144. London: Hogarth Press, 1958.

—— (1915), The unconscious. *Standard Edition*, 14:159–204. London: Hogarth Press, 1957.

—— (1916), Some character-types met with in psycho-analytic work. *Standard Edition*, 14:309–333. London: Hogarth Press, 1957.

—— (1917), A metapsychological supplement to the theory of dreams. *Standard Edition*, 14:217–235. London: Hogarth Press, 1957.

—— (1919a), ''A child is being beaten'': A contribution to the study of the origin of sexual perversions. *Standard Edition*, 17:175–204. London: Hogarth Press, 1955.

—— (1919b), The uncanny. *Standard Edition*, 17:219–258. London: Hogarth Press, 1955.

—— (1920a), Beyond the Pleasure Principle. *Standard Edition*, 18:1–64. London: Hogarth Press, 1955.

—— (1920b), The psychogenesis of homosexuality in a woman. *Standard Edition*, 18:145–172. London: Hogarth Press, 1955.

—— (1922), Dreams and telepathy. *Standard Edition*, 18:195–220. London: Hogarth Press, 1955.

—— (1923a), Remarks upon the theory and practice of dream interpretation. *Standard Edition*, 19:107–121. London: Hogarth Press, 1961.

—— (1923b), The Ego and the Id. *Standard Edition*, 19:1–59. London: Hogarth Press, 1961.

—— (1924), The economic problem of masochism. *Standard Edition*, 19:155–170. London: Hogarth Press, 1961.

—— (1925a), Negation. *Standard Edition*, 19:233–239. London: Hogarth Press, 1961.

—— (1925b), Inhibitions, symptoms, and anxiety. *Standard Edition*, 20:87–182. London: Hogarth Press, 1961.

—— (1925c), The occult significance of dreams. *Collected Papers*, 5:158–162. London: Hogarth Press, 1961.

———— (1927), Fetishism. *Standard Edition,* 21:147–157. London: Hogarth Press, 1961.

———— (1933), New Introductory Lectures. *Standard Edition,* 22. London: Hogarth Press, 1964.

———— (1937), Analysis terminable and interminable. *Standard Edition,* 23:209–253. London: Hogarth Press, 1964.

———— (1939), Moses and Monotheism. *Standard Edition,* 23:1–137. London: Hogarth Press, 1964.

———— (1940a), An Outline of Psycho-Analysis. *Standard Edition,* 23:139–207. London: Hogarth Press, 1964.

———— (1940b), Splitting of the ego in the process of defence. *Standard Edition,* 23:271–278. London: Hogarth Press, 1964.

Friedman, L. (1985), Towards a comprehensive theory of treatment. *Psychoanal. Inq.,* 5:589–600.

Furst, S. S. (1967), Psychic trauma: A survey. In: *Psychic Trauma,* ed. S. S. Furst. New York: Basic Books, pp. 3–50.

Gabbard, G. (1990), *Psychodynamic Psychiatry in Clinical Practice.* Washington, DC: American Psychiatric Press.

———— Twemlow, S. W. (1984), The metapsychology of altered mind/body perception. In: *With the Eyes of the Mind: An Empirical Analysis of Out-of-Body States.* New York: Praeger, pp. 169–183.

Gaddini, E. (1972), Aggression and the pleasure principle: Towards a psychoanalytic theory of aggression. *Internat. J. Psycho-Anal.,* 53:191–197.

Galenson, E., & Roiphe, H. (1972), The impact of early sexual discovery on mood, defensive organization, and symbolization. *The Psychoanalytic Study of the Child,* 26:195–216. Chicago: Quadrangle.

Gampel, Y. (1982), A daughter of silence. In: *Generations of the Holocaust,* ed. M. Bergmann & M. Jucovy. New York: Basic Books, pp. 120–136.

Garcia, E. E. (1990), A brief note on "Jekyll and Hyde" and M.P.D. *Dissociation,* 3:165–166.

Garma, A. (1971), Within the realm of the death instinct. *Internat. J. Psycho-Anal.,* 52:145–154.

Gedo, J. E. (1965), Unmarried motherhood. *Internat. J. Psycho-Anal.,* 46:352–357.

Gill, M. M. (1982), *Analysis of Transference,* Vol. 1. New York: International Universities Press.

Gillespie, W. H. (1940), A contribution to the study of fetishism. *Internat. J. Psycho-Anal.,* 21:401–415.

———— (1952), Notes on the analysis of sexual perversions. *Internat. J. Psycho-Anal.,* 33:397–402.

Glover, E. (1929), The screening function of traumatic memories. *Internat. J. Psycho-Anal.,* 10:90–93.

——— (1931), The therapeutic effect of inexact interpretation: A contribution to the theory of suggestion. *Internat. J. Psycho-Anal.,* 12:397–411.

——— (1933), The relation of perversion-formation to the development of reality-sense. *Internat. J. Psycho-Anal.,* 14:486–504.

——— (1943), The concept of dissociation. *Internat. J. Psycho-Anal.,* 24:7–13.

——— (1954), The indications for psychoanalysis. *J. Ment. Sci.,* 100:393–401.

——— (1955), The terminal phase. In: *The Technique of Psychoanalysis.* New York: International Universities Press, pp. 138–164.

——— (1958), *The Technique of Psychoanalysis,* 2nd ed. New York: International Universities Press.

Goldberg, A. (1990), *The Prison-house of Psychoanalysis.* Hillsdale, NJ: Analytic Press.

——— (1997), Writing case histories. *Internat. J. Psycho-Anal.,* 78:435–438.

——— Marcus, D. (1985), Natural termination: Ending analysis without setting a date. *Psychoanal. Quart.,* 54:46–65.

Good, M. I. (1994), The reconstruction of early childhood trauma: Fantasy, reality, and verification. *J. Amer. Psychoanal. Assn.,* 42:79–101.

Gray, P. (1973), Psychoanalytic technique: Ego capacity to view intrapsychic activity. *J. Amer. Psychoanal. Assn.,* 21:474–494.

Greaves, G. B. (1980), "Multiple personality"—165 years after Mary Reynolds. *J. Nerv. Ment. Dis.,* 168:577–596.

——— (1989), Precursors to integration in multiple personality disorder. *Dissociation,* 2:225–231.

——— (1993), A history of multiple personality disorder. In: *Clinical Perspectives on Multiple Personality Disorder,* ed. R. P. Kluft & C. G. Fine. Washington, DC: American Psychiatric Press, pp. 355–380.

Greenacre, P. (1968), Perversions: General considerations regarding their genetic and dynamic background. *The Psychoanalytic Study of the Child,* 23:4–62. New York: International Universities Press.

——— (1969), The fetish and the transitional object. *The Psychoanalytic Study of the Child,* 24:144–164. New York: International Universities Press.

Greenberg, J. (1995), Psychoanalytic technique and the interactive matrix. *Psychoanal. Quart.,* 64:1–22.

Greenson, R. (1967), *The Technique and Practice of Psychoanalysis.* New York: International Universities Press.

Greyson, B. (1981a), Toward a psychological explanation of near-death experiences. *Anabiosis,* 1:88–103.

——— (1981b), Near-death experiences and attempted suicide. *Suicide Life-Threat. Behav.,* 11:10–16.

———— (1983a), The psychodynamics of near-death experiences. *J. Nerv. Ment. Dis.*, 171:376–381.

———— (1983b), Increase in psychic phenomena following near-death experiences. *Theta*, 11:26–29.

———— (1997), Near death narratives. In: *The Varieties of Dissociative Experience: Implications for Theory, Research, and Treatment*, ed. S. Krippner & S. M. Powers. New York: Basic Books.

Grinberg, L. (1980), Closing phase treatment and the adult's "search for the truth about oneself." *Internat. J. Psycho-Anal.*, 61:25–37.

Grossman, L. (1992), An example of "character perversion" in a woman. *Psychoanal. Quart.*, 61:581–589.

———— (1993), The perverse attitude toward reality. *Psychoanal. Quart.*, 62:422–436.

Grossman, W. (1991), Pain, aggression, fantasy, and concepts of sadomasochism. *Psychoanal. Quart.*, 60:22–52.

Groth-Marnat, G. (1989), Paranormal phenomena and the near-death experience. In: *Exploring the Paranormal: Perspectives on Belief and Experience*, ed. G. Z. Zollschan, J. F. Schumaker, & G. F. Walsh. Dorset, U.K.: Prism, pp. 105–116.

Grubrich-Simitis, L. G. (1981), Extreme traumatization as cumulative trauma. *The Psychoanalytic Study of the Child*, 36:415–450. New Haven, CT: Yale University Press.

Gruenwald, D. (1977), "Multiple personality" and splitting phenomena: A reconceptualization. *J. Nerv. Ment. Dis.*, 164:385–393.

Hamburg, D. A. (1973), An evolutionary and developmental approach to human aggressiveness. *Psychoanal. Quart.*, 42:185–196.

Hamilton, J. (1976), Some comments about Freud's conceptualization of the death instinct. *Internat. Rev. Psycho-Anal.*, 3:151–164.

Hamilton, M., Ed. (1974), *Fish's Clinical Psychopathology*. Bristol, U.K.: John Wright.

Hann-Kende, F. (1933), On the role of transference and countertransference in psychoanalysis. In: *Psychoanalysis and the Occult*, ed. G. Devereux. New York: International Universities Press, 1953, pp. 158–167.

Hartlaub, G., Martin, G., & Rhine, M. (1986), Recontact with the analyst following termination: A survey of seventy-one cases. *J. Amer. Psychoanal. Assn.*, 35:895–910.

Hartmann, H. (1939), *Ego Psychology and the Problems of Adaptation*. New York: International Universities Press, 1958.

———— (1952), The mutual influence on the development of ego and id. In: *Essays on Ego Psychology*. New York: International Universities Press, pp. 151–181.

—————— Kris, E., & Lowenstein, R. M. (1949), Notes on the theory of aggression. *The Psychoanalytic Study of the Child,* 3/4:9–36. New York: International Universities Press.

Hastie, D. (1990), Telomere reduction in human colorectal cancer and with aging. *Nature,* 346:865–868.

Hayman, M. (1967), Drugs and the psychoanalyst. *Amer. J. Psychotherapy,* 21:644–654.

Herman, J. L. (1992), *Trauma and Recovery.* New York: Basic Books.

Herzog, J. (1982), World beyond metaphor: Thoughts on the transmission of trauma. In: *Generations of the Holocaust,* ed. M. Bergmann & M. Jucovy. New York: Basic Books, pp. 103–119.

Hilgard, E. (1977), *Divided Consciousness: Multiple Controls in Human Thought and Action.* New York: Wiley.

Hitchcock, J. (1984), The sinking feeling. *The Psychoanalytic Study of the Child,* 39:321–329. New Haven, CT: Yale University Press.

Hitschmann, E. (1924), Telepathy and psychoanalysis. *Internat. J. Psycho-Anal.,* 5:423–438.

—————— (1933), Telepathy during psychoanalysis. In: *Psychoanalysis and the Occult,* ed. G. Devereux. New York: International Universities Press, 1953, pp. 128–132.

Hollos, I. (1933), Psychopathologie alltaglicher telepathischer erscheinumgen. *Imago,* 19:529–546.

Hunter, R. C. (1967), On the experience of nearly dying. *Amer. J. Psychiatry,* 124:84–88.

Irwin, H. J. (1992), Origins and functions of paranormal belief: The role of childhood trauma and interpersonal control. *J. Amer. Soc. Psychic. Res.,* 86:199–208.

—————— (1994), Paranormal belief and proneness to dissociation. *Psychol. Rep.,* 75:1344–1346.

Isakower, O. (1938), A contribution to the pathopsychology associated with falling asleep. *Internat. J. Psycho-Anal.,* 19:331–345.

Jackel, M. (1966), Interruptions during psychoanalytic treatment and the wish for a child. *J. Amer. Psychoanal. Assn.,* 14:730–735.

Jacobs, T. (1973), Posture, gesture and movement in the analyst: Cues to interpretation and countertransference. *J. Amer. Psychoanal. Assn.,* 21:77–92.

—————— (1991), *The Use of the Self.* Madison, CT: International Universities Press.

Jacobson, E. (1964), *The Self and the Object World.* New York: International Universities Press.

James, W. (1890), *The Principles of Psychology.* New York: Dover, 1950.

Janet, P. (1889), *L'Automatisme Psychologique.* Paris: Baillière.

———— (1907), *The Major Symptoms of Hysteria.* New York: Macmillan.

Jaynes, J. (1976), *The Origin of Consciousness in the Breakdown of the Bicameral Mind.* Boston: Houghton Mifflin.

Jones, E. (1953), *The Life and Work of Sigmund Freud,* Vol. 1. New York: Basic Books.

———— (1957), *The Life and Work of Sigmund Freud,* Vol. 3. New York: Basic Books.

Jucovy, M. (1986), The Holocaust. In: *The Reconstruction of Trauma—Its Significance in Clinical Work,* ed. A. Rothstein. Madison, CT: International Universities Press, pp. 153–169.

Jung, C. G. (1902), *Zur Psychologie und Pathologie sogenannter okkulter Phanomene.* Leipzig: Mutze.

———— (1939), On the psychogenesis of schizophrenia. In: *The Collected Works of C. G. Jung,* Vol. 3. Princeton, NJ: Princeton University Press, 1960, pp. 233–249.

Kafka, J. (1969), The body as transitional object: A psychoanalytic study of a self-mutilating patient. *Brit. J. Med. Psychol.,* 42:207–212.

Kantrowitz, J., Katz, A., & Paolitto, F. (1990), Follow-up of psychoanalysis five to ten years after the termination: 1. Stability of change. *J. Amer. Psychoanal. Assn.,* 38:471–496.

Kanzer, M. (1985), Identification and its vicissitudes. *Internat. J. Psycho-Anal.,* 66:19–30.

Kernberg, O. (1975), *Borderline Conditions and Pathological Narcissism.* New York: Jason Aronson.

———— (1982), Self, ego, affects, and drives. *J. Amer. Psychoanal. Assn.,* 30:893–918.

———— (1991), Sadomasochism, sexual excitement, and perversion. *J. Amer. Psychoanal. Assn.,* 39:333–362.

———— (1992), *Aggression in Personality Disorders and Perversions.* New Haven, CT: Yale University Press.

Kessler, R. J. (1992), Medication and psychotherapy. In: *Psychotherapy: The Analytic Approach,* ed. M. J. Aronson & M. A. Scharfman. Northvale, NJ: Jason Aronson, pp. 163–182.

Kestenberg, J. (1972), Psychoanalytic contributions to the problem of children of survivors from Nazi persecution. *Israel Ann. Psychiatry & Rel. Disciplines,* 10:311–325.

———— (1975), From organ object imagery to self and object representation. In: *Children and Parents.* New York: Jason Aronson, pp. 215–234.

———— (1980), Psychoanalyses of children of survivors from the Holocaust: Case presentations and assessment. *J. Amer. Psychoanal. Assn.,* 28:775–804.

———— (1982), A metapsychological assessment based on an analysis of a survivor's child. In: *Generations of the Holocaust,* ed. M. Bergmann & M. Jucovy. New York: Basic Books, pp. 137–158.

———— Brenner, I. (1986), Children who survived the Holocaust. *Internat. J. Psycho-Anal.,* 67:309–316.

———— ———— (1988), Le narcissism au service de la survie. *Rev. Franç. Psychoanal.,* 6:1393–1408.

———— ———— (1995), Narcissism in the service of survival. In: *The Vulnerable Child,* Vol. 2, ed. T. Cohen, M. H. Etezady, & B. Pacella. Madison, CT: International Universities Press, pp. 35–50.

———— ———— (1996), *The Last Witness: The Child Survivor of the Holocaust.* Washington, DC: American Psychiatric Press.

———— Gampel, Y. (1983), Growing up in the Holocaust culture. *Israel J. Psychiatry,* 29:129–146.

Kevles, D. J., & Hood, L., Eds. (1992), *The Code of Codes: Scientific and Social Issues in the Human Genome Project.* Cambridge, MA: Harvard University Press.

Khan, M. M. R. (1963), The concept of cumulative trauma. *The Psychoanalytic Study of the Child,* 18:286–306. New York: International Universities Press.

Klauber, J. (1977), Analyses that cannot be terminated. *Internat. J. Psycho-Anal.,* 58:473–477.

Klein, H. (1973), Children of the Holocaust: Mourning and bereavement. In: *The Child in His Family, the Impact of Disease and Death,* ed. E. J. Anthony & C. Koupernik. New York: John Wiley, pp. 393–409.

Klein, M. (1921), The development of a child. In: *Love, Guilt and Reparation.* London: Delacorte Press, 1975, pp. 1–53.

———— (1933), The early development of conscience in the child. In: *Love, Guilt and Reparation, and Other Works 1921–1945.* New York: Free Press, 1975, pp. 248–256.

———— (1946), Notes on some schizoid mechanisms. In: *Developments in Psychoanalysis,* ed. J. Riviere. London: Hogarth Press, 1952, pp. 292–320.

———— (1952), The mutual influences in the development of ego and id. In: *Envy and Gratitude and Other Works 1946–1963.* New York: Free Press, 1975, pp. 57–60.

Klerman, G. (1992), Ideological conflicts in integrating pharmacotherapy and psychotherapy. In: *Integrating Pharmacotherapy and Psychotherapy.* Washington, DC: American Psychiatric Press, pp. 3–19.

Kletti, R., & Noyes, R. (1981), Mental states in mortal danger. *Essence,* 5:5–20.

Kluft, R. P. (1982), Varieties of hypnotic intervention in the treatment of multiple personality. *Amer. J. Clin. Hypn.,* 24:230–240.

———— (1984), Treatment of multiple personality: A study of 33 cases. *Psychiatric Clin. N. Amer.,* 7:9–29.

———— (1985), Childhood multiple personality disorder: Predictors, clinical findings, and treatment results. In: *Childhood Antecedents of Multiple Personality,* ed. R. P. Kluft. Washington, DC: American Psychiatric Press, pp. 167–196.

———— (1986a), Personality unification in multiple personality disorder: A follow-up study. In: *Treatment of Multiple Personality Disorder,* ed. B. G. Braun. Washington, DC: American Psychiatric Press, pp. 29–60.

———— (1986b), The place and role of fusion rituals in treating multiple personality. *Newsletter Amer. Soc. Clin. Hypn.,* 26:4–5.

———— (1986c), High-functioning multiple personality patients—Three cases. *J. Nerv. & Ment. Dis.,* 174:722–726.

———— (1987a), Unsuspected multiple personality disorder: An uncommon source of protracted resistances, interruption, and failure in psychoanalysis. *Hillside J. Clin. Psychiatry,* 9:100–115.

———— (1987b), First rank symptoms as a diagnostic clue to multiple personality disorder. *Amer. J. Psychiatry,* 144:293–298.

———— (1988), The post-unification treatment of multiple personality disorder: First findings. *Amer. J. Psychother.,* 43:212–228.

———— (1990), Incest and subsequent revictimization: The case of therapist-patient sexual exploitation, with a description of the sitting duck syndrome. In: *Incest-Related Syndromes of Adult Psychopathology,* ed. R. P. Kluft. Washington, DC: American Psychiatric Press, pp. 263–287.

———— (1991), Hospital treatment of multiple personality disorder. *Psychiatric Clin. N. Amer.,* 14:695–719.

———— (1993), Clinical approaches to the integration of personalities. In: *Clinical Perspectives on Multiple Personality Disorder,* ed. R. P. Kluft & C. G. Fine. Washington, DC: American Psychiatric Press, pp. 101–134.

———— (1994), Psychodynamic treatment of dissociative identity disorder and allied states. In: *Psychodynamic Treatment of Axis I Disorders,* ed. J. Barber & D. Crits-Christoph. New York: Basic Books.

Kogan, I. (1995), *The Cry of Mute Children.* London: Free Association.

Kohr, E. L. (1982), Near-death experience and its relationship to psi and various altered states. *Theta,* 10:50–53.

———— (1983), Near-death experience, altered states, and psi sensitivity. *Anabiosis,* 3:157–176.

Kohut, H. (1971), *The Analysis of the Self.* New York: International Universities Press.

—— (1977), *The Restoration of the Self.* New York: International Universities Press.

—— (1979), The two analyses of Mr. Z. *Internat. J. Psycho-Anal.,* 60:3–27.

Kramer, S. (1985), Object-coercive doubting: A pathological defense response to maternal incest. In: *Defense and Resistance,* ed. H. P. Blum. New York: International Universities Press, pp. 325–351.

—— (1990), Residues of incest. In: *Adult Analysis and Childhood Sexual Abuse,* ed. H. Levine. Hillsdale, NJ: Analytic Press, pp. 149–170.

Kris, E. (1956), The recovery of childhood memories in psychoanalysis. *The Psychoanalytic Study of the Child,* 11:54–88. New York: International Universities Press.

Krystal, H., Ed. (1968), *Massive Psychic Trauma.* New York: International Universities Press.

—— (1978), Trauma and affects. *The Psychoanalytic Study of the Child,* 33:81–116. New Haven, CT: Yale University Press.

Lansky, M. (1995), *Post-traumatic Nightmares.* Hillsdale, NJ: Analytic Press.

Laplanche, J., & Pontalis, J. B. (1973), *The Language of Psychoanalysis.* New York: W. W. Norton.

Lasky, R. (1978), The psychoanalytic treatment of a case of multiple personality. *Psychoanal. Rev.,* 65:353–380.

Laub, D., & Auerhahn, N. (1993), Knowing and not knowing massive psychic trauma: Forms of traumatic memory. *Internat. J. Psycho-Anal.,* 74:287–302.

Lawrence, M. (1995), Paranormal experiences of previously unconscious patients. In: *Parapsychology and Thanatology: Proceedings of an International Conference Held in Boston, Massachusetts, Nov. 6-7, 1993,* ed. L. Coly & J. McMahon. New York: Parapsychology Foundation, pp. 122–148.

Levin, F. M. (1991), *Mapping the Mind.* Hillside, NJ: Analytic Press.

Levine, H. B. (1990), Clinical issues in the analysis of adults who were sexually abused as children. In: *Adult Analysis and Childhood Sexual Abuse,* ed. H. Levine. Hillside, NJ: Analytic Press, pp. 197–218.

—— (1992), Discussion of Brenner's "Dissociative Character," Annual Meeting, American Psychoanalytic Association, Washington, DC, May.

Levinson, E. (1996), Aspects of self-revelation and self-disclosure. *Contemp. Psychoanal.,* 32:237–248.

Levy, S. T. (1977), Countertransference aspects of the pharmacotherapy of schizophrenics. *Internat. J. Psychoanal. Psychotherapy,* 6:15–30

—— (1992), Interpretations. In: *The Technique and Practice of Psychoanalysis,* Vol. 2, ed. A. Sugarman, R. A. Nemiroff, & D. P. Greenson. Madison, CT: International Universities Press.

Lewin, B. D. (1954), Sleep, narcissistic neurosis, and the analytic situation. *Psychoanal. Quart.,* 23:487–510.

———— (1955), Dream psychology and the analytic situation. *Psychoanal. Quart.,* 24:169–199.

Lichtenberg, J. D., & Slap, J. W. (1973), Notes on the concept of splitting and the defense mechanism of the splitting of representations. *J. Amer. Psychoanal. Assn.,* 21:772–787.

Lipton, S. (1961), The last hour. *J. Amer. Psychoanal. Assn.,* 9:325–330.

Litton, S. C. (1990), More on prophetic visions and the inner self-helper. *J. Near-Death Studies,* 8:261–263.

Loewald, H. W. (1955), Hypnoid state, repression, abreaction, and recollection. *J. Amer. Psychoanal. Assn.,* 3:201–210.

———— (1960), On the therapeutic action of psychoanalysis. *Internat. J. Psycho-Anal.,* 41:16–33.

———— (1977), Book review essay on *The Freud-Jung Letters.* In: *Papers on Psychoanalysis.* New Haven, CT: Yale University Press, 1980, pp. 405–418.

Lowenstein, R. J. (1993), Posttraumatic and dissociative aspects of transference and countertransference in the treatment of multiple personality disorder. In: *Clinical Perspectives on Multiple Personality Disorder,* ed. R. P. Kluft & C. G. Fine. Washington, DC: American Psychiatric Press, pp. 51–85.

Mahler, M. (1967), On human symbiosis and the vicissitudes of individuation. *J. Amer. Psychoanal. Assn.,* 15:740–763.

———— (1968), *On Human Symbiosis and the Vicissitudes of Individuation.* New York: International Universities Press.

———— Pine, A., & Bergman, A. (1975), *The Psychological Birth of the Human Infant.* New York: Basic Books.

Mandel, A. J. (1968), Psychoanalysis and psychopharmacology. In: *Modern Psychoanalysis,* ed. J. Marmer. New York: Basic Books, pp. 274–290.

Margolis, M. (1996), Termination issues in the analysis of a case of masochistic perversion. Presented to the Philadelphia Psychoanalytic Society, April 19, Philadelphia.

Marks, J. (1979), *The Search for the Manchurian Candidate: The CIA and Mind Control.* New York: Times Books.

Marmer, S. S. (1980), Psychoanalysis of "multiple personality." *Internat. J. Psycho-Anal.,* 61:439–459.

———— (1991), Multiple personality—A psychoanalytic perspective. *Psychiatric Clin. N. Amer.,* 14:677–693.

———— Fink, D. (1994), Rethinking the comparison of borderline personality disorder and multiple personality disorder. *Psychiatric Clin. N. Amer.,* 17:743–771.

Mayer, E. L. (1996), Subjectivity and intersubjectivity of clinical facts. *Internat. J. Psycho-Anal.,* 77:709–738.

McDougall, W. (1926), *An Outline of Abnormal Psychology.* London: Methuen.

McLaughlin, J. T. (1975), The sleepy analyst: Some observations on states of consciousness in the analyst at work. *J. Amer. Psychoanal. Assn.,* 23:363–382.

———— (1981), Transference, psychic reality, and countertransference. *Psychoanal. Quart.,* 50:639–669.

McWilliams, N. (1994), Dissociative personalities. In: *Psychoanalytic Diagnoses.* New York: Guilford, pp. 502–540.

Menninger, K. (1938), *Man Against Himself.* New York: Harcourt, Brace.

Merton, R. R. (1949), The self-fulfilling prophecy. In: *Social Theory and Social Structure.* Glencoe, IL: Free Press.

Modell, A. H. (1966), Psychotherapy plus drugs in severe depression: Technique. *Compreh. Psych.,* 7:224–231.

Moody, R. (1975), *Life After Life.* New York: Bantam Books.

Moore, B. E., & Fine, B. D., Eds. (1990), *Psychoanalytic Terms and Concepts.* New Haven, CT: Yale University Press.

Morgan, C. A., Grillon, C., Lubin, H., & Southwick, S. M. (1997), Startle reflex abnormalities in women with sexual assault-related posttraumatic stress disorder. *Amer. J. Psychiatry,* 154:1076–1080.

Moses, R. (1978), Adult psychic trauma: The question of early predisposition and some detailed mechanisms. *Internat. J. Psycho-Anal.,* 59:353–364.

Nasrallah, H. A. (1985), The unintegrated right cerebral hemispheric consciousness as alien intruder: A possible mechanism for Schneiderian delusions in schizophrenia. *Compreh. Psychiatry,* 26:273–282.

New Shorter Oxford English Dictionary. S. V. "Perversion."

Niederland, W. G. (1956), Clinical observations on the "little man" phenomenon. *The Psychoanalytic Study of the Child,* 11:381–395. New York: International Universities Press.

———— (1961), The problem of the survivor. *J. Hillside Hosp.,* 10:223–247.

Nunberg, H. (1955), *Principles of Psychoanalysis.* New York: International Universities Press.

———— (1956), Character and neurosis. *Internat. J. Psycho-Anal.,* 37:36–45.

Orens, M. (1955), Setting a termination date—An impetus to analysis. *J. Amer. Psychoanal. Assn.,* 3:651–665.

Orloff, J. (1996), *Second Sight.* New York: Warner Books.

Orne, M. T., Dinges, D. F., & Orne, E. C. (1984), The differential diagnosis of multiple personality disorder in the forensic context. *Internat. J. Clin. Exper. Hypnosis,* 32:118–167.

Ornstein, A. (1986), The Holocaust: Reconstruction and the establishment of psychic continuity. In: *The Reconstruction of Trauma—Its Significance in Clinical Work,* ed. A. Rothstein. Madison, CT: International Universities Press, pp. 171–191.

Ostow, M. (1960), The use of drugs to overcome technical difficulties in psychoanalysis. In: *The Dynamics of Psychiatric Drug Therapy,* ed. G. Sarwer-Foner. Springfield, IL: Charles Thomas, pp. 443–463.

——— (1962), *Drugs in Psychoanalysis and Psychotherapy.* New York: Basic Books.

——— (1966), The contemporary roles of psychoanalysis and drug therapy. In: *Psychiatric Drugs,* ed. P. Solomon. New York: Grune & Stratton, pp. 91–111.

Owens, J. (1995), Paranormal reports from a study of near-death experience and a case of an unusual near-death vision. In: *Parapsychology and Thanatology: Proceedings of an International Conference Held in Boston, Massachusetts, Nov. 6–7, 1993,* ed. L. Coly & J. McMahon. New York: Parapsychology Foundation, pp. 149–186.

Panel (1986), Identification in the perversions. Reporter: J. Arlow. *Internat. J. Psycho-Anal.,* 67:245–250.

——— (1989), Evaluation of outcome of psychoanalytic treatment: Should follow-up by the analyst be part of the post-analytic phase of analytic treatment? Reporter: M. Johan. *J. Amer. Psychoanal. Assn.,* 37:813–822.

Parens, H. (1979), *The Development of Aggression in Early Childhood.* New York: Jason Aronson.

——— (1993), Implications for the clinical situation of reformulations of the psychoanalytic theory of aggression. Presented at the Philadelphia Psychoanalytic Society, February 10.

——— (1977), The unique pathogenicity of sexual abuse. *Psychoanal. Inq.,* 17:250–266.

Peck, J. S. (1961), Dreams and interruptions in the treatment. *Psychoanal. Quart.,* 30:209–220.

Pederson-Krag, G. (1947), Telepathy and repression. *Psychoanal. Quart.,* 16:61–68.

Person, E., & Klar, H. (1994), Establishing trauma—Distinguishing unconscious fantasy from repressed memory. *J. Amer. Psychoanal. Assn.,* 42:1055–1082.

Pfister, O. (1930), Shockdenken und shock phantasien bei hochster todesgefahr. *Zeitschr. fur Psychoanal.,* 16:430–455.

Piper, A., Jr. (1995), A skeptical look at multiple personality disorder. In: *Dissociative Identity Disorder,* ed. L. Cohen, J. Berzoff, & M. Elin. Northvale, NJ: Jason Aronson, pp. 447–466.

Preston, R. (1994), *The Hot Zone.* New York: Random House.

Project MK ULTRA, The CIA's Program of Research in Behavioral Modifica-tion (1977), Joint hearing before the Select Committee on Intelligence and the Subcommittee on Health and Scientific Research of the Commit-tee on Human Resources, United States Senate, Ninety-fifth Congress, First Session, August 3, 1977. Washington, DC: U.S. Government Print-ing Office.

Pruyser, P. W. (1975), What splits in "splitting"? A scrutiny of the concept of splitting in psychoanalysis and psychiatry. *Bull. Menninger Clin.,* 39:1–46.

Pulver, S. E. (1987), The manifest dream in psychoanalysis: A clarification. *J. Amer. Psychoanal. Assn.,* 35:99–118.

Punzak, D. (1990), Prophetic visions and the "inner self-helper." *J. Near-Death Studies,* 8:193–196.

Putnam, F. W. (1984), The psychophysiological investigation of multiple personality disorder. *Psychiatric Clin. N. Amer.,* 7:31–39.

——— (1989), *Diagnosis and Treatment of Multiple Personality Disorder.* New York: Guilford.

——— Guroff, J. J., Silberman, E. K., Barban, L., & Post, R. M. (1986), The clinical phenomenology of multiple personality disorder: Review of 100 recent cases. *J. Clin. Psychiatry,* 47:285–293.

Raft, D., & Andresen, J. J. (1986), Transformations in self-understanding after near-death experiences. *Contemp. Psychoanal.,* 22:319–346.

Rangell, L. (1967), The metapsychology of psychic trauma. In: *Psychic Trauma,* ed. S. S. Furst. New York: Basic Books.

Rapaport, D. (1949), *Emotions and Memory.* The Menninger Clinic Mono-graph Series No. 2. Baltimore: Williams & Wilkins.

Raphling, D. L. (1994), A patient who was not sexually abused. *J. Amer. Psychoanal. Assn.,* 42:70–101.

Reich, W. (1949), *Character Analysis,* 3rd ed. New York: Orgone Institute Press.

Renik, O. (1978), The role of attention in depersonalization. *Psychoanal. Quart.,* 47:588–605.

——— (1991), One kind of negative therapeutic reaction. *J. Amer. Psy-choanal. Assn.,* 39:87–105.

——— (1993), Analytic interaction: Conceptualizing technique in the light of the analyst's irreducible subjectivity. *Psychoanal. Quart.,* 62:559–571.

——— (1995), The ideal of the anonymous analyst and the problem of self-disclosure. *Psychoanal. Quart.,* 64:466–496.

Richards, A. D. (1988), Self-mutilation and father-daughter incest: A psycho-analytic case report. In: *Fantasy, Myth, and Reality—Essays in Honor of Jacob A. Arlow, M.D.,* ed. H. Blum, Y. Kramer, A. Richards, & A. Richards. Madison, CT: International Universities Press, pp. 465–478.

Ring, K. (1981), Paranormal and other non-ordinary aspects of near-death: Implications for a new paradigm. *Essence*, 5:33–51.

——— (1982), Precognitive and prophetic visions in near-death experiences. *Anabiosis*, 2:47–74.

——— (1988), Prophetic visions in 1988: A critical reappraisal. *J. Near-Death Studies*, 7:4–18.

——— (1991), Paranormal antecedents and after effects of near-death experiences: Findings from new research. *Amer. Soc. Psychical Res. Newsletter*, 17:47–49.

——— Lawrence, M. (1993), Further evidence for veridical perception during near-death experiences. *J. Near-Death Studies*, 11:223–229.

Roheim, G. (1932), Telepathy in a dream. *Psychoanal. Quart.*, 1:227–291.

Rosenbaum, M. (1980), The role of the term schizophrenia in the decline of the diagnosis of a multiple personality. *Arch. Gen. Psychiatry*, 37:1383–1385.

Rosenfeld, H. (1971), A clinical approach to the psychoanalytic theory of the life and death instincts: An investigation into the aggressive aspects of narcissism. *Internat. J. Psycho-Anal.*, 52:169–178.

Ross, C. A. (1989), *Multiple Personality Disorder: Diagnosis, Clinical Features, and Treatment.* New York: Wiley.

Ross, D. R., & Lowenstein, R. J. (1992), Multiple personality and psychoanalysis: An introduction. Perspectives on multiple personality disorder. ed. D. R. Ross & R. J. Lowenstein, *Psychoanal. Inq.*, 12:3–48.

Ross, R., Ball, W., Sullivan, K., & Caroff, S. (1989), Sleep disturbance as the hallmark of posttraumatic stress disorder. *Amer. J. Psychiatry*, 146:697–707.

Sabom, M. B. (1982), *Recollections of Death.* New York: Harper & Row.

Sachs, H. (1923), On the genesis of sexual perversions. In: *Homosexuality*, ed. C. W. Socarides. New York: Jason Aronson, 1978, pp. 531–546.

Sachs, O. (1967), Distinction between fantasy and reality elements in memory and reconstruction. *Internat. J. Psycho-Anal.*, 48:416–423.

Sandler, J. (1988), Psychoanalytic technique and analysis terminable and interminable. *Internat. J. Psycho-Anal.*, 69:335–345.

Sanella, L. (1976), *Kundalini: Psychosis or Transcendence?* San Francisco, CA: H. S. Dakin.

Sarwer-Foner, G., Ed. (1960), *The Dynamics of Psychiatric Drug Therapy.* Springfield, IL: Charles C Thomas.

Satinover, J. (1986), Jung's lost contribution to the dilemma of narcissism. *J. Amer. Psychoanal. Assn.*, 34:401–438.

Saul, L. (1938), Telepathic sensitiveness as a neurotic symptom. *Psychoanal. Quart.*, 7:329–335.

Scheflin, A. W., & Optin, E. M. (1978), *The Mind Manipulators*. New York: Paddington Press.

Schimek, J. G. (1975), The interpretations of the past: Childhood trauma, psychical reality, and historical truth. *J. Amer. Psychoanal. Assn.*, 23:845–865.

Schur, M. (1966), *The Id and the Regulatory Principles of Mental Functioning*. New York: International Universities Press.

Schwartz, H. (1994), From dissociation to negotiation: A relational psychoanalytic perspective on multiple personality disorder. *Psychoanal. Psychol.*, 2:189–231.

Schwartz, P. (1988), A case of concurrent multiple personality disorder and transsexualism. *Dissociation*, 1:48–51.

Serdahely, W. (1992), Similarities between near-death experiences and multiple personality disorder. *J. Near-Death Studies*, 11:19–37.

——— (1993), Near-death experiences and dissociation: Two cases. *J. Near-Death Studies*, 12:85–94.

Servadio, E. (1955), A presumptively telepathic precognitive dream during analysis. *Internat. J. Psycho-Anal.*, 36:27–30.

Shakespeare, W. (1601), Twelfth Night. In: *The Annotated Shakespeare*, Vol. 1, ed. A. L. Rowse. New York: Clarkson N. Potter, 1978, pp. 508–557.

——— (1611), The Tempest. In: *The Annotated Shakespeare*, Vol. 3, ed. A. L. Rowse. New York: Clarkson N. Potter, 1978, pp. 866–907.

Shengold, L. (1967), The effects of overstimulation: Rat people. *Internat. J. Psycho-Anal.*, 48:403–415.

——— (1979), Child abuse and deprivation: Soul murder. *J. Amer. Psychoanal. Assn.*, 27:533–559.

——— (1989), *Soul Murder: The Effects of Child Abuse and Deprivation*. New Haven, CT: Yale University Press.

Silber, A. (1970), Functional phenomenon: Historical concept, contemporary defense. *J. Amer. Psychoanal. Assn.*, 18:519–538.

——— (1979), Childhood seduction, parental pathology, and hysterical symptomology: The genesis of an altered state of consciousness. *Internat. J. Psycho-Anal.*, 60:109–116.

Silberer, H. (1909), Report on a method of eliciting and observing certain symbolic hallucination-phenomena. In: *Organization and Pathology of Thought*, ed. D. Rapaport. New York: Columbia University Press, 1957, pp. 195–207.

Simmel, E. (1944), Self-preservation and the death instinct. *Psychoanal. Quart.*, 13:160–185.

Simon, B. (1992), "Incest—see under Oedipus complex": The history of an error in psychoanalysis. *J. Amer. Psychoanal. Assn.*, 40:955–988.

Singer, M. (1988), Fantasy or structural defect? The borderline dilemma as viewed from analysis of an experience of nonhumanness. *J. Amer. Psychoanal. Assn.*, 36:31–59.

Slap, J. W., & Trunnell, E. E. (1987), Reflections on the self state dream. *Psychoanal. Quart.*, 56:251–262.

Smith, B. L. (1989), Of many minds: A contribution on the dynamics of multiple personality. In: *The Facilitating Environment,* ed. M. G. Fromm & B. Smith. Madison, CT: International Universities Press.

Socarides, C. (1960), Development of a fetishistic perversion. *J. Amer. Psychoanal. Assn.*, 8:281–311.

———— (1989), *The Preoedipal Origin and Psychoanalytic Therapy of Sexual Perversion.* Madison, CT: International Universities Press.

———— (1992), Discussion of Brenner's "Dissociative Character," Annual Meeting, American Psychoanalytic Association, Washington, DC, May.

Sperry, R. W. (1968), Hemisphere deconnection and unity in conscious awareness. *Amer. Psychol.*, 23:723–733.

Spiegel, D., & Cardena, E. (1991), Distintegrated experience: The dissociative disorders revisited. *J. Abnorm. Psychol.*, 100:366–378.

Steele, B. F. (1970), Parental abuse of infants and small children. In: *Parenthood,* ed. E. J. Anthony & T. Benedek. Boston: Little, Brown, pp. 449–477.

Stein, M. H. (1965), States of consciousness in the analytic situation including a note on the traumatic dream. In: *Drives, Affects, Behavior,* Vol. 2, ed. M. Schur. New York: International Universities Press, pp. 60–68.

Steiner, G. (1995), Hermeneutics or Hermes-Mess. *Internat. J. Psycho-Anal.*, 76:435–446.

Stevenson, R. L. (1886), The Strange Case of Dr. Jekyll and Mr. Hyde. In: *The Complete Short Stories of Robert Louis Stevenson,* ed. C. Nader. Garden City: Doubleday & Co., 1969, pp. 458–533.

Stoller, R. (1975), *Perversion—The Erotic Form of Hatred.* Washington, DC: American Psychiatric Press.

Stolorow, R. D., Brandchaft, B., & Atwood, G. (1983), Intersubjectivity in psychoanalytic treatment. *Bull. Menninger. Clin.*, 47:2, 117–128.

Stone, L. (1954), The widening scope of indications for psychoanalysis. *J. Amer. Psychoanal. Assn.*, 2:567–594.

Stratton, F. J. (1957), An out of body experience combined with E.S.P. *J. Soc. Psychoanal. Res.*, 39:92–97.

Styron, W. (1979), *Sophie's Choice.* New York: Random House.

Sullivan, H. S. (1953), *The Interpersonal Theory of Psychiatry.* New York: W. W. Norton.

Sutherland, J. (1989), Psychic phenomena following near-death experiences: An Australian study. *J. Near-Death Studies,* 8:93–102.

Taylor, W. S., & Martin, M. F. (1944), Multiple personality. *J. Abnorm. Soc. Psychol.,* 49:135–151.

Terr, L. C. (1983), Chowchilla revisited: The effects of psychic trauma four years after a school bus kidnapping. *Amer. J. Psychiatry,* 140:1543–1550.

Thigpen, C., & Cleckley, H. (1957), *The Three Faces of Eve.* New York: McGraw-Hill.

Ticho, E. (1970), Differences between psychoanalysis and psychotherapy. *Bull. Menninger. Clin.,* 34:128–138.

———— (1972), Termination of psychoanalysis: Treatment goals, life goals. *Psychoanal. Quart.,* 41:315–333.

van der Kolk, B., & Kadish, W. (1987), Amnesia, dissociation, and the return of the repressed. In: *Psychological Trauma,* ed. B. van der Kolk. Washington, DC: American Psychiatric Press, pp. 173–190.

Volkan, V. (1976), *Primitive Internalized Object Relations.* New York: International Universities Press.

———— (1979), Transsexualism: As examined from the viewpoint of internalized object relations. In: *On Sexuality—Psychoanalytic Observations,* ed. T. Byram Karasu & C. W. Socarides. New York: International Universities Press.

———— (1981), *Linking Objects and Linking Phenomena.* New York: International Universities Press.

———— (1987), *Six Steps in the Treatment of Borderline Personality Organization.* Northvale, NJ: Jason Aronson.

———— (1995), Intergenerational transmission and "chosen" traumas: A link between the psychology of the individual and that of the ethnic group. In: *Psychoanalysis at the Political Border: Essays in Honor of Rafael Moses,* ed. L. Rangell & R. Moses. Madison, CT: International Universities Press, pp. 251–276.

———— (1996), Bosnia-Herzegovina: Ancient fuel of a modern inferno. *Mind and Human Interaction,* 7:110–127.

———— (1997), The seed of madness. In: *The Seed of Madness,* ed. V. Volkan & S. Akhtar. Madison, CT: International Universities Press, pp. 3–16.

———— Akhtar, S., Eds. (1997), *The Seed of Madness.* Madison, CT: International Universities Press.

Waelder, R. (1956), Critical discussion of the concept of an instinct of destruction. *Bull. Phila. Assn. Psychoanal.,* 6:97–109.

Watkins, J. G. (1992), *Hypnoanalytic Techniques: The Practice of Clinical Hypnosis,* Vol. 2. New York: Irvington.

———— Watkins, H. H. (1979–1980), Ego states hidden observers. *J. Alt. States Consc.,* 5:3–18.

———— ———— (1993), Ego state therapy in the treatment of dissociative disorders. In: *Clinical Perspectives on Multiple Personality Disorder,* ed. R. P. Kluft & C. G. Fine. Washington, DC: American Psychiatric Press, pp. 277–299.

Waugaman, R. (in press), Multiple personality disorder and one analyst's paradigm shift. *Psychoanal. Inq.*

Weinshel, E. (1977), "I didn't mean it"—Negation as a character trait. *The Psychoanalytic Study of the Child,* 32:387–419. New Haven, CT: Yale University Press.

Weinstein, H. W. (1990), *Psychiatry and the CIA: Victims of Mind Control.* Washington, DC: American Psychiatric Press.

Weiss, E. (1935), Todestrieb und Masochismus. *Imago,* 21:393–411.

West, M. D., Pereira-Smith, O. M., & Smith, J. R. (1989), Replicative senescence of human skin fibroblasts correlates with a loss of regulation and overexpression of collagenase activity. *Experiment. Cell Res.,* 189:138–147.

Whitman, R. M., Kramer, M., & Baldridge, B. J. (1969), Dreams about the patient: An approach to the problem of countertransference. *J. Amer. Psychoanal. Assn.,* 17:702–727.

Wholley, C. (1925), A case of multiple personality. *Psychoanal. Rev.,* 13:344–345.

Wilbur, C. (1988), Multiple personality disorder and transference. *Dissociation,* 1:73–76.

Winnicott, D. W. (1945), Primitive emotional development. *Internat. J. Psycho-Anal.,* 26:137–150.

———— (1953), Transitional objects and transitional phenomena. *Internat. J. Psycho-Anal.,* 34:89–105.

———— (1960), Ego distortion in terms of true and false self. In: *The Maturational Processes and the Facilitating Environment.* New York: International Universities Press, 1966, pp. 140–152.

Wylie, H. W., & Wylie, M. L. (1987), An effect of pharmacotherapy on the psychoanalytic process: Case report of a modified analysis. *Amer. J. Psychiatry,* 144:489–492.

Zavitzianos, G. (1971), Fetishism and exhibitionism in the female and their relationship to psychopathy and kleptomania. *Internat. J. Psycho-Anal.,* 52:297–305.

Zulliger, H. (1934), Prophetic dreams. *Internat. J. Psycho-Anal.,* 15:191–208.

NAME INDEX

Abraham, B., 96
Abse, D. W., xiii, 23
Adair, M., 54, 66
Adelman, S., 163
Adler, G., 195
Akhtar, S., xiii, 23, 33, 75, 105, 195, 200
Alexander, F., 107, 164
Andresen, J. J., 178
Anzieu, D., 202
Apprey, M., 98
Arlow, J. A., ix, xiv, 20, 22, 24, 26, 32, 69
Armstrong, J., 40
Atwood, G., 178
Auerhahn, N., 70, 73, 115
Azima, H., 164

Bader, M., 178
Bak, R. C., 54, 95
Baldridge, B. J., 202
Ball, W., 46, 47, 70, 81
Balter, L., 200
Baranger, M., 156, 202
Baranger, W., 156, 202
Barban, L., 19, 54
Barkin, R., 155
Barrett, D., 77
Beitman, B., 163
Bellak, L., 163, 164
Bergman, A., 94
Bergmann, H., 91, 95

Bergmann, M., xiii, 96
Berman, E., 22, 72
Berzoff, J., 42
Bibring, E., 73, 106
Blank, A. S., 17
Bleuler, J., 156
Bliss, E. L., 41
Blum, H., 89, 91, 96, 215
Boesky, D., 22
Bowan, E., 38, 40, 46
Bowers, M. D., Jr., 38
Brand-Bartlett, A., xiv
Brandchaft, B., 178
Braun, B. G., 19, 126, 155
Brenneis, B., 15, 45–46, 47, 70, 75
Brenner, C., xiv, 106
Brenner, I., xiii, 16, 24, 32, 33, 34, 37, 42, 47–48, 54, 55, 66n, 70, 72–73, 77, 78, 90, 92, 95, 97–98, 109–110, 112, 114, 120, 121, 154
Breuer, J., 21
Buchele, B., xiv
Buck, O. D., 24, 42
Burland, J. A., xiv
Burstin, K. J., 24, 42
Bush, N. E., 72, 194
Byerly, L., xiv

Calef, V., ix, 66

243

SUBJECT INDEX